sentence & proposition X

Logic 69

C ı c

ELEMENTARY
LOGIC OF SCIENCE
AND MATHEMATICS

BY

P. H. NIDDITCH, M.A., PH.D.

LECTURER IN PHILOSOPHY, UNIVERSITY OF BRISTOL

UNIVERSITY TUTORIAL PRESS LTD

CLIFTON HOUSE, EUSTON ROAD, LONDON, N.W.1

BY THE SAME AUTHOR

INTRODUCTORY FORMAL LOGIC OF MATHEMATICS

A book for University students of Mathematics and Logic, which expounds fundamental ideas of modern Mathematics, such as functions and sets, giving numerous explanatory examples and also presenting the logical apparatus whereby the relevant theorems are rigorously proved.

UNIVERSITY TUTORIAL PRESS LTD

Published 1960

PRINTED IN GREAT BRITAIN BY UNIVERSITY TUTORIAL PRESS LTD, FOXTON
NEAR CAMBRIDGE

PREFACE

THIS is a textbook intended to introduce the student to some of the basic ideas and doctrines of the methodology of the mathematical and empirical sciences. The book presents Logic as a unified subject: the theory of the sciences. Many exercises have been set for the more formal parts of the work, altogether about six hundred questions, including separate parts of distinctly numbered questions, being provided to help the serious student to master the subject, of which about half are supplied with answers or solutions; many teachers find it inconvenient if all the questions are provided with answers, and, besides, such provision would take up a great deal of space. Throughout, a selection of historical sources of the material covered is given, as well as guides to further expository reading.

The student must realise from the outset that Logic is primarily a technical subject; this is to be expected, for the sciences themselves are essentially technical in character. Logic, in so far as it is technical, belongs to the general field of Pure and Applied Mathematics. But the book presupposes only the most elementary, school knowledge of mathematics to be possessed by the reader.

The standard methodological discussions, such as those due to Mach, Poincaré, Borel, Whitehead, and Fisher, cannot in general be properly followed and evaluated except by those having a substantial knowledge of scientific technicalities, for they are the products of profound mathematical and scientific knowledge, and the technical knowledge in which this mainly consists is deeply involved in the writings of these eminent thinkers, moulding the content and configuration of the thoughts they seek to express. I have tried to choose enough technical topics among those widely regarded as important, which could be treated elementarily, for the reader to be set an instructive example.

There are also, however, certain aspects of methodology which have to be, or which at the elementary level may be, treated discursively rather than technically. Some of these aspects are considered in Chapters One, Five, Eight, Nine, and Ten, and in certain sections of some of the other chapters. It is possible, and it may be preferred, to study these portions first.

Logic embraces a large variety of topics many of which have several different facets. Therefore, I have had to make a selection of material. The nature of other aspects and portions of Logic can be learned by consulting some of the works referred to in the footnotes.

In dealing with matters about which various views are possible, I have usually put forward at some length just one of the possible views and have given references to the literature for other approaches. This seems pedagogically more satisfactory than to give brief and superficial accounts of the whole range of possible approaches. Since this is a textbook and not a treatise, the opinions offered in it are not always ones that I myself happen to share.

An early draft of the present book was read by Professor D. J. O'Connor of Exeter University, who gave me a number of useful criticisms. The substance of the penultimate draft was examined with great care by Mr J. A. Faris of Queen's University, Belfast, from whose comments the final version, especially of Chapters Two and Three, has benefited much. The final responsibility is of course my own.

Finally, three minor points: in quotations, expressions between square brackets are my interpolations, an exception being in the quotation on p. 204, while expressions between the solidi / / are footnotes in the originals; in exercises, starred questions are ones of greater (generally of much greater) difficulty; and I refer to my previous book, *Introductory Formal Logic of Mathematics* (University Tutorial Press, London) as *I.F.L.M.*

P. H. N.

TABLE OF CONTENTS

[Page numbers are in brackets.]

PAGE

CHAPTER ONE. LOGIC AND THE SCIENCES 1

1. The Deductive and Inductive Sciences [1]. 2. Mathematical and Inductive Logic [3]. 3. Logic of Mathematics [5]. 4. Logic of Science [7]. 5. Necessary and Sufficient Conditions [8].

CHAPTER TWO. THE PROPOSITIONAL CALCULUS .. 12

1. Introduction [12]. 2. Propositions [12]. 3. Propositional Schemata [13]. 4. Truth Table Method [15]. 5. Peano-Russell Notation [18]. 6. Applications of Truth Table Method [19]. 7. Indirect Truth Table Method [23]. 8. Deductive Systems of the PC [27]. 9. Foundations of an Axiomatic Deductive System [29]. 10. Whitehead and Russell's PC (PCWR) [32]. 11. Proof in PCWR [34]. 12. Łukasiewicz-Tarski Notation [35]. 13. Example of Proof in PCWR [36]. 14. Deductive Systems and Natural Language [38]. 15. Idea of an Axiom Schemata PC [38]. 16. Foundations of Tarski's Axiom Schemata System for the PC (PCT) [40]. 17. Examples of Proof Schemata in PCT [42]. 18. Deduction Theorem for PCT [44]. 19. Consistency of PCT [49]. 20. Completeness of PCT [53].

CHAPTER THREE. THE FUNCTIONAL CALCULUS .. 64

1. Introduction [64]. 2. Propositional Functions, Term Variables, and Formulae [64]. 3. Quantifiers [66]. 4. Free and Bound Occurrences of Term Variables [68]. 5. Functional Variables and Schemata [69]. 6. An Axiom Schemata System for the FC (FCT) [71]. 7. Suppositional Method of Proof [75]. 8. Suppositional Method Version of FCT (SFCT) [78]. 9. Intuitionist Logic [84]. 10. Examples of Deductions in SFCT and SFCIT [86]. 11. Consistency of FCT [90]. 12. Suppositional Method Version of FCT: Quantifier Rules [94]. 13. Further Examples of Deductions in SFCT and SFCIT [97].

v

PAGE

CHAPTER FOUR.   BOOLEAN ALGEBRA AND SET THEORY   101

1. Introduction [101]. 2. Huntington's First Axiomatic
System for Boolean Algebra (BAH₁) [101]. 3. Another
Huntington System for Boolean Algebra (BAH₂):
Independence of Axioms [108]. 4. Canonical Forms
of Boolean Polynomials [114]. 5. Sets, Set Membership,
Set Inclusion, Set Equality [118]. 6. Union, Intersection, Subtraction, and Complementation of Sets [123].
7. Systems of Sets: Modules, Rings, Fields [128].
8. Ordered Pairs and the Multiplication of Sets [131].
9. Functions and One-One Correspondences [136].
10. Indexed Families of Sets; General Unions and Intersections [139]. 11. Cardinal Numbers and Set-Theoretic
Paradoxes [143].

CHAPTER FIVE.   OBSERVATION AND THE OPERATIONAL
                PATTERN OF SCIENCE   149

1. Introduction [149]. 2. Science, Experience, and the
Rejection of Authority [149]. 3. The Operational Pattern
of Science [152]. 4. Selection of Problems or Group of
Phenomena for Study [154]. 5. Observation and Experiment [155]. 6. Formulation of Laws [156]. 7. Construction of Theories [161]. 8. Testing of Theories [164].
9. Continuance of Observational and Theoretical Research
[166]. 10. General Features of Scientific Observation [169].

CHAPTER SIX.   MEASUREMENT   175

1. Introduction [175]. 2. Counting [175]. 3. Units and
Measurement [178]. 4. Quantity-Types and Systems of
Units [181]. 5. The Number System: Integers, Rational
Numbers, Real Numbers [186]. 6. Units and Dimensions
[191]. 7. Method of Obtaining Dimensional Expressions
for Quantity-Types [193]. 8. Dimensional Analysis [195].
9. Errors of Observation [200]. 10. Limits of Error [205].
11. Arithmetic Mean and Measures of Dispersion [207].

CHAPTER SEVEN.   PROBABILITY   213

1. Introduction [213]. 2. Classical Definition of Probability [213]. 3. von Mises' Frequency Conception of
Probability [217]. 4. Probability, Statistics, and Experience
[221]. 5. Axioms and Fundamental Theorems of Probability Theory [225]. 6. Combinatory Analysis [231].
7. Conditional Probability and the Probability of Causes
[239].

PAGE

CHAPTER EIGHT. EXPERIMENTATION AND HYPOTHESIS 248

1. Introduction [248]. 2. Examples of Laboratory Experiments [248]. 3. Role and Sources of Laboratory Experimentation [255]. 4. General Nature of Statistics [262]. 5. Sampling (268). 6. Normal Distribution [273]. 7. Tests of Significance for Statistical Hypotheses [278].

CHAPTER NINE. MATHEMATICS AND DEDUCTION .. 282

1. Introduction [282]. 2. Demonstration and Proof [282]. 3. Mathematical Truth [284]. 4. Mathematics and Axiomatics [289]. 5. Advantages of the Postulational Method [297]. 6. Discovery and Proof in Mathematics [302].

CHAPTER TEN. DEDUCTION AND HYPOTHESIS IN THE INDUCTIVE SCIENCES 309

1. Introduction [309]. 2. Scientific Explanation and Deduction [309]. 3. Nature of Abduction (Hypothesis) and Induction [314]. 4. Induction and Inductive Hypotheses [319]. 5. Induction and the Rule of Succession [326]. 6. Science and the Hypothetico-Deductive Method [333]. 7. Operationalism [336].

ANSWERS AND HINTS FOR SOLUTIONS TO EXERCISES 341

LIST OF ABBREVIATIONS 357

LIST OF SYMBOLS 363

INDEX OF AUTHORS 365

INDEX OF TERMS AND SUBJECTS 369

and for the advancement of, these sciences. Without Pure Mathematics as an auxiliary, there would have been no modern Mathematical Physics, with all its ramifications, nor indeed any substantial Classical Physics, for this depended on the work of Newton and without geometry there would have been no Newtonian Mechanics or Optics. (ii) The mathematical theory of probability (which is, besides, used as an auxiliary to, *e.g.* Wave Mechanics) is employed, particularly in Physics and Biology, for the techniques of inference which it supplies. For instance, that theory, as the Calculus of Observations, is used in Physics (including Astronomy) to help in the determination of the most probable value of the magnitude of a measured quantity, this help being required because repeated, refined measurements of a quantity, such as the distance between two points or the time of a star's transit, do not produce results that are identical but ones that differ to some small degree.

Again, the mathematical theory of probability is used in Biology (including Experimental Medicine) to help in the determination of the likelihood of certain hypotheses that are entertained and tested in that field, as for instance the genetic hypothesis that a pair of characters are not distributed in a population in accordance with Mendel's Second Law of Independent Assortment, or the surgical hypothesis that for a cancer of the breast which has not reached the local axilla a radical mastectomy gives in the long run better results than a simple mastectomy. On the other hand, (iii) a large number of advances within the general field of Pure Mathematics have been initiated or otherwise influenced by problems arising in the inductive sciences; much of the Calculus, of the Calculus of Variations and of the Theory of Differential Equations has had its source in questions prompted by the course of Physics. Again, not inconsiderable portions of the modern mathematical theory of probability, especially on the statistical side (though that is usually classified as Applied rather than as Pure Mathematics), have grown up in response to the needs of research workers in the biological sciences or in the domain of production engineering. (iv) Progress in the design and construction of computing machines assists the mathematician, by supplying him with additional numerical data or with the solutions to his problems that are otherwise, in practice, insoluble; from the materials thus mechanically obtained, the mathematician can proceed to build up his subject further. Such machines as electrical and electronic ones depend on advances in the inductive sciences.

Accordingly, the deductive and inductive sciences, while distinct from each other, do not exist in anything like complete isolation; the members of each group stimulate and react to the activities of the members of the other. Each group has its own methods and its own limitations; the other group helps to provide it with additional methods and to broaden and deepen its scope.

1·02 Mathematical and Inductive Logic

There are not many subjects of whose content an illuminating and informative account can be given in a sentence or two; this is because most subjects are many-sided and have been formed by many contributors not all of whom have had the same objective or regarded the subject from the same standpoint. The nature and aims of a subject can be understood adequately only after an unsuperficial study of it; yet such a study can hardly fail to bring with it a consciousness of the manifold character of what has been studied. One is then forced to describe the subject in terms of certain general methods which it uses or in terms of a catalogue of certain general topics with which it is concerned. Before he has studied it a person may be satisfied with that account of Physics according to which it is the study of inanimate nature and the laws thereof; when he has learned some Physics, he may well feel obliged to accept no description of it as adequate which does not explicitly point to the experimental and theoretical aspects of the study or to the topics of Mechanics, Heat, Light, Sound, Electricity, Magnetism, Atomic Energy, and Cosmic Radiation. This sort of situation applies to Logic. In a state of ignorance, such an account of Logic as that it is the theory of the syllogism, or that it is the theory of valid reasoning, or that it is the science of the laws of thought, might be acceptable; but an actual acquaintance with what logicians do and the kind of problems with which they deal, brings out the superficiality, exaggeration, imprecision and inadequacy of such accounts.

In this book Logic is dealt with from the point of view which sees it as primarily concerned with the methods of the sciences, deductive and inductive. For us, Logic is the logic of (inductive) science and mathematics. Logic is the methodology of the sciences. One great advantage of this conception is that it manages to include under it almost all that logicians are interested in and, at the same time, to indicate the idea that has been the main driving force in the development of modern Logic; for, on the one hand, that half of Logic called *Mathematical Logic* is, as its name suggests, occupied with the deductive sciences, Mathematics in particular, and, on the other hand, that half of Logic called (the theory of) *Scientific Method* or *Inductive Logic* is, as its name suggests, occupied with the inductive sciences. However, the "half" has to be interpreted in a somewhat inexact sense; there are portions of Logic, especially portions that interest philosophers, that do not have the methods of the sciences as their ultimate subject-matter. At present, perhaps the most important of these portions is what is known as *Modal Logic*; this is, in intention, concerned with systematically presenting the properties of, and connections between, the notions of possibility, impossibility, and necessity. An example of what might be a theorem in Modal Logic is: if it is possible that both the propositions *p* and *q* are true, then it is not necessary that either *p* is false or that *q* is false.

Our purpose in this text, then, is to elucidate the methods of the deductive and inductive sciences. The studies of such methods are what we call the *Logic of Mathematics* and the *Logic of Science*. About each of these a few more words must now be said.

1·03 Logic of Mathematics

The Logic of Mathematics is the logic of the deductive sciences; although unquestionably Mathematics is the chief member of the group of deductive sciences, it is not the only member, and to that extent the name we have assigned to the logic of the deductive sciences might seem inappropriate. However, there is this to be remarked by way of explanation and defence: the deductive sciences, apart from Mathematics, are branches of Deductive Logic, and these branches have been largely offshoots from the body of Mathematics itself. There is here the paradox that the Logic of Mathematics (in the narrow sense) is itself a branch of Deductive Logic, and Deductive Logic is concerned with the deductive sciences—of which Deductive Logic is a member. The paradox is resolved by drawing attention to the following feature of Deductive Logic in general. Deductive Logic has two levels. At one level one constructs deductive systems relating to the notions dealt with; for example, a deductive system of Modal Logic can be constructed, in which a few "truths" involving the modal notions of possibility, etc., are taken as axioms, and then other such "truths" are derived from these basic ones by definite procedures of deduction. This level of Deductive Logic is often called *Formal Logic*: in Formal Logic the concentration is on the construction and internal development (establishment of theorems) of deductive systems involving logical notions. At the second level, which presupposes the constructions of the first level, the task of Deductive Logic is to determine and demonstrate, usually by informal procedures of a deductive kind, truths *about* the deductive systems constructed at the first level; truths such as that the system is free from self-contradiction, that the system contains as theorems all the formulae (statements, etc.) of a specified variety. These truths about the deductive systems are truths concerning *provability* within the systems. For instance, it can legitimately be asserted that a system is free from self-contradiction if and only if it can be shown that there is no formula F such that both F is *provable* within the system while also the negation of F is *provable* within the system; more generally, in fact, a formula is a theorem if and only if it is provable within the system, so that a system is free from self-contradiction if and only if there is not a pair of theorems such that one contradicts the other. Accordingly, Deductive Logic takes Deductive Logic as its subject matter in the sense that Deductive Logic at the second level deals with provability within deductive systems of Deductive Logic at the first level.

For our purposes and without making any claims whatever to exhaustive classification, Deductive Logic can be divided into Modal Logic on the one side and Mathematical Logic on the other; Mathematical Logic, with which alone of the two we shall be dealing, can be classified into: the descriptive and informal methodology of mathematics, in which the nature and role of mathematical systems are discussed (cf. Chap. X); the Propositional Calculus (cf. Chap. II), and the Functional Calculi of various Orders (cf. Chap. III for the Functional Calculus of Order 1); Boolean Algebra (Chap. IV); and Set Theory (Chap. IV). Apart from the fact that theorems of the Propositional and Functional Calculi are used, albeit implicitly, in all careful reasoning, and therefore in scientific reasoning, they have a special importance for Mathematics, which needs them for its own deductive development. These Calculi can also be looked on, and by mathematical logicians are often looked on, as themselves (at level one) simple mathematical systems; as such, they can be treated as providing simple examples for the understanding of the methods of the Deductive Sciences as a whole and of Mathematics especially. Boolean Algebra and Set Theory lie at the foundations of Mathematics and have numerous applications within it; for the present work they will be required for the treatment of Probability Theory. See the table on p. 10.

1·04 Logic of Science

The Logic of Science, or Inductive Logic, can be classified into: the descriptive methodology of the inductive sciences (cf. Chaps V, VIII, and X); the Theory of Measurement (cf. Chap. VI); and Probability Theory (cf. Chaps VII and VIII).

The descriptive methodology of the inductive sciences deals with such fundamental aspects of science as observation, experiment, and theory in an informal way, by discussion and description. The Theory of Measurement falls into three parts; firstly, there is that part which deals with the general nature and role of measurement in the inductive sciences; secondly, there is the mathematical Theory of Errors of Observation (Calculus of Observations), which is in reality a branch of Statistical Theory, and deals with the methods of inference in connection with the varied results of measurement processes; and thirdly, there is

Dimensional Analysis, which deals with the methods whereby interrelationships between physical quantities can be deduced from the nature of the "units" into which the quantities can be analysed. Finally, Probability Theory has two sides. There is the Pure Mathematics of probability, and there is the Applied Mathematics of probability—Statistics; and the latter deals, *inter alia*, with the Design of Statistical Experiments, *i.e.* with the design of those experiments in which the behaviour of the individual components in the subject-matter, such as molecules or genes, cannot be predicted, and deals with the Theory of Statistical Inference, which is the theory of the methods of drawing reasonable conclusions from sets of statistical data. See the table on p. 10.

It was remarked in the Preface that this book is an elementary one, supposing no greater knowledge of Mathematics than what is learned in the lower forms of secondary schools. This limitation is a severe one, particularly for a treatment of Inductive Logic; for the Theory of Measurement and Probability Theory are essentially advanced mathematical theories which make extensive use of the Calculus. The reader must, therefore, bear in mind that the treatment offered in this text is no more than an introductory one. Plenty of references to the sources of the material given and for further reading are provided in the footnotes. The reader should make appropriate use of them.

1·05 Necessary and Sufficient Conditions

Before proceeding to the main work of the book, it may be useful to explain the significance of certain logical phrases with which the reader is doubtless already familiar and which will recur continually in the course of what follows, but about which he might not have altogether clear ideas.

Let the letters F and G stand for any formulae each of which is either to be accepted or rejected; and let not-F be the negation or denial of F and not-G the negation or denial of G. Consider the statement: if F, then G. In such a case, F is said to be a *sufficient condition* for G, and G is said to be a *necessary condition* for F, and, particularly important, if "if F, then G" denotes a theorem (*e.g.* "if the triangle ABC is right-angled, then the square on the hypotenuse is equal to the sum of the squares on the other two sides"), then "if G, then F" is said to be the *converse* (*e.g.* "if the square on the hypotenuse is equal to the sum of the squares on the other two sides, then the triangle ABC is right-angled"). The reason why F in "if F, then G" is described as being a sufficient condition for G is self-evident: whoever asserts "if F, then G" is, in effect, asserting that F is sufficient to yield G, or that G follows from F no matter what else may be the case. And the reason why G in "if F, then G" is described as being a necessary condition for F is that whoever asserts "if F, then G" is asserting that G *must be* accepted if F is accepted. To clarify this a little more, suppose that F and G are true-or-false propositions; *e.g.* if "if F, then G" denotes "if Newton's mechanics is true, then the moon's orbit is round the earth", then the moon's orbit *must be* round the earth *if* Newton's mechanics is true, and, were the moon's orbit *not* to be round the earth, the truth of Newton's mechanics would have to be denied.

"If F, then G" is taken as being synonymous with "F implies G". Suppose one wanted to maintain both "F implies G" and the converse "G implies F", as one would do, for example, with respect to the theorem of Pythagoras. In "F implies G", F is a sufficient condition for G, and in "G implies F", F is a necessary condition for G. Hence, instead of saying "F implies G and G implies F", one can say "F is a sufficient and necessary

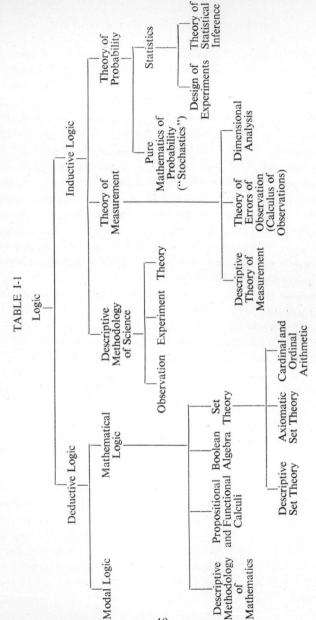

TABLE 1-1

Logic

condition for G". But one can also say, in such a case, "G is a sufficient and necessary condition for F", for in "G implies F", G is a sufficient, and in "F implies G", G is a necessary condition, for F.

Finally, instead of saying "F is a sufficient and necessary condition for G", one can say "G if and only if F": "G if F" corresponds to the part "F is a sufficient condition for G", and "G only if F" corresponds to the part "F is a necessary condition for G".

To summarise, the following four are logically equivalent: if F, then G; F implies G; F is a sufficient condition for G; G is a necessary condition for F. And the following seven are logically equivalent: F implies G and G implies F; F implies G and conversely; G implies F and conversely; F is a sufficient and necessary condition for G; G is a sufficient and necessary condition for F; F if and only if G; G if and only if F.

CHAPTER TWO

THE PROPOSITIONAL CALCULUS

2·01 Introduction

In this chapter we shall be concerned with some of the fundamentals of deductive logic. In particular, we shall present two systems for the Propositional Calculus (PC), which is generally regarded as the basic part of deductive logic; followed by an important part of the epitheory of the PC, this epitheory being about the PC itself. An epitheory deals with such questions about a Calculus as the consistency of the Calculus and as the scope of provability within the Calculus.

We begin by introducing the notions of a proposition and of a propositional schema. Next we explain the direct and indirect Truth Table Methods. These methods enable one to decide whether a given proposition or propositional schema is logically valid and so permit the logical evaluation of a large variety of arguments and inferences. We proceed to consider in detail two types of postulational theory for the PC, in which all the possible valid propositional schemata and only these occur as theorems. Finally, we demonstrate some typical theorems belonging to the epitheory of the PC, one of these theorems being that the second deductive system we have presented for the PC is consistent, and another, that it is complete.

2·02 Propositions

In Classical logic, in which alone we shall be concerned in this chapter, a proposition is a sentence that is either-true-or-false, in the ordinary senses of these terms. The truth or falsity, as the case may be, of a proposition is called its *truth-value*[1] (t.v.). So the t.v. of a true proposition is truth and that of a false proposition is falsity. By extension, sentences which are not true-or-false in the ordinary senses of these terms but which are conventionally thought and spoken of as if they were just plainly true-or-false are also classed as propositions. Mathematical sentences are the outstanding ones of this kind. Whereas a sentence such as "Monozygotic twins belong to the same

[1] Term due to Frege, G. (1848-1925): *Grundgesetze der Arithmetik I* (Jena, 1893).

blood group on the present classification of blood groups" is considered to be really true—true of the system of nature—a mathematical sentence such as "The sum of the interior angles of a plane triangle is equal to the sum of two right angles" cannot, as a purely mathematical sentence, be considered as really true or really false but as true or false only with respect to certain ranges of mathematical systems, being true for some systems—Euclidean Geometries—and false for others—Non-Euclidean Geometries. Thus whereas a proposition about matter-of-fact has a unique t.v., for nature's system is exclusive, the t.v. of at least some mathematical propositions is not unique but varies from one mathematical system to another. To say that a mathematical proposition is true for a certain system is to say merely that the proposition is provable within the system; and to say that a mathematical proposition is false for a certain system is to say merely that the negation of the proposition is provable within the system. Nevertheless, although there is this distinction between mathematical and ordinary propositions, we shall be able to disregard it in what immediately follows; but we shall recur to it in a later chapter.

2·03 Propositional Schemata

It is convenient in logic to introduce letters to stand for any propositions whatever, much as it is convenient in algebra to introduce letters to stand for any numbers whatever. We shall use "p", "q", "r", with or without positive whole number subscripts, as propositional variables, that is as letters which denote any propositions whatever.

(2·031) p, therefore p

and

(2·032) p, therefore p or q

are schemata that represent actual arguments when

propositions are put in for the propositional variables
(p.v.s); and any such actual argument will obviously be
logically valid.   It will be valid by virtue of its logical form
and not at all by virtue of its subject-matter.   Two arguments of the form (2·032) may have no subject-matter in
common and yet they will both be valid because their form
is a logically valid one.   A central task of the logician is to
discover general properties of logically valid forms and to
organise his results so that they may be a fruitful basis for
further research in logic itself and for applications to other
spheres.   Accordingly the logician is led to construct
systems in which all the valid forms of argument of some
type or types are theorems and in which no invalid form of
argument of any type is a theorem.   However, for
theoretical as well as practical purposes it proves more
satisfactory to consider implications rather than arguments.
Hence the logician is interested in valid schemata of the
type

(2·033) p implies p

and

(2·034) p implies (p or q)

rather than of the argument types (2·031) and (2·032).
We shall describe all the expressions illustrated by (2·033)
and (2·034) as being *propositional schemata* (p.s.s), and it
will be seen in due course that not all p.s.s have an implicational character.   What p.s.s (except for p.s.s that are
p.v.s) share is containing occurrences of p.v.s connected
by words like "implies", "and", "or", "not".   The
theory of the whole PC may be characterised as a deductive
theory in which all the valid p.s.s and no p.s.s that are not
valid are provable, as theorems.   In this chapter we shall
use "s", "t", "u", with or without positive whole number
subscripts, as p.s. variables, that is as letters which denote
any p.s.s whatever.

2·04 The Truth Table Method

Before investigating the PC as a theoretical system it will be better for heuristic reasons as well as for subsequent developments to present a method whereby one can determine whether any given p.s. is a valid one or is an invalid one. This method is the Truth Table Method.[1] It will be seen that this method is applicable to p.s.s that are not implicational in form as well as to those that are.

We have agreed that p denotes any proposition whatever. With any proposition is associated its negation. The negation of "The Sun is a star" may be expressed as "The Sun is not a star", and the negation of "The Sun is a star or mercury is a metal" may be expressed as "Neither the Sun is a star nor is mercury a metal". In natural languages there is no standard way of expressing the negation of a proposition. But in logic it is useful to adopt one. The negation of any proposition p will be symbolised by "not-p".

The truth table for negation is:

	not-p
(2·041)	1 0
	0 1

The truth table method presupposes that the negation of a proposition is itself a proposition. If any proposition p has the t.v. truth, which we symbolise by "0", then not-p has the t.v. falsity, which we symbolise by "1". Hence the first row in the body of (2·041). If any proposition p has the t.v. falsity, then not-p has the t.v. truth. Hence the second row in the body of (2·041). For example, the

[1] First formulated systematically by Łukasiewicz, J. (1878-1956): O logice trójwartościowej, *Ruch filoz.* (Lwów), 1920, **5**, 169-71; by Post, E. L. (1897-1954): "Introduction to a general theory of elementary propositions", *Amer. J. Math*, 1921, **43**, 163-85; and by Wittgenstein, L. (1889-1951): *Tractatus Logico-Philosophicus*, §§ 4·3 and 4·4, London, 1922, (first published 1921).

t.v. of "The Sun is a star" is truth, so the t.v. of "The Sun is not a star" is falsity; and conversely, since the t.v. of "The Sun is not of greater mass than the Earth" is falsity, the t.v. of "The Sun is of greater mass than the Earth" is truth.

The truth tables for non-exclusive alternation and for conjunction are:

	p or q		p and q
	0 0 0		0 0 0
(2·042)	0 0 1	(2·043)	0 1 1
	1 0 0		1 1 0
	1 1 1		1 1 1

The truth table method presupposes that the sentence consisting of the alternation of two propositions is itself a proposition; and similarly for a sentence consisting of the conjunction of two propositions. Given then any proposition of the form symbolised by "p or q" or of the form symbolised by "p and q", there are four possible combinations of t.v.s for the components denoted by p and q. Both may be true—first row in the body of the tables, columns one and three. The first may be true and the second false—second row, columns one and three (always these columns). The first component may be false and the second true—third row. Finally the first and the second may both be false—fourth row. According to (2·042) any proposition of the form denoted by "p or q" has the t.v. truth except in the last case when both components are false, in which case the whole alternative proposition is false. According to (2·043) any proposition of the form denoted by "p and q" has the t.v. falsity except in the first case when both components are true, in which case the whole conjunctive proposition is itself true. The t.v.s for the whole alternative and for the whole conjunctive proposition are listed under the connective word in the tables.

We have said that the truth table method presupposes that the negation, alternation and conjunction of propositions form themselves into propositions. A slightly different approach is possible. One may say instead that the method poses these as definitions. And the truth tables (2·041) to (2·043) may in turn be treated as definitions for the t.v.s of such "molecular" propositions. Regarding the tables as providing definitions, it is to be noted that these definitions are entirely in conformity with ordinary ideas about negation, alternation and conjunction. The definition of "implication" given through the next table is not in conformity with ordinary ideas. For instance, according to the table "$2 + 2 = 5$ implies $7 + 5 = 12$" is a true proposition. The sort of implication the table defines was originally called by Russell "material implication" to distinguish it from other varieties.[1] The properties of material implication are used in everyday *mathematical reasoning*; hence their importance.

The truth table for (material) implication is:

	p implies q	
0	0	0
0	1	1
1	0	0
1	0	1

(2·044)

According to (2·044) any proposition of the form symbolised by "p (materially) implies q" is true except when the antecedent p of the implicative proposition is true and the consequent q is false, in which case the whole implicative proposition is defined to be false.

---

[1] Modern conception of material implication arises with Peirce, C. S. (1839-1914): "On the algebra of logic", *Amer. J. Math.*, 1885, **7**, 180-202, especially 186-7. The name and the elaboration of the conception are due to Russell, B. A. W. (1872-): *The Principles of Mathematics I* (Cambridge, 1903).

2·05 The Peano-Russell Notation

Just as the algebraist uses artificial symbols to denote the operator such as addition and multiplication in which he is interested, so the logician uses artificial symbols to denote the "operators" such as alternation and implication in which he is interested. There are several reasons for the introduction of artificial symbols to stand for operators, of which we may mention three. (i) The first reason is to gain the advantage of brevity. It is shorter to write "$a + (b + c)$" than to write say "The sum of a and (the sum of b and c)". (ii) The second reason is the better to ensure that only the technical meanings are read into the statements made. If, for example, we use the hook sign " $\supset$ " for material implication, there is less chance of anyone being misled about the significance to be attached to a p.s. containing this sign than if the ordinary word "implies" and synonymous words were employed, for the ordinary words have meanings and overtones additional and superfluous to the defined technical term. (iii) The third reason is to allow of a more consistent notation. For example, a single type of symbol can be used for and restricted to all the operators on propositions, so that one can tell at a glance what the role of an instance of such a type of symbol is.

There are two main sets of notation in current use in deductive logic. One is the Peano-Russell notation, the other is the Łukasiewicz-Tarski notation. We shall postpone the explanation of the latter to 2·12. In the present section we explain the former notation.[1]

---

[1] Peano, G. (1858-1932): *Notations de logique mathématique* (Turin, 1894); and *Formulaire de Mathématique II* (Turin, 1896-8). Russell: "Sur la logique des relations . . .", *Riv. di mat*, 1900-1, **7**, 115-48; and with Whitehead, A. N. (1861-1947): *Principia Mathematica I* (Cambridge, 1910). A distinctive feature, due to Peano, of this symbolism is the use of dots as brackets. Thus $p \supset .q \supset p$ corresponds to $p \supset (q \supset p)$, and $p \supset q . \supset : r \supset p . \supset . r \supset q$ corresponds to $(p \supset q) \supset ((r \supset p) \supset (r \supset q))$.

Negation is indicated by the tilde sign "$\sim$". This is prefixed to the appropriate proposition or p.s.   Thus $\sim p$ is the negation of p.

Non-exclusive alternation is indicated by the v sign "$\mathbf{V}$". This is infixed between the appropriate propositions or p.s.s.   Thus $p \mathbf{V} q$ is the alternation of p and q: p is true or q is true or both.

Conjunction is indicated by the dot sign ". " and material implication by the hook sign "$\supset$".   These are also infixed between the appropriate propositions or p.s.s. Thus $p.q$ and $p \supset q$ are the conjunction and the implication of p and q.

For example:

(2·051) $\qquad [p \supset q] \supset [\sim q \supset \sim p]$

means: "(p implies q) implies (not-q implies not-p)".   In order to save brackets the tilde sign is regarded as applying only to what immediately follows it, so that $\sim q \supset \sim p$ is to be interpreted as $(\sim q) \supset (\sim p)$ and not as $\sim (q \supset \sim p)$.

(2·052) $\qquad [p \supset (q \supset r)] \supset [q \supset (p \supset r)]$

means: "(p implies that q implies r) implies (q implies that p implies r)".

(2·053) $\qquad [\sim (p \mathbf{V} q)] \supset [\sim p.\sim q]$

means: "not-(p or q) implies both not-p and not-q".

2·06 Applications of the Truth Table Method

We now show how to apply the truth table definitions (2·041) to (2·044) to schemata such as (2·051) to (2·053).

	[p	$\supset$	q]	$\supset$	[$\sim$	q	$\supset$	$\sim$	p]
	0	0	0	0	1	0	0	1	0
(2·061)	0	1	1	0	0	1	1	1	0
	1	0	0	0	1	0	0	0	1
	1	0	1	0	0	1	0	0	1

The first step in the construction of this table for the p.s. (2·051) is to set out under the occurrences of the p.v.s all the possible combinations of t.v.s. There are four such combinations, so the body of the table contains four rows, one row for each combination. (If the p.s. contained n different p.v.s, there would be 2^n possible combinations of t.v.s, so the body of the table would contain 2^n rows.) The second step is to fill in the columns which can be completed from the data provided by the first step, by using the truth table definitions (2·041) and (2·044). Thus columns 2 (using columns 1 and 3), 5 (using column 6), and 8 (using column 9) are filled in. The third step is to fill in the columns which can be completed from the data provided by the second step, by using (2·044). Thus column 7 is filled in (using columns 5 and 8). The fourth and final step is to fill in the remaining column, column 4 (using columns 2 and 7), which may be called the "principal column" of the p.s. since it gives the t.v. of the whole schema for each possible combination of t.v.s for the p.v.s entering into the schema. It is to be noticed that the principal column in the present case contains only 0s.

$$[p \supset (q \supset r)] \supset [q \supset (p \supset r)]$$

$[p$	$\supset$	$(q$	$\supset$	$r)]$	$\supset$	$[q$	$\supset$	$(p$	$\supset$	$r)]$
0	0	0	0	0	0	0	0	0	0	0
0	1	0	1	1	0	0	1	0	1	1
0	0	1	0	0	0	1	0	0	0	0
0	0	1	0	1	0	1	0	0	1	1
1	0	0	0	0	0	0	0	1	0	0
1	0	0	1	1	0	0	0	1	0	1
1	0	1	0	0	0	1	0	1	0	0
1	0	1	0	1	0	1	0	1	0	1

(2·062)

The first step in the construction of this table is to fill in the columns (1, 3, 5, 7, 9, 11) under the occurrences of the p.v.s, covering all the possible combinations of t.v.s. There are 2^3 of these, so the body of the table has 8 rows.

(The best way to ensure coverage of all the possible combinations of t.v.s for a p.s. of order n, *i.e.* one that contains n different p.v.s,[1] is to write down $2^n/2$ "0"s followed by $2^n/2$ "1"s under each occurrence of the alphabetically first p.v.; then to write down $2^n/4$ "0"s followed by $2^n/4$ "1"s, twice, under each occurrence of the alphabetically second p.v.; next to write down $2^n/8$ "0"s followed by $2^n/8$ "1"s, thrice, under each occurrence of the alphabetically third p.v.; and so on.) The second step is to fill in columns 4 (using columns 3 and 5) and 10 (using columns 9 and 11). The third step is to fill in columns 2 (using columns 1 and 4) and 8 (using columns 7 and 10). And the final step is to fill in the principal column—column 6 (using columns 2 and 8). It is to be noticed that again the principal column contains only 0s.

$$[\sim (p \quad \lor \quad q)] \supset [\sim \quad p \quad . \quad \sim \quad q]$$

(2·063)

1	0	0	0	0	1	0	1	1	0
1	0	0	1	0	1	0	1	0	1
1	1	0	0	0	0	1	1	1	0
0	1	1	1	0	0	1	0	0	1

The first step in the construction of this table is to fill in columns 2, 4, 7 and 10. The second step is to fill in columns 3, 6 and 9. The third step is to fill in columns 1 (using column 3) and 8 (using columns 6 and 9). And the final step is to fill in the principal column—column 5 (using columns 1 and 8). It is to be noticed that yet again the principal column in this case contains only 0s.

$$[p] \supset [p \quad . \quad q]$$

(2·064)

0	0	0	0	0
0	1	0	1	1
1	0	1	1	0
1	0	1	1	1

$$[p \quad \lor \quad q] \supset [p]$$

(2·065)

0	0	0	0	0
0	0	1	0	0
1	0	0	1	1
1	1	1	0	1

[1] The term "order" in this connection is due to Post: *Amer. J. Math.*, 1921, **43**, 163-85.

It will be seen that the principal columns in (2·064) and (2·065) do not contain only 0s.

A p.s. whose principal column in its truth table has only 0s is said to be a *tautologous propositional schema* (t.p.s.). When propositions are substituted for the p.v.s in a t.p.s., the resulting proposition is said to be a *tautology*.[1] All the p.s.s that one would affirm on intuitive grounds to express valid logical principles turn out to be t.p.s.s, and this leads the logician to adopt the truth table method as providing a criterion for valid p.s.s. Accordingly a p.s. is held to be valid if and only if it is a t.p.s.

EXERCISES

Express E2·6·1 to E2·6·5 in the Peano-Russell notation, construct the truth tables for the resulting schemata, and hence determine the validity or otherwise of the schemata. (Treat "if . . ., then - - -" as synonymous with ". . . implies - - -".)

E2·6·1. If p, then q implies p.

E2·6·2. Either p is true or p is false.

E2·6·3. If (p or not-r) and r is false, then p is false.

E2·6·4. If (p implies q) and p is false, then q is false.

E2·6·5. Either (it is not the case that p is false) or q is true, or (q is false or p is true).

E2·6·6. Calling a p.s. whose principal column in its truth table contains only 1s *tautologically self-contradictory*, describe two ways in which a t.p.s. can be constructed out of such a schema by means of one or more of $\sim$, $\vee$, ., and $\supset$.

E2·6·7. Two p.s.s s_1 and s_2 each of order n in the same p.v.s. are said to be *truth-tabularly* or *truth-functionally* equivalent—symbolically, $s_1 \equiv s_2$—if and only if the t.v. of s_1 is the same as that of s_2 for each of the possible 2^n combinations of t.v.s. Thus for any particular combination of t.v.s for the component p.v.s, we define $s_1 \equiv s_2$ to take the t.v. truth if and only if the t.v. of s_1 is the same as the t.v. of s_2. Is $[q \supset p] \equiv [\sim p \supset \sim q]$ a t.p.s?

E2·6·8. Is $[p \vee q] \equiv [q \vee p]$ a t.p.s.? Is $[\sim (p \supset q)] \equiv [p . \sim q]$?

E2·6·9. If $s_1 \equiv s_2$ and $s_2 \equiv s_3$, show that $s_1 \equiv s_3$.

---

[1] This technical sense of "tautology" is due to Wittgenstein: *Tractatus Logico-Philosophicus*, § 4·46.

E2·6·10. If s_1 and s_2 are t.p.s.s of order 2 in the same p.v.s, is $s_1 \equiv s_2$?

E2·6·11. Show that $[p \equiv q] \equiv [(p \supset q).(q \supset p)]$. (Hence as far as concerns the truth table method " $\equiv$ " symbolises mutual material implication.)

2·07 The Indirect Truth Table Method

The test of a p.s. for validity by the truth table method is often laborious and lengthy, especially if a schema contains more than two or three variables. Because of these practical drawbacks to the straightforward use of the method an indirect procedure has been devised which on the one hand preserves the principles of the direct truth table method and on the other hand is simpler and shorter to apply. The indirect truth table method proceeds by *reductio ad absurdum*. One begins by supposing that a given p.s. is not a t.p.s. There are then just two possibilities that might arise. (i) An inconsistent result is subsequently obtained. In this case one affirms that the given schema is indeed a t.p.s., for the supposition that it is not one leads to an inconsistency (*ad absurdum*). (ii) An inconsistent result is not subsequently obtained. In this case one affirms that the given schema is not a t.p.s.

Let us consider whether

(2·071) $[p \supset q] \supset [(p \supset (q \supset r)) \supset (p \supset r)]$

is a t.p.s. Begin by supposing that it is not a t.p.s. Then in the full truth table for (2·071) there will be at least one 1 in the principal column (column 4). Write "1" in the principal column and add a subscript "1" to indicate the first step. Now if (2·071) has the t.v. falsity, the antecedent must be true and the consequent false, by the second row of (2·044). Write "0" in column 2 and "1" in column 10, adding subscripts "2" to indicate the second step. The third step is to write "0_3" in column 6 and and "1_3" in column 12, on the basis of 1_2 in column 10. The reason we follow up the right-hand side rather than the left of (2·071) is that it has unique t.v. possibilities whereas the left side has not, since $p \supset q$ can be true for three different combinations of t.v.s for p and q. The fourth step is to write "0_4" in column 11 and "1_4" in column 13. The fifth step is to write "0_5" in columns 1 and 5 (by virtue of column 11) and "1_5" in column 9 (by virtue of column 13). Thus so far we have

$$[p \supset q] \supset [(p \supset (q \supset r)) \supset (p \supset r)$$

	0_5	0_2		1_1	0_5	0_3		1_5	1_2	0_4	1_3	1_4
(2·072)

| 1 | 2 | 3 | 4 | 5 | 6 | 7 | 8 | 9 | 10 | 11 | 12 | 13 |

Now $p \supset q$ is true and p is true; therefore q must be true. Hence step 6 is to write "0_6" in column 3. Step 7 is to write "0_7" in column 7 on the strength of 0_6. Step 8 is to write "1_8" in column 8, for $q \supset r$ has a true antecedent and a false consequent. But—and here is the climax—we then have that $p \supset (q \supset r)$ is true, although it has a true antecedent (p) and a false consequent ($q \supset r$)—which is impossible. Accordingly we have to reject the supposition that (2·071) is not a t.p.s. since that supposition has led to an inconsistency. So it is affirmed that (2·071) is a t.p.s.

The schema $[(p \lor q) \supset r] \supset [p \supset (q \lor r)]$ is a t.p.s. but the schema $p \supset (p.q)$ is not. We set out the results of the working of the indirect truth table method for these schemata in (2·073) and (2·074).

$$[(p \lor q) \supset r] \supset [p \supset (q \lor r)]$$

(2·073) 0_5 0_6 1_5 0_2 1_5 1_1 0_3 1_2 1_4 1_3 1_4

$$p \supset (p . q)$$

(2·074) 0_2 1_1 0_3 1_2 1_4

In (2·073) there is an inconsistency between 0_2 in relation to 0_6 and the 1_5 in column 5. In (2·074) there is no inconsistency.

It is not always possible to test the validity of a p.s. by the indirect truth table method using only one row below the schema. Consider for example

(2·075) $\qquad [p \supset (q.r)] \supset [(p \supset q).(p \supset r)].$

Proceeding as in the previous examples we put "1_1" in column 6, "0_2" in column 2 and "1_2" in column 10. So on the supposition that (2·075) is false for some combination of t.v.s for its component p.v.s, the antecedent, implicative schema $p \supset (q.r)$ is true and the consequent, conjunctive schema $(p \supset q).(p \supset r)$ is false. But an implicative schema can be true for three combinations of t.v.s and a conjunctive schema can be false for three combinations of t.v.s. We reason thus: p is either-true-or-false; suppose first that p is true, and when the row involving that extra supposition has been completed, suppose next that p is false and fill in a second row of t.v.s. The extra suppositions are indicated by italicising "0" and "1". The final result for (2·075) is (2·076). In the first row of t.v.s there is an inconsistency between 1_2 and the two occurrences of 0_8. In the second row of t.v.s the two occurrences of 0_5 are justified by the fact that an implicative schema is true if it has a false antecedent. In this second row there is an inconsistency between 1_2 and the two occurrences of 0_8; one stops filling in columns as soon as an inconsistency arises.

$$[p \ \supset \ (q \ . \ r)] \ \supset \ [(p \ \supset \ q) \ . \ (p \ \supset \ r)]$$

(2·076)	0_4	0_2	0_6	0_5	0_6	1_1	0_3	0_8	0_7	1_2	0_4	0_8	0_7
	1_4	0_2				1_1	$\mathit{1}_3$	0_5		1_2	1_4	0_5	

(To remove all danger of the reader's being misled let us remark that expressions such as "an implicative schema is true if it has a false antecedent" are of course elliptical, just as truth tables in relation to p.s.s are elliptical. Such expressions suggest that a p.s. can have t.v.s, which is not the case. These elliptical expressions are to be interpreted as meaning that the corresponding actual propositions take such t.v.s. Thus, whatever proposition is denoted by an implicative schema is true if whatever proposition is denoted by the antecedent in the schema is false, is the interpretation to be assigned to the elliptical expression just quoted.)

EXERCISES

Determine by the indirect truth table method which of the p.s.s E2·7·12 to E2·7·16 are t.p.s.s.

E2·7·12. $[p] \supset [\sim p \supset q]$.

E2·7·13. $[(p.q) \supset r] \supset [(p \supset r).(q \supset r)]$.

E2·7·14. $[\sim (p \supset q)] \supset [p \vee q]$.

E2·7·15. $[\sim (\sim p \vee \sim p)] \supset [p]$.

E2·7·16. $[(p \supset q)] \supset [((r_1.r_2) \vee p) \supset ((r_1.r_2) \vee q)]$.

Express the arguments in E2·7·17 and E2·7·18 in schematic form using the Peano-Russell notation, and determine their validity by applying the indirect truth table method. (Treat "s_1, therefore s_2" as equal to "s_1 implies s_2".)

E2·7·17. If $\overset{\infty}{\underset{r=1}{\Sigma}} u_r$ is convergent, then $\underset{n \to \infty}{L} u_n$ exists and is equal to 0; therefore if $\underset{n \to \infty}{L} u_n$ does not exist or does not equal 0, then $\overset{\infty}{\underset{r=1}{\Sigma}} u_r$ is divergent [= not convergent].

E2·7·18. If $x \in s\_(t\_u)$, then $x \in s$ and $x \in t\_u$; and if $x \in t\_u$, then $x \in t$ or $x \in u$. Therefore if $x \in s\_(t\_u)$, then $(x \in s$ and $x \in t)$ or $(x \in s$ and $x \in u)$.

E2·7·19. If we make "$1 - s$" synonymous with "not-s", "st" with "s or t", "$s + t - st$" with "s and t", and "$(1 - s) t$" with "s implies t", then a p.s. of order n is a t.p.s. if and only if it is equal to 0 (truth) for all the 2^n combinations of the t.v.s 0 and 1 for its p.v.s.[1] *E.g.* (a) $p \supset (q \supset p)$ is a t.p.s. since it becomes (a') $(1 - p)$ $(1 - q) p$; simply, if $p = 0$, the final factor of (a') is 0 and so (a') $= 0$, while if $p = 1$, the first factor of (a') becomes zero and so (a') $= 0$. Express "s if and only if t" in algebraic terms.

---

[1] For the derivation of these algebraic analogues, cf. Goodstein, R. L. (1912-): *Recursive Number Theory* (Amsterdam, 1957).

E2·7·20. Express each of the following schemata in algebraic terms
and determine which are t.p.s.s. (a) $[p] \supset [p]$.
(b) $[\sim(p.q)] \supset [\sim p \lor \sim q]$. (c) $[\sim p \supset p] \supset [p]$.
(d) $[p.(\sim q \lor r)] \supset [(p.q) \supset r]$. (e) $[p \supset (q.r)] \supset$
$[(\sim p \lor \sim q) \supset r]$.

2·08 Deductive Systems of the PC

It is easy to show that there is a very large number of distinct
t.p.s.s, that in fact there are infinitely many of them. Choose any
two distinct t.p.s.s T_1 and T_2. Then $T_1 \supset T_2$ is a (third) t.p.s.,
$T_2 \supset (T_1 \supset T_2)$ is a (fourth) t.p.s., $T_1 \supset (T_2 \supset (T_1 \supset T_2))$ is a (fifth) t.p.s.,
$T_2 \supset (T_1 \supset (T_2 \supset (T_1 \supset T_2)))$ is a (sixth) t.p.s., and so on indefinitely.
A less trivial mode of constructing an infinite sequence of t.p.s.s is
this. Choose first any t.p.s. T and choose next any p.s. s_1 whatever,
whether it be tautologous or not. Then $s_1 \supset T$ is a t.p.s. Choose
next a p.s. s_2 distinct from s_1 and from T. Then $s_2 \supset (s_1 \supset T)$ is a
t.p.s. Choose next a p.s. s_3 distinct from s_1, s_2, and T. Then
$s_3 \supset (s_2 \supset (s_1 \supset T))$ is a t.p.s. And so on indefinitely. There is the
material available for this process to be continued indefinitely for by
virtue of what is said at the beginning of 2·03, there are available the
three different infinite sequences of (trivial) p.s.s $p_1, p_2, p_3, p_4, p_5, \ldots$;
$q_1, q_2, q_3, q_4, q_5, \ldots$; $r_1, r_2, r_3, r_4, r_5, \ldots$.

When the mathematician realises that he is in actual or potential
possession of a very large class of "truths" about a subject-matter or
connected group of subject-matters and he wishes to establish these
truths in a rigorous way, he usually tries to construct a deductive
system in which a few of the truths are taken as initial data and all
the other truths have to be proved as theorems from these initial ones.
Similarly the logician, having at hand a large number of valid logical
principles of the sort we have been considering, desires to construct
a deductive system in which a few of these principles are accepted as
true without justification within the system, all the others having to
be made provable from them.

Another kind of d.s. (deductive system) is possible—a d.s. without
any postulates at all, and with only rules of proof—but we shall
postpone consideration of such a d.s. to the next chapter, limiting
ourselves for the present to the more familiar type of d.s. in which
there are postulates.

There are two kinds of postulational d.s. for the whole PC. One
is that in which there is a finite, usually very small, number of axioms.
We shall say that such a d.s. is an *axiomatic d.s.* This sort of d.s.
was inaugurated, for the case of geometry, by Euclid (floruit *c.* 300 B.C.)
in his *Elements.* Because of the pervasive influence of that work all
subsequent d.s.s for mathematics and logic, until recently, have been
of the axiomatic type and it is this type of d.s. with which all educated

people are acquainted. The other kind of postulational d.s. is that in which there are infinitely many axioms, although all the axioms belong to one or another of a very few forms. It is these forms, each of which gives rise to infinitely many axioms, that are postulated. These forms are called *axiom schemata*. Within the d.s. each concrete instance of an axiom schema is an axiom, somewhat as a concrete instance of a p.v. is a proposition. We shall say that a d.s. with axiom schemata is an *axiom schemata d.s.*

We are using the term "postulate" as a generic term to cover the initial truths of both the kinds of d.s. we have been mentioning. Thus the axioms of an axiomatic d.s. and the axiom schemata of an axiom schema d.s. are described as being postulates. This, we may add, is not the ordinary use of the term "postulate", which makes the term synonymous with "axiom".[1]

---

[1] The modern conception of a postulational d.s. has developed from the ideas to be found in the following. Frege: *Begriffschrift*, Halle (1879). Burali-Forti, C. (1861-1931): *Logica matematica* (Milan, 1894). Hilbert, D. (1862-1943): *Die Grundlagen der Geometrie* (Leipzig, 1899); articles reprinted in *op. cit.* 7. Ausgabe, Leipzig, Berlin, 1930, 247-61 (1905), 262-88 (1926), 289-312 (1928), and in *Gesammelte Abhandlungen III* (Berlin, 1935), 146-56 (1918), 157-77 (1922); with Ackermann, W. (1896-): *Grundzüge der theoretischen Logik* (Berlin, 1928); and with Bernays, P. (1888-): *Grundlagen der Mathematik I, II* (Berlin, 1934-9). Leśniewski, St. (1886-1939): "Grundzüge eines neuen Systems der Grundlagen der Mathematik", *Fund. Math.*, 1929, **14**, 1-81; and "Über die Grundlagen der Ontologie", *C. R. Soc. Sc. Lett. Varsovie* cl. III, 1930, **23**, 111-32. Łukasiewicz: *Elementy logiki matematycznej* (Warsaw, 1929). Tarski, A. (1902-): "Fundamentale Begriffe der Methodologie der deduktiven Wissenschaften I", *Monatsh. Math. Phys*, 1930, **37**, 361-404; "Grundzüge des Systemenkalküls, Erster Teil", *Fund. Math.*, 1935, **25**, 503-26; and *Introduction to Logic and to the Methodology of the Deductive Sciences*, translated by Olaf Helmer (London, 1941, first published in Polish, 1936). Carnap, R. (1891-): *Logical Syntax of Language*, translated by Amethe Smeaton (London, 1937, first published in German, 1934). Neumann, J. von (1903-57): "Zur Hilbertschen Beweistheorie", *Math. Z.*, 1927, **26**, 1-46. Church, A. (1903-): "A set of postulates for the foundation of logic", *Ann of Math.* (2), 1932, **33**, 346-66 and 1933, **34**, 839-64. Curry, H. B. (1900-): "Some aspects of the problem of mathematical rigor", *Bull. Amer. Math. Soc.*, 1941, **47**, 221-41; *A Theory of Formal Deducibility* (Notre Dame, Indiana, 1950); and *Leçons de logique algébrique* (Paris, Louvain, 1952). (The above-mentioned authors are listed as nearly as possible in order of their influential activity, not dependent solely on dates of publication; for example, Leśniewski was exercising a major influence through his lectures at Warsaw from about 1920.) Cf. also **9·04**.

2·09 The Foundations of an Axiomatic Deductive System

The foundations of any axiomatic d.s. consist of at least two and usually of three parts. The first two parts are necessary, the third is not necessary but is convenient. In order these three parts are (i) a group of axioms, (ii) a group of rules of deduction and (iii) a group of definitions.

(i) The axioms are required to provide the basic material from which to build all the other truths (theorems, provable statements) of the system.

(ii) The rules of deduction are required to provide definite modes for the demonstration of these other truths. They enable the question of whether an alleged proof of a statement s and therefore the question of whether s is rationally acceptable as a theorem of the system, to be decisively settled. By explicitly formulating all the principles of inference that are allowed to be used in the system, one prevents arguments that might otherwise be interminable—since there would be no definite and explicit criteria for settling them—about whether some statement does or does not "follow" from certain others. The rules of proof are an essential part of a d.s. for they are the means of passing from the initial truths and from already established truths to further truths.

(iii) In a PC of the usual, axiomatic type the only definitions are those of connectives. In any d.s. for the PC some of the connectives are taken as primitive—as undefined—so that these are the only connectives contained in the axioms.[1] If other connectives are introduced into the system, they are introduced by means of definitions in terms of the primitive connectives. For example, if alternation symbolised by "∨" and negation symbolised by "∼" are taken as the sole primitive connectives, then

[1] The first postulational d.s. for the PC was given by Frege: *Begriffschrift*. He had six axioms with implication and negation as the primitive connectives. Cf. E2·20·109.

implication symbolised by " $\supset$ " and conjunction symbolised by " . " can be defined by (2·091) and (2·092), where as usual s and t denote any p.s.s, and where " $\leftrightarrow$ " indicates a definitional equality.

(2·091) $\qquad$ $[s \supset t] \leftrightarrow [\sim s \vee t]$.

(2·092) $\qquad$ $[s.t] \leftrightarrow [\sim(\sim s \vee \sim t)]$.

A d.s. which makes no use of natural language we shall describe as being a symbolic d.s. For symbolic d.s.s of logic it is customary to provide what are called *formation rules*.[1] These rules determine which groups of symbols belong to certain categories; for instance, which groups of symbols are to be counted as statements in the system. For the PC the only formation rules given are those which determine which groups of symbols are p.s.s, these being the statements of the system. However, the formation rules are not a part of the deductive apparatus of the system but belong to the preliminaries which are employed in the enunciation of the deductive apparatus. The formation rules constitute a fourth part of the foundations of an axiomatic, symbolic d.s. Explicit and precise formation rules are not given for d.s.s making use of natural language since the rules would tend to be too lengthy and complicated. In the case of the PC it is in fact scarcely more difficult to give formation rules in relation to a natural language than in relation to a purely symbolic one, as will be seen in **2·14**.

EXERCISES

Show by constructing complete truth tables that E2·9·21 to E2·9·26 are tautologous (and hence, substituting " $\leftrightarrow$ " for " $\equiv$ ", can be used as definitions). Cf. **9·02**.

E2·9·21. $[p \supset q] \equiv [\sim p \vee q]$.

E2·9·22. $[p.q] \equiv [\sim(\sim p \vee \sim q)]$.

E2·9·23. $[p \vee q] \equiv [\sim p \supset q]$.

---

[1] Terminology due to Carnap: *Logical Syntax of Language*,

E2·9·24. $[p.q] \equiv [\sim(p \supset \sim q)]$.

E2·9·25. $[p \lor q] \equiv [\sim(\sim p.\sim q)]$.

E2·9·26. $[p \supset q] \equiv [\sim(p.\sim q)]$.

Show by the indirect truth table method that E2·9·27 to E2·9·31 are tautologous.

E2·9·27. $[p \lor q] \supset [p \lor (\sim p.q)]$, and the converse.

E2·9·28. $[\sim(p \equiv q)] \supset [(p.\sim q) \lor (\sim p.q)]$, and the converse.

E2·9·29. $[p.\sim(p.q)] \supset [p.\sim q]$, and the converse.

E2·9·30. $[(p.\sim q).r] \supset [(p.r).\sim(q.r)]$, and the converse.

E2·9·31. $[(p.\sim q) \supset r] \supset [p \supset (q \lor r)]$, and the converse.

Show by the algebraic method of E2·7·19 that E2·9·32 to E2·9·37 are tautologous.

E2·9·32. $[(p \supset q) \equiv (q \supset p)] \supset [p \equiv q]$, and the converse.

E2·9·33. $[(p \supset q) \supset p] \supset [p]$, and the converse.

E2·9·34. $[p \supset (q \supset r)] \supset [(p \supset q) \supset (p \supset r)]$, and the converse.

E2·9·35. $[p \equiv (q \supset p)] \supset [\sim p \supset q]$, and the converse.

E2·9·36. $[p \equiv (q \equiv r)] \supset [(p \equiv q) \equiv r]$, and the converse.

E2·9·37. $[(p \equiv q) \equiv (r_1 \equiv r_2)] \supset [(p \equiv r_1) \equiv (q \equiv r_2)]$.

*E2·9·38. **Leśniewski's Theorem.**[1] Every p.s. containing only p.v.s and occurrences of " $\equiv$ " and perhaps brackets is a t.p.s. if and only if each p.v. occurs an even number of times.

E2·9·39. If s/t (where "/" is known as Sheffer's stroke[2]) means that s and t are incompatible, *i.e.* that not both s and t are true, then if / is taken as the sole primitive connective, give definitions of (a) $\sim$, (b) $\lor$, (c) ., and (d) $\supset$ in terms /.

E2·9·40. If s\t means that neither s nor t is true, then if \ is taken as the sole primitive connective, give definitions of (a) $\sim$, (b) $\lor$, (c) ., (d) $\supset$, and (e) / in terms of \.

*E2·9·41. **Zyliński's Theorem:**[3] / and \ denote the only connectives (operating on one or two p.s.s) in terms of which all the other connectives (operating on one or two p.s.s) can be defined.

---

[1] *Fund. Math.*, 1929, **14**, 1-81, especially 26-7.

[2] Sheffer, H. M. (1883-): "A set of five independent postulates for Boolean algebras . . .", *Trans. Amer. Math. Soc.*, 1913, **14**, 481-8. Sheffer used a vertical bar.

[3] Zyliński, E.: "Some remarks concerning the theory of deduction", *Fund. Math*, 1925, **7**, 203-209, especially 208.

2·10 Whitehead and Russell's Propositional Calculus (PCWR)

The first d.s. we shall present for the PC is that to be found in Whitehead and Russell's *Principia Mathematica*.[1] We shall call this system "PCWR". In PCWR there are four independent axioms (a fifth axiom in the original system was later found by Bernays to be provable from the other four), three rules of deduction, and some definitions in terms of the sole primitive connectives of negation and alternation of which we shall give the most important three.

The axioms of PCWR are:

(2·101) $[\sim (p \lor p)] \lor [p]$.

(2·102) $[\sim p] \lor [q \lor p]$.

(2·103) $[\sim (p \lor q)] \lor [q \lor p]$.

(2·104) $[\sim (\sim p \lor q)] \lor [\sim (r \lor p) \lor (r \lor q)]$.

The definitions of PCWR are:

(2·105) $[s \supset t] \leftrightarrow [\sim s \lor t]$.

(2·106) $[s . t] \leftrightarrow [\sim (\sim s \lor \sim t)]$.

(2·107) $[s \equiv t] \leftrightarrow [\sim (\sim (\sim s \lor t) \lor \sim (\sim t \lor s))]$.

The rules of deduction of PCWR are:

Rule of Substitution (for p.v.s): If s is an axiom or already proved theorem and there are one or more occurrences of a p.v. v in s, then it is legitimate to affirm that t, which is identical with s except that each occurrence of v in s has been changed for an occurrence of s_1, is a theorem. (*E.g.* if it has been shown that $p \supset p$ is a theorem, then one can claim $(q \lor \sim r) \supset (q \lor \sim r)$ to be a theorem since the latter is identical with the former except that each occurrence of "p" has been changed for one of "$(q \lor \sim r)$".)   It is

---

[1] *Principia Mathematica I*, Part I, Section A: "The theory of Deduction".   We present a subsequently improved version of the original which formulated, for example, no rule of substitution.   The original system was first published by Russell: "Mathematical logic as based on the theory of types", *Amer. J. Math.*, 1908, **30**, 222-62.

permissible to substitute simultaneously for any number of distinct p.v.s in s.

Rule of Replacement (for connectives): If s is an axiom or already proved theorem and there are one or more occurrences of an expression of the form of one of those on the right-hand side (left-hand side) in (2·105) to (2·107), then it is legitimate to affirm that t, which is identical with s except that at least one but not necessarily all of such occurrences has been replaced by an instance of the corresponding expression on the left-hand side (right-hand side) of (2·105) to (2·107), is a theorem. (*E.g.* if it has been shown that $(\sim p \vee p) \vee (\sim q \vee r)$ is a theorem, then one can claim $(p \supset p) \vee (\sim q \vee r)$ and $(p \supset p) \vee (q \supset r)$ to be theorems, by virtue of (2·105).)

Rule of Modus Ponens: If s and $\sim s \vee t$ (or $s \supset t$) are axioms or already proved theorems, then it is legitimate to affirm that t is a theorem.

If it is desired to give formation rules for PCWR one can proceed as follows, where, however, we have altogether neglected considerations relating to brackets which are being used for our present purposes in a way that is governed primarily by the wish to help the reader to grasp the formulae than by strict, prescribed rules. It should be stated that, on the one hand, many brackets that ought to appear are omitted from our version of the formulae in order to simplify these and that, on the other hand, strict prescribed rules about brackets can be given and obeyed without very much trouble, though at the cost of making the formulae considerably longer and less intelligible; cf. **2·14**.

Rules of Formation (for p.s.s): (i) *p*, *q* and *r*, with or without positive integral subscripts, are p.s.s; (ii) an expression consisting of $\sim$ followed on its right by a p.s. is a p.s.; (iii) an expression consisting of $\vee$, ., $\supset$ or $\equiv$

between two p.s.s is a p.s.; (iv) (i) to (iii) determine the only p.s.s in PCWR.

2·11 Proof in PCWR

We now lay down definitions of what constitutes being a proof and being a theorem in PCWR. Something is a proof if and only if (i) it consists of a finite sequence of p.s.s such that each p.s. of the sequence is (*a*) an axiom, or (*b*) a consequence by the Rule of Substitution (RS) of one previous member of the sequence, or (*c*) a consequence by the Rule of Replacement (RR) of one previous member of the sequence, or (*d*) a consequence by the Rule of Modus Ponens (MP) of two previous members of the sequence; (ii) no member of the sequence is formed by the application of more than one rule of deduction at a time; and (iii) for each member of the sequence explicit reference is made to such of the axioms, definitions, rules of deduction and already established steps as serve to account for its occurrence. Something is a theorem if and only if it is a p.s. which occurs as a step in a proof.

Our way for explicitly accounting for each step of a proof is this. All the steps are numbered, the first part of each number indicating as usual our chapter and section. We set out all the references at the end of the sequence of steps, initiating each reference by using the final part of the number assigned to each step, this final part being called for convenience the *proof number*. If a step is an axiom, we write "ax" followed by the appropriate number (2·101) to (2·104). If a step s_1 follows from a step s_2 by RS, we write the proof number of s_2, then "RS", and finally an occurrence of the substituted p.v. followed by /, followed by an occurrence of the substituting p.s. If a step s_1 follows from a step s_2 by RR, we write the proof number of s_2, then "RR", and finally "df" followed by the appropriate number (2·105) to (2·107). And if a step s_1 follows

from steps s_2 and s_3 by MP, where s_3 is of the form
$\sim s_2 \vee s_1$ (or $s_2 \supset s_1$), then we write the proof numbers of s_2
and s_3 in that order, followed by "MP". Finally we remark
that if a step can be variously accounted for, we give only
one of the possible accounts.

2·12 The Łukasiewicz-Tarski Notation

Before giving a proof in PCWR we shall introduce the
Łukasiewicz-Tarski notation for the PC.[1] We can then
express the steps of the proof in the Peano-Russell notation
and provide the corresponding schemata in the Łukasiewicz-
Tarski notation so that the reader may master the latter by
comparing schemata in it with the same schemata in the
former notation.

We can compile a little dictionary thus:

	Peano-Russell	*Łukasiewicz-Tarski*
(2·121)	$\sim s$	Ns
(2·122)	$s \vee t$	Ast
(2·123)	$s \cdot t$	Kst
(2·124)	$s \supset t$	Cst
(2·125)	$s \equiv t$	Est

The characteristic feature of the Łukasiewicz-Tarski
notation is that signs for connectives are prefixed.
Accordingly, brackets become superfluous. *E.g.* "p or
(q or r)" becomes in stages "p or Aqr" and finally "$ApAqr$",
whereas "(p or q) or r" becomes in stages "Apq or r"
and finally "$AApqr$"; again, "(not-p and not-q) implies
((p if and only if q) or (p and not-q))" becomes in stages
"(Np and Nq) implies (Epq or $KpNq$)", "$KNpNq$ implies
$AEpqKpNq$" and finally "$CKNpNqAEpqKpNq$".

---

[1] This notation was developed entirely on his own by Łukasiewicz
in 1924, but it was inspired originally by an idea due to Tarski.
(Information given by Łukasiewicz to author.)

2·13 An Example of Proof in PCWR

(2·131) $[\sim(p \lor p)] \lor [p]$ $ANAppp$

(2·132) $[p \lor p] \supset [p]$ $CApppp$ ... $CAppp$

(2·133) $[\sim p] \lor [q \lor p]$ $ANpAqp$

(2·134) $[p] \supset [q \lor p]$ $CpAqp$

(2·135) $[p] \supset [p \lor p]$ $CpApp$

(2·136) $[\sim(\sim p \lor q)] \lor [\sim(r \lor p) \lor (r \lor q)]$

$ANANpqANArpArq$

(2·137) $[p \supset q] \supset [(r \lor p) \supset (r \lor q)]$

$CCpqCArpArq$

(2·138) $[(p \lor p) \supset p] \supset [(\sim p \lor (p \lor p)) \supset (\sim p \lor p)]$

$CCApppCANpAppANpp$

(2·139) $[\sim p \lor (p \lor p)] \supset [\sim p \lor p]$

$CANpAppANpp$

(2·1310) $[p \supset (p \lor p)] \supset [\sim p \lor p]$

$CCpAppANpp$

(2·1311) $[\sim p] \lor [p]$ $ANpp$

(2·1312) $[p] \supset [p]$ Cpp

(2·1313) $[\sim(p \lor q)] \lor [q \lor p]$ $ANApqAqp$

(2·1314) $[p \lor q] \supset [q \lor p]$ $CApqAqp$

(2·1315) $[\sim p \lor p] \supset [p \lor \sim p]$ $CANppApNp$

(2·1316) $[p] \lor [\sim p]$ $ApNp$

(2·1317) $[\sim p] \lor [\sim \sim p]$ $ANpNNp$

(2·1318) $[p] \supset [\sim \sim p]$ $CpNNp$

References. 1: ax (2·101). 2: 1, RR, df (2·105). 3: ax (2·102). 4: 3, RR, df (2·105). 5: 4, RS, q/p. 6: ax (2·104). 7: 6, RR, df (2·105). 8: 7, RS, $p/p \lor p$, q/p, $r/\sim p$. 9: 2, 8, MP. 10: 9, RR, df (2·105). 11: 5, 10, MP. 12: 11, RR, df (2·105). 13: ax (2·103). 14: 13, RR, df (2·105). 15: 14, RS, $p/\sim p$, q/p. 16: 11, 15, MP. 17: 16, RS, $p/\sim p$. 18: 17, RR, df (2·105).

EXERCISES

Prove schemata E2·13·42 to E2·13·47 to be theorems in PCWR.

E2·13·42. $[p] \supset [q \supset p]$.

E2·13·43. $[p \supset q] \supset [(q \supset p) \supset (q \supset q)]$.

E2·13·44. $[p \supset q] \supset [(r \supset p) \supset (r \supset q)]$.

E2·13·45. $[p.q] \mathbf{V} [p \supset \sim q]$.

*E2·13·46. $[p \mathbf{V} \sim p] \supset [p \mathbf{V} \sim \sim \sim p]$.

E2·13·47. $[\sim \sim p] \supset [p]$.

E2·13·48.   Give formation rules (covering brackets) for PCWR taking the "alphabet" to be: $p, p_1, p_2, \ldots, q, q_1, q_2, \ldots, r, r_1, r_2, \ldots ; \sim, \mathbf{V}, ., \supset, \equiv, (,)$.

E2·13·49.   Express schemata E2·13·42 to E2·13·47 in the Łukasiewicz-Tarski notation.

E2·13·50.   Łukasiewicz gave as axioms for the PC:[1]
(a) $CCpqCCqrCpr$;   (b) $CCNppp$;   (c) $CpCNpq$. C and N denote the primitive connectives.   (d) $Ast \leftrightarrow CNst$; (e) $Kst \leftrightarrow NCsNt$;   (f) $Est \leftrightarrow NCCstNCts$.   Bearing in mind the differences of notation, the rules of proof are essentially the same as those for PCWR.   Calling Łukasiewicz's system "PCŁ", provide the rules of formation for PCŁ.

Prove schemata E2·13·51 to E2·13·54 to be theorems in PCŁ.

E2·13·51. Cpp.

E2·13·52. $ApNp$.

E2·13·53. $CpApq$.

E2·13·54. $CCApqrCpr$.   Construct a truth table for this and confirm that it is tautologous (which surprises some people) and construct a truth table for $CACprCqrCpr$ and confirm that this is not tautologous, and so not equivalent to the former.

E2·13·55.   Express the associative law of addition in algebra $[(a + b) + c = a + (b + c)]$ without using brackets.

E2·13·56.   Express the left distributive law of multiplication over addition in algebra $[a \times (b + c) = (a \times b) + (a \times c)]$ without using brackets.

E2·13·57.   Express in more usual form: $CK \times ab = acNa = 0b = c$.

*E2·13·58.   **Bernays' Theorem:**[2] $[\sim (p \mathbf{V} (q \mathbf{V} r))] \mathbf{V} [q \mathbf{V} (p \mathbf{V} r)]$ can be proved as a theorem in PCWR.   (This schema was taken as a fifth axiom in Whitehead and Russell's original system.   Bernays' Theorem shows it is not independent of the other axioms.)

---

[1] Łukasiewicz: *Elementy logiki matematycznej.*

[2] "Axiomatische Untersuchung des Aussagen-Kalküls der 'Principia Mathematica'", *Math. Z.*, 1926, **25**, 305-20.   Cf. E9·5·10 and reference there.

2·14   Deductive Systems and Natural Language

It is important to emphasise the fact that although logicians create their d.s.s using only artificial symbols and not words of a natural language, nevertheless, the essentials of their d.s.s do not at all depend on the symbolism employed. For the PC in particular, it is easy to construct a system without artificial symbols other than those for p.v.s. For instance, with English words, the axioms of PCWR can be stated thus: [not-(p or p)] or [p]; [not-p] or [q or p]; [not-(p or q)] or [q or p]; [not-(not-p or q)] or [not-(r or p) or (r or q)]. Again leaving aside matters to do with bracketing, formation rules for this modified system could be given thus: (i) p, q, and r with or without positive integral subscripts are p.s.s; (ii) an expression consisting of "not-" followed on its right by a p.s. is a p.s.; (iii) an expression consisting of "or", "and", "implies", or "if and only if" between two p.s.s is a p.s.; (iv) the only p.s.s in the system are those given by (i) to (iii). If the parentheses (,) are to be taken into account, one need modify (i) to (iii) by requiring only that each schematic expression be surrounded by a pair of round brackets. Thus: (i)′ p, q, and r, with or without positive integral subscripts are p.s.s, if they are surrounded by a pair of round brackets; (ii)′ an expression consisting of "not-" followed on its right by a p.s. is a p.s. if it is surrounded by a pair of round brackets; (iii)′ an expression consisting of "or", "and", "implies" or "if and only if" between two p.s.s is a p.s., if it is surrounded by a pair of round brackets.

Nevertheless, in spite of the possibility of constructing d.s.s for logic in which natural language is used, it is customary for the sorts of reasons indicated at the beginning of 2·05 to make d.s.s for logic purely symbolic ones. The reader must, therefore, be prepared to acclimatise himself to thinking directly in terms of the artificial symbolism currently employed by logicians, and so in terms of both the Peano-Russell and of the Łukasiewicz-Tarski notations. The reader is advised to concentrate on mastering the latter notation since it is, in the opinion of the present author, in every respect superior. In what follows we shall as often as is practicable give formulae in both notations; but where it is not practicable preference is usually given to the Peano-Russell notation since this is still more favoured by the majority of teachers of logic in this country.

2·15   The Idea of an Axiom Schemata PC

We pointed out in 2·08 that there are two kinds of postulational d.s. for the PC. One kind is an axiomatic d.s.; this is exemplified by PCWR. The other kind is an axiom schemata d.s. We now proceed to explain and exemplify this.[1]

The totality of p.s.s in the Peano-Russell notation will be labelled " L_1PR " and the totality of p.s.s in the Łukasiewicz-Tarski notation will be labelled " $L_1ŁT$ ". " L_1 " will serve as the generic name for these totalities.

In the preceding section s and t, with or without positive integral subscripts, have been used to denote any p.s.s whatever. We shall henceforth use also "u", with or without positive integral subscripts, for the same purpose. p, q and r, etc., were described as being propositional variables—p.v.s. Similarly, s, t, and u, etc., may be described as being metalinguistic propositional variables— m.p.v.s. s, t, and u are employed for speaking about what belongs to L_1. L_1 in relation to expressions used for speaking about what belongs to it is said to be the *object language* and expressions, such as s, t, and u, which are used for speaking about what belongs to the object language are said to belong to the *metalanguage*.[2] Our metalanguage, which may be labelled " L_2 ", has two species, just as L_1 has two species— L_1PR and $L_1ŁT$. L_2PR is the totality of metalinguistic propositional schemata (m.p.s.s) expressed in the Peano-Russell symbolism. (i) s, t, and u, with or without positive integral subscripts, are m.p.s.s, if they are surrounded by a pair of round brackets; (ii) an expression consisting of $\sim$ followed on its right by a m.p.s. is a m.p.s., if it is surrounded by a pair of round brackets; (iii) an expression consisting of **V**, ., or $\supset$ between two m.p.s.s is a m.p.s., if it is surrounded by a pair of round brackets; (iv) (i) to (iii) give the only m.p.s.s (constituting L_2PR). Similarly $L_2ŁT$ is the totality of m.p.s.s expressed in the Łukasiewicz-Tarski symbolism. (i) s, t, and u,

[1] The idea of an axiom schemata d.s. is due to von Neumann: *Math. Z.*, 1927, **26**, 1-46.

[2] The distinction between object language and metalanguage was introduced by Leśniewski and Tarski about 1930.

with or without positive integral subscripts, are m.p.s.s; (ii) an expression consisting of N followed on its right by a m.p.s. is a m.p.s.; (iii) an expression consisting of A, K, or C followed on its right by two m.p.s.s is a m.p.s.; (iv) (i) to (iii) give the only m.p.s.s (constituting L_2LT).

The foundations of the axiom schemata d.s. for the PC which we shall present consists of two parts: the axiom schemata themselves and a rule of deduction. The axiom schemata used are due to Tarski.[1] The whole system will be called "PCT". If W denotes an axiom schema of PCT, then W gives rise to infinitely many axioms in terms of L_1, each of these being of the same form as that expressed by W. *E.g.* if $s \supset (t \supset s)$ is an axiom schema, then $p \supset (q \supset p)$ and $(r.q) \supset ((p \supset r) \supset (r.q))$ are axioms. Similarly if W denotes a provable statement—a theorem schema—of PCT, then W gives rise to infinitely many theorems in terms of L_1; for each proof (schema) belonging to PCT gives rise to infinitely many proofs in terms of L_1. The aim in forming PCT is to allow all and only the t.p.s.s expressible in terms of L_1 to become derivable as theorems. Each proof schema of a theorem schema in PCT provides the pattern for a proof of all the corresponding theorems in terms of L_1. The chief difference between an axiom and an axiom schemata d.s. is that the latter, unlike the former, has no rule of substitution.

2·16 The Foundations of Tarski's Axiom Schemata System for the PC (PCT)

The axiom schemata of PCT are:

(2·161) $s \supset (t \supset s)$ $CsCts$

(2·162) $[s \supset (t \supset u)] \supset [(s \supset t) \supset (s \supset u)]$

                                $CCsCtuCCstCsu$

---

[1] The axiom schemata are taken in a slightly modified form from Tarski: "Der Aussagenkalkül und die Topologie", *Fund. Math*, 1938, **31**, 103-34, especially 105. Tarski uses Peano-Russell notation for connectives except that Hilbert's $\rightarrow$ replaces $\supset$.

(2·163) $s \supset (s \lor t)$ $CsAst$

(2·164) $t \supset (s \lor t)$ $CtAst$

(2·165) $[s \supset u] \supset [(t \supset u) \supset ((s \lor t) \supset u)]$

$CCsuCCtuCAstu$

(2·166) $(s.t) \supset s$ $CKsts$

(2·167) $(s.t) \supset t$ $CKstt$

(2·168) $[u \supset s] \supset [(u \supset t) \supset (u \supset (s.t))]$

$CCusCCutCuKst$

(2·169) $\sim s \supset (s \supset t)$ $CNsCst$

(2·1610) $(\sim s \supset s) \supset s$ $CCNsss.$

Here, as before, and as subsequently, our use of brackets is informal.

Rule of Modus Ponens: If s and $s \supset t$ [Cst] are steps in a proof, then it is legitimate to affirm t as a subsequent step in the proof.

Something is a categorical proof if and only if (i) it consists of a finite sequence of p.s.s such that each p.s. of the sequence is (*a*) an axiom obtainable from the schemata in the list (2·161) to (2·1610) by putting in some p.s. for each occurrence of a m.p.v., or (*b*) a consequence by the Rule of Modus Ponens of two preceding members of the sequence; (ii) for each member of the sequence explicit reference is made to such among the axiom schemata, rule of deduction and already established steps as serve to account for its occurrence. Something is a categorical theorem if and only if it is a p.s. which occurs as a step in a categorical proof. If s denotes a p.s., "⊢ s" is used to express the assertion that s is a categorical theorem.

Something is a hypothetical proof if and only if (i) it consists of a finite sequence of p.s.s such that each p.s. of the sequence is (*a*) an axiom obtainable from the schemata in the list (2·161) to (2·1610) by putting in some p.s. for each occurrence of a m.p.v., or (*a′*) a hypothesis, or (*b*) . . .—

the ellipsis being filled in by an exact repetition of the corresponding portion of the previous paragraph. Something is a (merely) hypothetical theorem if and only if it is a step in a hypothetical (and in no categorical) proof. If s_i $(i = 1, 2, \ldots, n)$ denotes a p.s., then "$s_1, s_2, \ldots, s_{n-1} \vdash s_n$" is used to express the assertion that s_n is a theorem obtainable as a step in a proof in which, if there are any hypotheses, then the only ones are in the list $s_1, s_2, \ldots, s_n$.[1]

Something is a proof (theorem) if and only if it is either a categorical or a hypothetical proof (theorem).

Our way of setting out proofs and proof schemata is substantially the same as in **2·13**, the only notable differences being that "axs" replaces "ax" in proof schemata and that, in the case of hypothetical proofs and proof schemata, we indicate those p.s.s and m.p.s.s that are adopted as hypotheses by putting a small superscript circle ° to their right.

2·17 Examples of Proof Schemata in PCT

We begin by constructing a hypothetical proof schema to justify the assertion

(2·171) $\sim\sim s \vdash s$ $NNs \vdash s$.

An appropriate proof schema is as follows:

(2·172) $\sim\sim s°$ $NNs°$

(2·173) $\sim\sim s \supset (\sim s \supset s)$ $CNNsCNss$

(2·174) $\sim s \supset s$ $CNss$

(2·175) $(\sim s \supset s) \supset s$ $CCNsss$

(2·176) s s

References.—3: axs (2·169). 4: 2, 3, MP. 5: axs (2·1610). 6: 4, 5, MP.

---

[1] The use of $\vdash$ goes back to Frege: *Begriffschrift*. The current use, covering hypothetical as well as categorical provability, is due to Rosser, J. B. (1907-) and to Kleene, S. C. (1909-). Cf. Kleene: "Proof by cases in formal logic", *Ann. of Math* (2), 1934, **35**, 529-44, especially 534 and footnote 8 there.

This proof schema shows how to prove say $p \cdot q$ on the hypothesis $\sim\sim(p \cdot q)$. One simply transforms the proof schema by writing $p \cdot q$ for s throughout and changes the references by modifying "axs" to "ax".

Thus one has the following hypothetical proof:

(2·177)	$\sim\sim(p \cdot q)^{\circ}$	$NNKpq^{\circ}$
(2·178)	$\sim\sim(p \cdot q) \supset [\sim(p \cdot q) \supset (p \cdot q)]$	
		$CNNKpqCNKpqKpq$
(2·179)	$\sim(p \cdot q) \supset (p \cdot q)$	$CNKpqKpq$
(2·1710)	$[\sim(p \cdot q) \supset (p \cdot q)] \supset (p \cdot q)$	$CCNKpqKpqKpq$
(2·1711)	$p \cdot q$	Kpq

References.—8: ax (2·169). 9: 7, 8, MP. 10: ax (2·1610). 11: 9, 10, MP.

(2·1712)	s°	s°
(2·1713)	t°	t°
(2·1714)	$s \supset (t \supset u)^{\circ}$	$CsCtu^{\circ}$
(2·1715)	$t \supset u$	Ctu
(2·1716)	u	u

References.—15: 12, 14, MP. 16: 13, 15, MP.

(2·1712) to (2·1716) and the accompanying references constitute a hypothetical proof schema which justifies the assertion

(2·1717)	$s, t, s \supset (t \supset u) \vdash u$	$s, t, CsCtu \vdash u.$

We next give an example of a categorical proof schema; this proof schema serves to justify the assertion

(2·1718)	$\vdash s \supset s$	$\vdash Css.$
(2·1719)	$s \supset [(t \supset s) \supset s]$	$CsCCtss$
(2·1720)	$[s \supset ((t \supset s) \supset s)] \supset [(s \supset (t \supset s)) \supset (s \supset s)]$	
		$CCsCCtssCCsCtsCss$
(2·1721)	$[s \supset (t \supset s)] \supset (s \supset s)$	$CCsCtsCss$

(2·1722)   s ⊃ (t ⊃ s)   *CsCts*

(2·1723)   s ⊃ s   *Css*

References.—19: axs (2·161).   20: axs (2·162).   21: 19, 20, MP.   22: axs (2·161).   23: 22, 21, MP.

EXERCISES

Justify the assertions E2·17·59 to E2·17·70.

E2·17·59.   s ⊢ s.

E2·17·60.   If s, s ⊢ t, then s ⊢ t.

E2·17·61.   If t, s ⊢ u, then s, t ⊢ u.

E2·17·62.   If s ⊢ t, then u, s ⊢ t.

E2·17·63.   If s ⊢ s_1 and s_1 ⊢ u, then s ⊢ u.

E2·17·64.   s, t ⊢ s.

E2·17·65.   s ⊢ s **V** t.

E2·17·66.   t, s ⊃ (t ⊃ u) ⊢ s ⊃ u.

E2·17·67.   s, t, *CKstu* ⊢ u.

E2·17·68.   u, *C*us, *C*ut ⊢ *K*st.

E2·17·69.   *N*s ⊢ *C*st.

E2·17·70.   *C*ts ⊢ *CA*sts.

E2·17·71.   Construct a categorical proof of $[p \supset (\sim q.r)] \supset [p \supset (\sim q.r)]$.

2·18   The Deduction Theorem for PCT

It is important that the exact significance of an expression such as s ⊢ t or as ⊢ s ⊃ t be realised.   Such expressions are obviously not in our object language L_1, for s and t are m.p.v.s and not p.s.s.   Less obviously neither are such expressions in our metalanguage L_2; the sign ⊢ is not in the alphabet of L_2, and although s ⊃ t is a well-formed statement—a m.p.s.—of L_2, ⊢ s ⊃ t is not.   The sign ⊢ belongs to the *U-language*[1] (also called the *syntax language*), that is, to the language that is used in communicating assertions belonging to the epitheory[2] of our object language

---

[1] Term due to Curry: *A Theory of Formal Deducibility*, p. 11.

[2] The term "epitheory" was introduced by Curry: "Languages and formal systems", *Proc. Xth International Congress of Philosophy*, 1949, 770-2.   The usual term is "metatheory", but as Curry has pointed out, this might misleadingly suggest that the metalanguage is used therein.

system PCT. The statement s, s $\supset$ (t $\supset$ u) $\vdash$ s $\supset$ u is an epitheoretical statement about p.s.s and not about m.p.s.s. One must not think that the statement makes an assertion to the effect that a hypothetical proof schema of s $\supset$ u can be constructed on the L_2 schematic hypotheses s and s $\supset$ (t $\supset$ u). That this is not an appropriate interpretation is clear from the fact that, as will shortly be seen, "if s $\vdash$ t, then $\vdash \sim$ (s $\supset$ t)" is a false statement of the epitheory of PCT, but it is evident that from the axiom schemata (2·161) to (2·1610) and MP it is impossible to deduce the actual m.p.s. t itself from the m.p.s. s, and so that hypothetical statement, having a false antecedent, would always be true.

We are now going to demonstrate a useful epitheorem of PCT: it is a theorem about PCT, not in PCT, The demonstration we shall give proceeds by that mode of inference called *course-of-values induction*. One version of the principle of this mode of inference is describable thus: if (i) a statement b (1) about the positive integer 1 has been shown to be valid, and (ii) the hypothesis that b (k), about the arbitrary positive integer k, is valid for all $k \leq m$ has been shown to yield the consequence that b ($m + 1$) is also valid, then it is legitimate to assert that b (k) is valid for all positive integers k.

(2·181) **The Deduction Theorem for PCT:** If $s_1, s_2, \ldots, s_n \vdash$ t, then $s_1, s_2, \ldots, s_{n-1} \vdash s_n \supset$ t (Cs_nt), where $n = 1, 2, \ldots$.

Demonstration: This will be by course-of-values induction on the length, *i.e.* on the number of steps, k in the hypothetical proof of t. It will be convenient to introduce two abbreviating notations. Firstly, "$s_1, s_2, \ldots, s_m$" will be abbreviated to "s (1, m)". Secondly, an expression such as "s $\vdash_1$ t" will be used to signify the assertion that there is a hypothetical proof of length 1 of the p.s. denoted by t on the hypothesis denoted by s; and an expression such as "s $\vdash_{k \leq m}$ t" will be used to signify that there is a hypothetical proof of length not greater than m of the p.s. denoted by t on the hypothesis denoted by s.

We want first to show that if s $(1, n)$ $\vdash_1$ t, then s $(1, n - 1)$ $\vdash$ $s_n \supset$ t $(Cs_n t)$. If s $(1, n)$ $\vdash_1$ t, then there is a hypothetical proof of (what is denoted by) t on the hypotheses (denoted by) s_i $(i = 1, 2, \ldots, n)$, the proof containing a single step. (We shall henceforth omit the ever-to-be present phrase "denoted by" and similar phrases, for the sake of simplicity and economy.)   Hence t is either (a) an axiom, or (b) one of the s_i $(i = 1, 2, \ldots, n - 1)$ or (c) s_n.

(a) If t is an axiom, then the hypothetical proof of $s_n \supset$ t $[Cs_n t]$ on the hypotheses s_1 to s_{n-1} may be constructed as follows:

(2·182)   t   t
(2·183)   t $\supset$ ($s_n \supset$ t) $CtCs_n t$
(2·184) $s_n \supset$ t $Cs_n t$

References.—2: given as axiom.   3: ax (2·161).   4: 2, 3, MP.

(b) If t is one of the hypotheses in the list s $(1, n - 1)$, then the hypothetical proof of $s_n \supset$ t $[Cs_n t]$ on the hypotheses s_1 to s_{n-1} may be constructed as follows:

(2·185)   t   t
(2·186)   t $\supset$ ($s_n \supset$ t) $CtCs_n t$
(2·187) $s_n \supset$ t $Cs_n t$

References.—5: given as hypothesis.   6:   ax (2·161).   7:   5, 6, MP.

(c) If t is s_n, then the hypothetical proof of $s_n \supset$ t $[Cs_n t]$ on the hypotheses s_1 to s_{n-1} (all of which are superfluous) is given by (2·1719) to (2·1723) with s_n instead of s, and the references accompanying those steps.

Thus we have shown that if s $(1, n)$ $\vdash_1$ t, then s $(1, n - 1)$ $\vdash$ $s_n \supset$ t $(Cs_n t)$.

Next, let b $(k \leq m)$ represent the assertion that

(2·188) if s $(1, n)$ $\vdash_{k \leq m}$ t, then s $(1, n - 1)$ $\vdash s_n \supset t$ $(Cs_n t)$.

We suppose the validity of b $(k \leq m)$ and aim to show that b $(m + 1)$ is consequently valid. Now b $(m + 1)$ represents the assertion that

(2·189) if s $(1, n)$ $\vdash_{m+1} t$, then s $(1, n - 1)$ $\vdash s_n \supset t$ $(Cs_n t)$.

We adopt the antecedent in (2·189) and aim to obtain the consequent therein.

Since *ex hypothesi* s $(1, n)$ $\vdash_{m+1}$ t, there is a proof of t in $m + 1$ steps on the hypotheses in the list s $(1, n)$. Either t occurs in this hypothetical proof of length $m + 1$ before the $(m + 1)$ st step or it does not. If it does occur before the $(m + 1)$ st step, then by virtue of the supposed validity of (2·188) the consequent in (2·189) is obtained; and so the aim to establish (2·189) on the supposition of (2·188) would be accomplished.

Alternatively, if t does not occur until the $(m + 1)$ st step, then there are several possibilities. t is either (*a*) an axiom, or (*b*) one of the hypotheses in the list s $(1, n - 1)$, or (*c*) s_n, or (*d*) a consequence by the Rule of Modus Ponens of two preceding steps. If (*a*), (*b*), or (*c*), the proof of $s_n \supset t$ $[Cs_n t]$ on the hypotheses s_1 to s_{n-1} is constructed as in the cases (*a*), (*b*), and (*c*) above. If (*d*), then t follows from two preceding steps s and s $\supset$ t $[Cst]$. Since s and s $\supset$ t $[Cst]$ occur earlier than the $(m + 1)$ st step, proofs of $s_n \supset s$ $[Cs_n s]$ and of $s_n \supset (s \supset t)$ $[Cs_n Cst]$ on the hypotheses s_1 to s_{n-1} can be constructed by virtue of the supposed validity of (2·188). The proof of $s_n \supset t$ $[Cs_n t]$ on the hypotheses s_1 to s_{n-1} may be constructed as follows:

(2·1810) $s_n \supset s$ $Cs_n s$

(2·1811) $s_n \supset (s \supset t)$ $Cs_n Cst$

(2·1812) $[s_n \supset (s \supset t)] \supset [(s_n \supset s) \supset (s_n \supset t)]$

                                     $CCs_n CstCCs_n sCs_n t$

(2·1813) $(s_n \supset s) \supset (s_n \supset t)$ $CCs_n sCs_n t$

(2·1814) $s_n \supset t$ $Cs_n t$

References.—10: obtainable by supposed validity of (2·188). 11: obtainable by supposed validity of (2·188). 12: ax (2·162). 13: 11, 12, MP. 14: 10, 13, MP.

Thus we have shown that if the validity of (2·188) is supposed, the validity of (2·189) can be established. And we showed previously that (2·188) is valid if $m = 1$. Accordingly, by the principle of course-of-values induction, we have succeeded in demonstrating (2·181).[1]

EXERCISES

Making use of the Deduction Theorem, justify the epitheoretic theorems E2·18·72 to E2·18·82.

E2·18·72.   If Ast, $s \vdash u$ and Ast, $t \vdash u$, then Ast $\vdash u$.

E2·18·73. $s \supset t, t \supset u \vdash s \supset u$.

E2·18·74. $(s.t) \supset u \vdash s \supset (t \supset u)$.

E2·18·75. $s \vdash \sim s \supset t$.

E2·18·76. $\vdash s \supset (\sim s \supset t)$.

E2.18.77. $\vdash (s \supset t) \supset [(u \supset s) \supset (u \supset t)]$.

E2·18·78. $s, u \vdash CC$stu.

E2·18·79. $\vdash C A$st$A$ts.

E2·18·80. $s \vdash CtK$ts.

E2·18·81. $\vdash CC$sCtuCtCsu.

E2·18·82.   If $s(1, n) \vdash t$, then $\vdash Cs_n Cs_{n-1} Cs_{n-2} \ldots Cs_2 Cs_1 t$.

E2·18·83.   Show by means of the Deduction Theorem that the t.p.s. $CCqrCCpqCpr$ is categorically provable in PCT.

E2·18·84.   Show by means of the Deduction Theorem that the Łukasiewicz axioms (E2·13·50) are categorically provable in PCT.

---

[1] The Deduction Theorem was first established by Herbrand, J. (1908-31): *Recherches sur la théorie de la démonstration* (Paris, 1930). The theorem and its extensions only formalises for logic the long-used principle of mathematical inference according to which, if the supposition of p enables one to obtain q, then it is legitimate to assert that p implies q. The name *Deduction Theorem* is due to Hilbert and Bernays: *Grundlagen der Mathematik I*, p. 155.

E2·18·85.   Construct full truth tables for each of the axiom schemata (2·161) to (2·1610) and confirm that each schema is tautologous.

E2·18·86.   Show that if p.s.s are put in consistently for the m.p.v.s in any of the axiom schemata (2·161) to (2·1610), the resultant expression is a t.p.s.

E2·18·87.   Show that if s and s $\supset$ t [Cst] are (denote) t.p.s.s, then t is a t.p.s.

E2·18·88.   Show that if $\vdash$ s and $\vdash \sim$ s in PCT, then, for any well-formed statement t in L_1PR, $\vdash$ t in PCT.

Justify the epitheoretic theorems E2·18·89 to E2·18·93.

E2·18·89.   If $\vdash$ s and s, t $\vdash$ u, then t $\vdash$ u.

E2·18·90.   If s, t $\vdash$ u and s, t $\vdash \sim$ u, then s, t $\vdash$ u. $\sim$ u.

*E2·18·91.   If s $\vdash$ t. $\sim$ t, then $\vdash \sim$ s.

E2·18·92.   If s, t $\vdash$ u and s, $\sim$ t $\vdash$ u, then s, t $\mathbf{V} \sim$ t $\vdash$ u.

E2·18·93.   A chain of theorems: (a) NAsNs, s $\vdash$ $As$$Ns$; (b) NAsNs, s $\vdash$ NAsNs; (c) NAsNs $\vdash$ Ns; (d) NAsNs, Ns $\vdash$ $As$$Ns$; (e) NAsNs, Ns $\vdash$ NAsNs; (f) NAsNs $\vdash$ NNs; (g) $\vdash$ NNAsNs; (h) $\vdash$ $As$$Ns$.

2·19 The Consistency of PCT

Any d.s. should be consistent, for in general from a pair of contradictory statements any well-formed statement whatever in the system can be deduced. With respect to PCT in particular, if both $\vdash$ s and $\vdash \sim$ s, then it is easy, by means of (2·169) and two applications of MP, to obtain $\vdash$ t, where t is any p.s. whatever in L_1PR. But if, for instance, $\vdash p \supset (p.q)$, then PCT would have failed in its purpose, for it was intended to allow only t.p.s.s to be categorically provable in the system.

There are two elementary notions of consistency and correspondingly of inconsistency. A d.s. with negation is said to be *simply-consistent* (or *relatively consistent*) if and only if there is no well-formed statement belonging to the language used therein such that both the statement and its negation are categorically provable. The system is said to be *simply-inconsistent* if and only if it is not simply-consistent. This is the ordinary notion of consistency, and if we use the term consistency, or inconsistency, without further qualification, it will be to simple-consistency, or simple-inconsistency, that we are referring. With the second notion of consistency[1] a d.s. is said to be *absolutely consistent* if and only if there is at least one well-formed statement belonging to the language used therein which is not categorically provable, and is *absolutely inconsistent* if and only if it is not absolutely consistent. At any rate for symbolic d.s.s, the scope of the notion of absolute consistency is wider than that of the notion of simple-consistency, since it is applicable also to d.s.s without negation.

(2·191) The Tautology Theorem for PCT: If s denotes a p.s. belonging to L_1 and $\vdash$ s, then s denotes a t.p.s.

Demonstration: We proceed by course-of-values induction on the length (= number of steps) k in the categorical proof of what is denoted by s. (As before we shall omit, in this and the next section, the ever-to-be present phrase "denoted by" and similar phrases.)

If $\vdash_1$ s, then s must be an axiom of PCT. Hence, cf. E2·18·85 and E2·18·86, s is a t.p.s.

Next, we suppose the validity of the assertion that for all s

(2·192)   if $\vdash_{k \leq m}$ s, then s is a t.p.s.,

and aim to show that, for all s,

(2·193)   if $\vdash_{m+1}$ s, then s is a t.p.s.

is consequently also a valid assertion. We adopt the antecedent in (2·193) and aim to obtain the consequent therein.

Since *ex hypothesi* $\vdash_{m+1}$ s, there is a categorical proof of s in $m + 1$ steps. Either (i) s occurs before the $(m + 1)$ st step or (ii) it does not occur until the $(m + 1)$ st

[1] Due to Tarski, *Monatsh. Math. Phys.*, 1930, **37**, 361-404.

step. If (i), then by virtue of (2·192) the validity of (2·193) would be immediately established. If (ii), then there are two possibilities. (*a*) s is an axiom, or (*b*) s is a consequence by MP of two preceding steps. If (*a*), then, cf. E2·18·85 and E2·18·86, s is a t.p.s. And if (*b*), then, cf. E2·18·87, s is a t.p.s. by virtue of (2·192). Accordingly (2·193) may be asserted.

Therefore, by the principle of course-of-values induction, Theorem (2·191) may be asserted.

(2·194) **The Simple-Consistency Theorem for PCT:** It is not the case that there is some well-formed statement s belonging to L_1 such that both $\vdash$ s and $\vdash \sim$ s [$\vdash Ns$].

Demonstration: We proceed by *reductio ad absurdum*. Suppose there is some s such that both $\vdash$ s and $\vdash \sim$ s [$\vdash Ns$]. Since *ex hypothesi* $\vdash$ s, then by the previous theorem (i) s is a t.p.s. (ii) If s is a t.p.s., then $\sim$ s [Ns] is not a t.p.s. since by the defining truth table for negation it will have at least one sign of falsity in its principal column. Applying an intuitive modus ponens to (i) and (ii) yields the conclusion that (iii) $\sim$ s [Ns] is not a t.p.s. But *ex hypothesi* $\vdash \sim$ s [$\vdash Ns$], and hence, by Theorem (2·191), (iv) $\sim$ s [Ns] is a t.p.s. (iii) and (iv) contradict one another. Therefore we reject the supposition that leads to the contradiction. Consequently we affirm that it is not the case that there is some s such that both $\vdash$ s and $\vdash \sim$ s [$\vdash Ns$].[1]

(2·195) **The Consistency Equivalence Theorem for PCT:** If PCT is simply-consistent, then it is absolutely consistent, and conversely.

Demonstration: If PCT is simply-consistent, then (i) there is at least one well-formed statement s in L_1 for which it is not the case that $\vdash$ s; for it is not the case, by virtue of

---

[1] Theorem (2·194), for PCWR, was the first Consistency Theorem to be established for logic. It was given by Post: *Amer. J. Math.*, 1921, **43**, 163-85.

Theorem (2·191), that $\vdash p . \sim p \; [KpNp]$, for $p . \sim p \; [KpNp]$ is not a t.p.s. But (i) expresses the necessary and sufficient condition for the absolute consistency of PCT. Therefore, if PCT is simply-consistent, it is absolutely consistent. To consider the converse, if PCT is absolutely consistent, then, from the definition of absolute consistency, (ii) there is some s in L_1 for which it is not the case that $\vdash s$. Now let it be supposed that PCT is not simply-consistent. Then, for some t in L_1, both $\vdash t$ and $\vdash \sim t \; [\vdash Nt]$. But if both $\vdash t$ and $\vdash \sim t \; [\vdash Nt]$, then $\vdash s$; for a categorical proof of s, *i.e.* a categorical proof containing s as a step, can be constructed thus: (a) t—given to be categorically provable; (b) $\sim t \; [Nt]$—given to be categorically provable; (c) $\sim t \supset (t \supset s) \; [CNtCts]$—ax (2·169); (d) $t \supset s \; [Cts]$— (b) and (c), MP; (e) s—(a) and (d), MP. Hence $\vdash s$, which contradicts (ii). Therefore we reject the supposition, that PCT is not simply-consistent, that leads to the contradiction. Accordingly, if PCT is absolutely consistent, then it is simply-consistent.

(2·196) **The Absolute Consistency Theorem for PCT:** PCT is absolutely consistent.

Demonstration: By virtue of Theorem (2·194) PCT is simply-consistent and by virtue of Theorem (2·195) if PCT is simply-consistent then it is absolutely consistent. By an intuitive modus ponens we obtain the conclusion that PCT is absolutely consistent. (What we mean by an "intuitive modus ponens" is an application of the principle of modus ponens which belongs to the unsystematised and nonexplicitly formulated inferential apparatus for the epitheory of PCT.)

EXERCISES

Demonstrate the epitheorems E2·19·94 to E2·19·100.

E2·19·94. If $s \vdash u_1$ and $t \vdash u_2$, then s, $t \vdash u_1 \lor u_2$.

E2·19·95. If $s \vdash u_1$ and $t \vdash u_2$, then s, $t \vdash u_1 . u_2$.

*E2·19·96. If $\sim s \vee \sim t \vdash \sim (s.t)$.

E2·19·97. If $s \vdash t$ and $s_1 \vdash \sim u$, then $s.s_1 \vdash \sim (t \supset u)$.

E2·19·98. Justify E2·17·60 to E2·17·63 by use of the Deduction Theorem.

E2·19·99. $s \vdash \sim \sim s$.

*E2·19·100. If $\sim s. \sim t \vdash \sim (s \vee t)$.

E2·19·101. If $s \vdash t \supset u$ and $\vdash t$, then $s \vdash u$.

2·20 The Completeness of PCT

There are two notions of completeness for a postulational d.s. of the PC. With the first notion,[1] a simply-consistent system S is said to be *tautologically* (or *relatively*) *complete* if and only if every t.p.s. is categorically provable by means of the postulates and rules of deduction. (Definitions can be transformed into rules of replacement.) With the second notion,[2] S is said to be *absolutely complete* if and only if S would cease to be simply-consistent were a non-tautologous p.s., or m.p.s., added to the axioms, or axiom schemata. S will be said to be *tautologically* (*absolutely*) *incomplete* if and only if it is not tautologically (absolutely) complete.

In this section we shall show that PCT is complete in both the senses just mentioned. We base our demonstration of completeness in the generic sense on what we call *The p.v. Sequence Theorem*. Our demonstration is the first detailed one along these lines. This approach to the Completeness Theorems for the PC is due to Kalmár.[3] The usual approach is more complicated. It is followed by the generality of writers and teachers in this field because it was used by Post who was the first to enunciate and demonstrate a Completeness Theorem,[4] and because

---

[1] Due to Post: *Amer. J. Math.*, 1921, **43**, 163-85.

[2] Due to Tarski: *Monatsh. Math. Phys.*, 1930, **37**, 361-404.

[3] Kalmár, L. (c. 1908-): "Über die Axiomatisierbarkeit des Aussagenkalküls", *Acta scientiarum mathematicarum* (Szeged), 1934-5, **7**, 222-43.

[4] *Amer. J. Math.*, 1921, **43**, 163-85. He showed the tautological completeness of PCWR.

subsequent influential texts, such as Hilbert and Ackermann's *Grundzüge der theoretischen Logik*, were written
before Kalmár's work was published and they adopted
Post's own procedure. However, the reader should
perhaps be warned that the full demonstration of the
Completeness Theorems even along Kalmár's lines is very
prolix, although not especially difficult. Indeed, the
individual details are easy to follow; the only difficulty
lies in not losing grasp of the general trend amidst the
multiplicity of particular cases. To help the reader to
avoid all distractions from his concentrating on the essentials
of the argument, we shall use only one notation, the
Peano-Russell one.

If s is a p.s. of L_1 whose distinct constituent p.v.s are in
the list of distinct p.v.s v_1, v_2, ..., v_n ($n = 1, 2, 3, ...$),
then if the t.v. of s for a given combination Q of t.v.s for
v_1 to v_n is truth we write "$Q(s) = 0$". and if the t.v. of s
for Q is falsity we write "$Q(s) = 1$". If the t.v. of
v_i ($i = 1, 2, ..., n$) for Q is truth (falsity) we write
"$Q(v_i) = 0(1)$"; and similarly for other sub-p.s.s of s.
By definition, the expression "the p.v. sequence corresponding to $v(1, n)$ for Q" signifies the sequence
v_1', v_2', ..., v_n', which will be abbreviated to $v'(1, n)$,
where, for each i from 1 to n, $v_i' = v_i$ if $Q(v_i) = 0$ and
$v_i' = \sim v_i$ if $Q(v_i) = 1$, the sign $=$ here indicating
identity. Thus if s is (denotes) $p.q$, the original p.v.
sequence is p, q, r, and the t.v.s assigned to the members
of the list are truth, falsity, falsity respectively, then
$Q(s) = 1$ and the p.v. sequence corresponding to p, q, r
for Q is p, $\sim q$, $\sim r$.

(2·201) **The p.v. Sequence Theorem for PCT:** If s is a p.s.
in L_1 whose distinct constituent p.v.s are among those in
the list $v(1, n)$, then (i) if $Q(s) = 0$, then $v'(1, n) \vdash s$, and
(ii) if $Q(s) = 1$, then $v'(1, n) \vdash \sim s$.

Demonstration: We proceed by course-of-values induction on the degree $k\ (= 0, 1, 2, \ldots)$ of s, the degree being the number of occurrences of connectives in s. We shall use that form of course-of-values induction which is derived from the formulation in **2·18** by substituting "0" for "1" and "non-negative" for "positive".

If s is of degree 0, then for some p.v. v_1 we have $s = v_1$. (I) If $Q(s) = 0$, then $Q(v_1) = 0$. But if $Q(v_1) = 0$, then $v_1' = v_1$. Since $v_1' \vdash v_1'$, it follows from the two identities that $v_1' \vdash s$. Therefore, if $Q(s) = 0$, then $v'(1, n) \vdash s$. (n can be just 1 here.) (II) If $Q(s) = 1$, then $Q(v_1) = 1$. If $Q(v_1) = 1$, then $v_1' = \sim v_1$. From this identity and the fact that $v_1' \vdash v_1'$ we obtain $v_1' \vdash \sim s$. Therefore, if $Q(s) = 1$, then $v'(1, n) \vdash \sim s$. (Here again n can be just 1.) Thus the theorem for the case $k = 0$ has been established.

Next, we suppose the validity of the assertion that, for all s,

(2·202) if s is of degree $k\ (= 0, 1, 2, \ldots)$ and $k \leq m$, then

(I) if $Q(s) = 0$, then $v'(1, n) \vdash s$, and (II) if $Q(s) = 1$, then $v'(1, n) \vdash \sim s$,

and aim to show that, for all s,

(2·203) if s is of degree $m + 1$, then (I) if $Q(s) = 0$, then

$v'(1, n) \vdash s$, and (II) if $Q(s) = 1$, then $v'(1, n) \vdash \sim s$

is consequently also a valid assertion. We adopt the antecedent in (2·203) and aim to obtain the consequent therein.

The meaning of the expression "the principal connective of s" is readily understood. In $p \supset (q \supset r)$ the principal connective is the first $\supset$ reading from the left, and in $((p.q) \supset (r \supset p_1)) \mathbf{V} (\sim q \mathbf{V} \sim p_1)$ the principal connective is the first $\mathbf{V}$ reading from the left.

Since *ex hypothesi* s is of degree $m + 1$, its principal connective is (i) $\sim$, (ii) $\mathbf{V}$, (iii) ., or (iv) $\supset$. What we shall do is to show, for each of these four cases, that the consequent of (2·203) is obtainable, by virtue of the supposed validity of (2·202).

(i) If $\sim$ is the principal connective, then there must be some t of degree m such that s $= \sim$ t, t having the same constituent p.v.s as s.   By virtue of (2·202)

(2·204) (I) if Q (t) = 0, then v' (1, n) ⊢ t, and (II) if
  Q (t) = 1, then v' (1, n) ⊢ $\sim$ t.

(I) If Q (s) = 0, then by the truth table for negation Q (t) = 1.   Hence by (II) in (2·204) v' (1, n) ⊢ $\sim$ t.   Since $\sim$ t is identically s

(2·205) if Q (s) = 0, then v' (1, n) ⊢ s.

(II) If Q (s) = 1, then by the truth table for negation Q (t) = 0.   Hence by (I) in (2·204) v' (1, n) ⊢ t.   If v' (1, n) ⊢ t, then, cf. E2·19·99, v' (1, n) ⊢ $\sim \sim$ t.   Since s $= \sim$ t.

(2·206) if Q (s) = 1, then v' (1, n) ⊢ $\sim$ s.

Therefore, by (2·205) and (2·206),

(2·207) (I) if Q (s) = 0, then v' (1, n) ⊢ s, and (II) if Q (s) = 1,
  then v' (1, n) ⊢ $\sim$ s;

which completes the case of negation.

(ii) If ∨ is the principal connective, then there must be some t and some u each of degree not greater than m such that s $=$ (t ∨ u), the constituent p.v.s of t being in the list v (1, i), those of u being in the list v (1, j), and the p.v.s in the list v (1, n) for s being formed out of these two lists by a suitable ordering and by the exclusion of repetitions.

(I) If Q (s) = 0, then (a) Q (t) = 0 and Q (u) = 0, or (b) Q (t) = 0 and Q (u) = 1, or (c) Q (t) = 1 and Q (u) = 0.

(a) If Q (t) = 0 and Q (u) = 0, then by virtue of (2·202) v' (1, i) ⊢ t and   v' (1, j) ⊢ u.   Hence, cf. E2·19·94, v' (1, i), v' (1, j) ⊢ t ∨ u.   So v' (1, i), v' (1, j) ⊢ s.   Therefore v' (1, n) ⊢ s.

(b) If $Q(t) = 0$ and $Q(u) = 1$, then by virtue of (2·202) $v'(1, i) \vdash t$. Hence, cf. E2·17·62, $v'(1, i)$, $v'(1, j) \vdash t$. And so, cf. E2·17·65, $v'(1, i)$, $v'(1, j) \vdash t \lor u$. Therefore again $v'(1, n) \vdash s$.

(c) If $Q(t) = 1$ and $Q(u) = 0$, then by virtue of (2·202) $v'(1, j) \vdash u$, and so, analogously to (b), $v'(1, i)$, $v'(1, j) \vdash t \lor u$. Therefore yet again $v'(1, n) \vdash s$.

Accordingly, by (a), (b), and (c),

(2·208)   if $Q(s) = 0$, then $v'(1, n) \vdash s$.

(II) If $Q(s) = 1$, then $Q(t) = 1$ and $Q(u) = 1$. By virtue of (2·202) it follows that $v'(1, i) \vdash \sim t$ and $v'(1, j) \vdash \sim u$. Hence, cf. E2·19·95, $v'(1, i)$, $v'(1, j) \vdash \sim t. \sim u$. But also, cf. E2·19·100, $\sim t. \sim u \vdash \sim (t \lor u)$. And so, cf. E2·17·63, $v'(1, i)$, $v'(1, j) \vdash \sim (t \lor u)$. Accordingly, since $s = (t \lor u)$, $v'(1, i)$, $v'(1, j) \vdash \sim s$. Therefore

(2·209) if $Q(s) = 1$, $v'(1, n) \vdash \sim s$.

By (2·208) and (2·209)

(2·2010) (I) if $Q(s) = 0$, then $v'(1, n) \vdash s$, and (II) if
          $Q(s) = 1$, then $v'(1, n) \vdash \sim s$;

which completes the case of alternation.

(iii) If . is the principal connective, then there must be some t and some u each of degree not greater than m such that $s = (t.u)$, the constituent p.v.s of t being in the list $v(1, i)$, etc., as in (ii).

(I) If $Q(s) = 0$, then $Q(t) = 0$ and $Q(u) = 0$. Hence by virtue of (2·202), $v'(1, i) \vdash t$ and $v'(1, j) \vdash u$. So, cf. E2·19·95, $v'(1, i)$, $v'(1, j) \vdash t.u$. Accordingly

(2·2011) if $Q(s) = 0$, then $v'(1, n) \vdash s$.

(II) If $Q(s) = 1$, then (a) $Q(t) = 0$ and $Q(u) = 1$, or (b) $Q(t) = 1$ and $Q(u) = 0$, or (c) $Q(t) = 1$ and $Q(u) = 1$.

(a) If $Q(t) = 0$ and $Q(u) = 1$, then by virtue of (2·202) $v'(1, j) \vdash \sim u$. Hence, by virtue of axiom schema (2·164), $v'(1, j) \vdash \sim t \lor \sim u$. But, cf. E2·19·96, $\sim t \lor \sim u \vdash \sim (t.u)$; and so $v'(1, j) \vdash \sim s$. Therefore, cf. E2·17·62, $v'(1, i)$, $v'(1, j) \vdash \sim s$. Thus, $v'(1, n) \vdash \sim s$.

(b) If $Q(t) = 1$ and $Q(u) = 0$, then by virtue of (2·202) $v'(1, i) \vdash \sim t$, and so, by virtue of axiom schema (2·163), $v'(1, i) \vdash \sim t \lor \sim u$. Hence, as in (a), $v'(1, i)$, $v'(1, j) \vdash \sim s$. Therefore $v'(1, n) \vdash \sim s$.

(c) If $Q(t) = 1$ and $Q(u) = 1$, then by virtue of (2·202) $v'(1, i) \vdash \sim t$, and so, by reasoning exactly as in (b), again $v'(1, n) \vdash \sim s$.

Accordingly, by (a), (b), and (c),

(2·2012) if $Q(s) = 1$, then $v'(1, n) \vdash \sim s$.

By (2·2011) and (2·2012)

(2·2013) (I) if $Q(s) = 0$, then $v'(1, n) \vdash s$, and (II) if $Q(s) = 1$, then $v'(1, n) \vdash \sim s$;

which completes the case of conjunction.

(iv) If $\supset$ is the principal connective, then there must be some t and some u each of degree not greater than m such that $s = (t \supset u)$, the constituent p.v.s of t being in the list $v(1, i)$, etc., as in (ii).

(I) If $Q(s) = 0$, then (a) $Q(t) = 0$ and $Q(u) = 0$, or (b) $Q(t) = 1$ and $Q(u) = 0$, or (c) $Q(t) = 1$ and $Q(u) = 1$.

(a) If $Q(t) = 0$ and $Q(u) = 0$, then by virtue of (2·202) $v'(1, i) \vdash t$ and $v'(1, j) \vdash u$. Hence $v'(1, i)$, $v'(1, j) \vdash t \supset u$; for, cf. E2·17·62, $v'(1, i)$, $v'(1, j)$, $t \vdash u$, and so, by the Deduction Theorem, $v'(1, i)$, $v'(1, j) \vdash t \supset u$. Therefore $v'(1, n) \vdash s$.

(b) If $Q(t) = 1$ and $Q(u) = 0$, then by virtue of (2·202) $v'(1, j) \vdash u$. Hence $v'(1, i)$, $v'(1, j) \vdash t \supset u$; for $v'(1, j) \vdash u$ and so, cf. E2·17·62, $v'(1, i)$, $v'(1, j)$, $t \vdash u$, which yields the assertion made, by virtue of the Deduction Theorem. Therefore $v'(1, n) \vdash s$.

(c) If $Q(t) = 1$ and $Q(u) = 1$, then by virtue of (2·202) $v'(1, i) \vdash \sim t$. Hence $v'(1, i)$, $v'(1, j) \vdash t \supset u$; for $v'(1, i) \vdash \sim t$ and, by virtue of axiom schema (2·169), $\sim t \vdash t \supset u$. Therefore $v'(1, n) \vdash s$.

Accordingly, by (a), (b), and (c),

(2·2014)   if $Q(s) = 0$, then $v'(1, n) \vdash s$.

(II) If $Q(s) = 1$, then $Q(t) = 0$ and $Q(u) = 1$. Hence, by virtue of (2·202), $v'(1, i) \vdash t$ and $v'(1, j) \vdash \sim u$, so, cf. E2·19·95, $v'(1, i)$, $v'(1, j) \vdash t. \sim u$. Now therefore, cf. E2·18·90 and E2·18·91, $t. \sim u \vdash \sim (t \supset u)$. Accordingly $v'(1, i)$, $v'(1, j) \vdash \sim (t \supset u)$. Thus, $v'(1, n) \vdash \sim s$. So

(2·2015)   if $Q(s) = 1$, then $v'(1, n) \vdash \sim s$.

By (2·2014) and (2·2015)

(2·2016)   (I) if $Q(s) = 0$, then $v'(1, n) \vdash s$, and (II) if $Q(s) = 1$, then $v'(1, n) \vdash \sim s$;

which completes the case of implication.

Thus, on the supposition of (2·202) we have succeeded in demonstrating (2·203). Hence the demonstration of Theorem (2·201) is completed, by the principle of course-of-values induction.

We want next to show that

(2·2017) If $s(1, n-1)$, $s \vdash u$ and $s(1, n-1)$, $t \vdash u$, then $s(1, n-1)$, $s \lor t \vdash u$.

Suppose the antecedents in (2·2017). Then, by the Deduction Theorem, (i) $s(1, n-1) \vdash s \supset u$ and (ii) $s(1, n-1) \vdash t \supset u$. A proof of u on the hypotheses $s(1, n-1)$ and $s \lor t$ can be constructed as follows: $(a_1)\, s_1{}^\circ$; $(a_2)\, s_2{}^\circ$; ...; $(a_{n-1})\, s_{n-1}{}^\circ$; ...; (b) $s \supset u$ — by (i) and the preceding steps; (c) $t \supset u$ — by (ii) and preceding steps except (b); (d) $(s \supset u) \supset ((t \supset u) \supset ((s \lor t) \supset u))$ — ax

(2·165);   (e) $(t \supset u) \supset ((s \lor t) \supset u)$ — (b),   (d),   MP;
(f) $((s \lor t) \supset u$ — (c), (e), MP;   (g) $s \lor t^\circ$; (h) u—(g), (f),
MP.

(2·2018) **The Tautological Completeness Theorem for PCT:**
If s is a tautologous propositional schema, then $\vdash s$.

Demonstration: Let the distinct constituent p.v.s of s
be those in the list $v(1, n)$. Since s is a t.p.s., it follows from
the P.V. Sequence Theorem that, for all 2^n possible t.v.
combinations, $v'(1, n) \vdash s$. Applying (2·2017) repeatedly
(in fact at least $2^{n-1} + 2^{n-2} + \ldots + 1$ times) to the U-language
formula $v'(1, n) \vdash s$ yields

$$(2·2019) \qquad v_1 \lor \sim v_1, \; v_2 \lor \sim v_2, \; \ldots, \; v_n \lor \sim v_n \vdash s.$$

Consider, as an illustration, one application of (2·2017).
Since s is a t.p.s., $v'(1, n-1), \; v_n \vdash s$, and $v'(1, n-1),$
$\sim v_n \vdash s$. Consequently, by (2·2017), $v'(1, n-1),$
$v_n \lor \sim v_n \vdash s$.

Since, cf. E2·18·93, $\vdash v_i \lor \sim v_i$ for each i from 1 to n,
it follows, cf. E2·19·89, that $\vdash s$.   Thus, PCT is tautologically
complete.

(2·2020) **The Mutual Implication Theorem for PCT:** If s
and t are of the same order n and for each of the 2^n possible
t.v. combinations Q assignable to their constituent p.v.s
$Q(s) \equiv Q(t)$, then $\vdash s \supset t$ and $\vdash t \supset s$.

Demonstration: From the hypothesis that, for all 2^n
possible t.v. combinations assignable to the constituent
p.v.s. of s and t, $Q(s) \equiv Q(t)$, it follows that $s \supset t$ and
$t \supset s$ are t.p.s.s. For suppose that $s \supset t \, (t \supset s)$ is not a
t.p.s. Then, for some Q, $Q(s) = 0$ and $Q(t) = 1 \, (Q(s) = 1,$
and $Q(t) = 0$), which contradicts the hypothesis that
$Q(s) \equiv Q(t)$. Therefore both $s \supset t$ and $t \supset s$ are
t.p.s.s.   Hence, by the Tautological Completeness Theorem,
$\vdash s \supset t$ and $\vdash t \supset s$.

(2·2021) **The Absolute Completeness Theorem for PCT:** If a non-tautologous m.p.s. be added to the postulates (2·161) to (2·1610), then, for some p.s. t, both $\vdash$ t and $\vdash \sim$ t.

Demonstration: If W is added as a non-tautologous axiom schema, then it takes the t.v. falsity for at least one combination Q of t.v.s assignable to its constituent m.p.v.s. For any such combination Q put in $V \lor \sim V$ for each occurrence of the constituent m.p.v. V for which $Q(V) = 0$ and put in $V . \sim V$ for each occurrence of the constituent m.p.v. V for which $Q(V) = 1$. If the resulting m.p.s. is labelled "W_1", then W_1 is tautologically self-contradictory (cf. E2·6·6). If W_1 is of order n, its constituent m.p.v.s being exactly those in the list $V(1, n)$, then the m.p.s. denoted by W_2 which consists of the conjunction of all the $V_i . \sim V_i$ ($i = 1, 2, \ldots, n$) is also of order n and is tautologically self-contradictory.

Let s denoted any p.s. of the form of the m.p.s. denoted by W_1, and let t denoted any p.s. of the form of the m.p.s. denoted by W_2 provided that s and t are of the same order. Both s and t are tautologically self-contradictory, so by the Mutual Implication Theorem $\vdash s \supset t$. But s is (denotes) an axiom, and therefore $\vdash s$. Hence $\vdash t$. But since t is tautologically self-contradictory, $\sim t$ is a t.p.s. By the Tautological Completeness Theorem, $\vdash \sim t$. Accordingly, both $\vdash$ t and $\vdash \sim$ t.

Consider an example. Let W denoted $s \supset (s.t)$; then W_1 denotes $(s \lor \sim s) \supset ((s \lor \sim s).(t. \sim t))$. Thus the number n of the constituent m.p.v.s of W is 2, the m.p.v.s in the list $V(1, 2)$ being s and t. Hence W_2 denotes $(s. \sim s).(t. \sim t)$. s can denote

(2·2022)

$((p \supset r) \lor \sim (p \supset r)) \supset (((p \supset r) \lor \sim (p \supset r)).(q. \sim q));$

then t can denote, for example,

(2·2023) $((q.r). \sim (q.r)).((p \lor r). \sim (p \lor r)).$

If $s \supset (s.t)$ is an axiom schema, then obviously (2·2022) is an axiom and so categorically provable; again, obviously, (2·2022) is tautologically self-contradictory, for its antecedent is always true and its consequent always false. Also (2·2023) is clearly tautologically self-contradictory, being the conjunction of two p.s.s each of which is tautologically self-contradictory. By the Mutual Implication Theorem and the fact that (2·2022) is an axiom, it follows that (2·2023) is categorically provable. But by the Tautological Completeness Theorem the negation of (2·2023), which is a t.p.s., is also categorically provable.

*EXERCISES

E2·20·102. For an axiomatic d.s. of the PC, a p.s. s is said to be a *variant* of the p.s. t if and only if s is identical with t except that for each occurrence of at least one p.v. v of t there has been a substitution by the p.v. v_1, that is different from v. Show that a variant of a categorical theorem in (i) PCWR and (ii) PCŁ, is a categorical theorem.

E2·20·103. For an axiomatic d.s. of the PC we may disregard having a rule of replacement even if there are definitions; regarding s and t as identical if they differ only in so far as that by the further use of definitional equivalencies they could be made literally identical. Then the notation "$s(1, n) \vdash t$" means (assuming MP and Substitution): there is a finite sequence of p.s.s $t_1, t_2, \ldots, t_m (= t)$, where for each i ($i = 1, 2, \ldots, m$) either (i) t_i is s_j for some j; or (ii) t_i is an axiom; or (iii) t_i is a variant of an axiom; or (iv) t_i is inferred by MP from t_j and t_k ($j < i, k < i$); or (v) t_i is inferred by Substitution from t_j ($j < i$) *where the variable substituted for does not occur in* $s(1, n)$. Establish

The Deduction Theorem for PCWR: If $s(1, n) \vdash t$, then $s(1, n-1) \vdash s \supset t$.
PCWR   PCWR

E2·20·104. **The Deduction Theorem for PCŁ**: If $s(1, n) \vdash t$, then $s(1, n-1) \vdash Cs_n t$.
PCŁ   PCŁ

E2·20·105. **The Simple-Consistency Theorem for PCWR**: PCWR is simply-consistent.

E2·20·106. **The Absolute Consistency Theorem for PCWR**: PCWR is absolutely consistent.

E2·20·107. **The Tautological Completeness Theorem**: PCWR is tautologically complete.

E2·20·108. **The Tautological Completeness Theorem for PCŁ**: PCŁ is tautologically complete.

E2·20·109. The axiomatic d.s. PCF[1] has the rules MP and Substitution, and the axioms: (a) $p \supset (q \supset p)$;
(b) $[r \supset (p \supset q)] \supset [(r \supset p) \supset (r \supset q)]$;
(c) $[p \supset (q \supset r)] \supset [q \supset (p \supset r)]$;
(d) $(p \supset q) \supset (\sim q \supset \sim p)$; (e) $\sim \sim p \supset p$;
(f) $p \supset \sim \sim p$. Demonstrate:

The Simple-Consistency Theorem for PCF: PCF is simply-consistent.

E2·20·110. **The Tautological Completeness Theorem for PCF**: PCF is tautologically complete.

E2·20·111. Establish (2·2021) without using (2·2020).

---

[1] Frege: *Begriffschrift*.

CHAPTER THREE

THE FUNCTIONAL CALCULUS

3·01 Introduction

In this chapter we are concerned with the Pure Functional Calculus of the First Order (FC). This part of logic constitutes a generalisation of the PC. It can be regarded as the theory of unanalysed propositions, on the one hand, and of propositional functions, whether or not governed by quantifiers for term variables, on the other. For the FC a propositional function is an expression that contains variables for subjects, individuals, not for properties or relations, and which would become a proposition if appropriate names or descriptions were substituted for the variables. *E.g.* "*p* is a prime number" is a propositional function; as it stands it is neither true nor false, but it would become true-or-false if *p* were replaced by a positive integer, say by "3" or by "4". Quantifiers are expressions (or what is signified by expressions) such as "for all" and "for some". They play a fundamental role in all sciences since they are involved in all general statements.

We begin the chapter by explaining the nature of propositional functions and of quantifiers. After introducing Peano-Russell and Łukasiewicz-Tarski "languages" for the FC, we then present an axiom schemata system for the FC, which we label "FCT". It is formally the same as PCT but has two additional postulates and two additional rules, all four of which relate to quantifiers. We take over without further comment the notions and symbols connected with proof and provability that were introduced when we dealt with PCT.

Next we describe the Suppositional Method of proof for the FC; this method requires the use of only rules of deduction, no postulates at all. The rules are derived from epitheorems of FCT. The advantage of this method is that it makes the constructive proof of theorems a great deal simpler. The rules of this method for FCT also form a large part of the body of rules that is needed for the application of this method of deduction to mathematics.

3·02 Propositional Functions, Term Variables, and Formulae

We shall use the term "formula" as a generic term, of which there are two species: propositions and propositional functions.[1] About the nature of propositions we need

---

[1] The name *propositional function* is due to Russell: *Principles of Mathematics*. What we are here calling a propositional function is often called a *propositional form*.

here say no more. A propositional function is the sort of statement that mathematical statements commonly are, for these, typically, contain free variables. A free variable is, subject to refinements we shall mention later on, a letter denoting arbitrary members of a certain class, such as the class of integers, the class of rational numbers or the class of points in a Cartesian plane, the letter being used in such a way as to allow of other letters denoting arbitrary members, or denoting a particular member, of the same class to be substituted for the original letter. Thus, if the letters a, b, c, i, j, and m are used for integers, then the statement "if $a > b$ and $b > c$, then $a > c$" is a propositional function; and that statement can be transformed, by substituting other variables, into "if $i > j$ and $j > m$, then $i > m$", and can again be transformed, now by substituting constants denoting particular individuals, into "if $68 > 40$ and $40 > 80$, then $68 > 80$", which is a proposition and a true one; cf. **2·04**. It may be noticed in passing that, at least when the connective symbols are replaced by appropriate words in ordinary language, all the schemata of L_1 and L_2 are propositional functions (p.f.s) and not propositions, the p.v.s in a p.s. of L_1 denoting arbitrary members of the class of propositions, and the m.p.v.s in a m.p.s. of L_2 denoting arbitrary members of the class of p.s.s of L_1; if constants are substituted for the p.v.s in a p.s., actual (ordinary) propositions are obtained, and if constants are substituted for the m.p.v.s in a m.p.s., abstract (theoretical) propositions are obtained.

It is seen, then, that the statement "m is a prime number" is not a proposition but a p.f. It is neither true nor false. However, it can be transformed into a proposition by making appropriate substitutions for m in terms of constants. For instance, "4 is a prime number" and "5 is a prime number" are propositions obtainable from the given p.f. Again, the statement "if $i = j$, then $j = i$" is not a proposition but a p.f. It can be transformed into a proposition by making appropriate substitutions for "i" and "j" in terms of constants. For instance, "if $(1 + 1) + 1 = 3$, then $3 = (1 + 1) + 1$" is a proposition.

In the examples we have presented concerning p.f.s the variables are term variables, that is they denote arbitrary *objects* of a physical or conceptual kind, and do not denote arbitrary *properties* or *qualities*. A term variable is akin to a variable noun rather than akin to a variable adjective.

A p.f. is a p.f. of n term variables ($n = 1, 2, 3, \ldots$) if and only if there is at least one occurrence in it of n distinct term variables. *E.g.* "m is a prime number" is a p.f. of 1 term variable, "if m_1 and m_2 are prime numbers, then the product of m_1 and m_2 is not a prime number" is a p.f. of 2 term variables, and "if $i = j$ and $j = m$, then $i = m$" is a p.f. of 3 term variables.

It will occasionally be useful to have a term to stand for what, in this section, we have been calling a *statement*. We have been using the term "statement" to denote indiscriminately both propositions and p.f.s. As indicated at the beginning of this section, we shall employ the term "formula" for this generic purpose. Hence, "m is a prime number", "3 is a prime number", and "41 is a prime number" are formulae.

3·03 Quantifiers

The formula "m is a prime number" is a p.f. But the formula "There is at least one m such that m is a prime number" is not a p.f. It is a proposition and a true one, for what it says is that there is at least one prime number; and this is true since, *e.g.* 2 is a prime number. Again, the formula "No matter what (positive integer) m is, m is a prime number" is not a p.f. It is a proposition and a false one, for what it says is that every positive integer is a prime number; and this is false since, *e.g.* 4 is not a prime number. Expressions (or what they denote) of the sort "There is at least one—such that" and of the sort "No matter what—is" are called *quantifiers*.[1] An expression of the former sort is said to be a *particular quantifier* or *existential quantifier*. An expression of the latter sort is said to be a *universal quantifier*. In the Peano-Russell notation the particular quantifier is represented by "($\exists$)" and the universal quantifier by "( )". Thus, "There is at least one *m* such that" is translated into "($\exists m$)", and "No matter what *m* is" is translated into "(m)". In the Łukasiewicz-Tarski notation the particular quantifier is represented by the capital sigma Σ and the universal quantifier by the capital pi Π.[2] Regardless of what symbolism is employed, it is convenient in English to read the particular quantifier as "for some" and the universal quantifier as "for all" or "for each".

We shall call the expression consisting of a quantifier followed on its right by a term variable, a *quantificational expression* (q.e.). For instance, in the formula "($\exists i$) (j) ($i + j = j$)", there are two q.e.s: ($\exists i$) and (j). In the usual employment of both the Peano-Russell and the Łukasiewicz-Tarski notations a q.e. can contain an occurrence of only a single term variable, so that an expression such as (xy) or as Σxyz would not be permitted. We shall follow the usual practice when presenting formulae in the Peano-Russell notation, but the Łukasiewicz-Tarski notation will be modified in two respects. In the first

[1] Quantifiers were introduced by Peirce: *Amer. J. Math.*, 1885, **7**, 180-202.

[2] The notation ( ) is due to Whitehead and Russell: *Principia Mathematica I*. The notation ($\exists$) is due to Peano; he used the notation $\supset_x$ for the universal quantifier in implicative formulae; *e.g.* $(a > b) \supset_{ab} (a - b > 0)$. Cf. Peano: *Arithmetices Principia*, (Turin, 1889). The symbol ($\forall$) for the universal quantifier was introduced by Heyting, A. (1898-): "Die formalen Regeln der intuitionistischen Logik", *Sitzungsber. preuss. Akad. Wiss. Berlin*, 1930, 42-56; it is rapidly replacing ( ).

place, S and P will be used instead of Σ and Π respectively; that is, in bracket-free formulae S will be the particular, and P the universal, quantifier. In the second place, we shall allow expressions such as Sxy and $Pyzxx_1$ to rank as q.e.s.

3·04 Free and Bound Occurrences of Term Variables

The occurrence of m in "m is a prime number" is said to be a *free* occurrence of the variable m. Similarly, all the occurrences of "i" and "j" in the formula "for every prime number m, if m is a factor of $i \times j$, then m is a factor of either i or j" are free; on the other hand, each occurrence of m in this formula is said to be *bound*.

By definition, an occurrence of a term variable is bound if and only if it is either (i) in a q.e. or (ii) within the scope of a q.e. that contains an occurrence of that term variable. Thus, in the last example, the first occurrence of m is bound because it is in the q.e. "for every (prime number) m", the bracketed phrase indicating only the class of objects for any one of whose members m is standing; the second and third occurrences of m are bound because they are within the scope of a q.e. that contains an occurrence of m. Again, in

$$(3·041) \qquad (i)\,(j)\,(m)\,[(i > j . m > 0) \supset (mi > mj)],$$

all the occurrences of the variables are bound. By definition, an occurrence of a term variable is said to be *free* if and only if it is not bound. In

$$(3·042) \qquad (i)\,[(m > 0) \supset (mi > 0 \equiv i > 0)],$$

each occurrence of i is bound and each occurrence of m is free. In

$$(3·043) \qquad [(\exists i)\,(i > 0)] \supset [(j)\,(ij > m)],$$

the first two occurrences of i are bound and the third is

free; both the occurrences of j are bound, but the occurrence of m is free.[1]

3·05 Functional Variables and Schemata

The general theory of formulae, in so far as the only variables to occur in q.e.s are term variables, is the subject-matter of that part of logic called the *Functional Calculus* (*of first order*), the *Predicate Calculus* (*of first order*) or the *Quantificational Calculus*. We shall employ the first of these names and, for simplicity, we shall omit the parenthetical qualification. The Functional Calculus (FC) is that part of logic which deals not only with propositions but also with propositional functions; it therefore contains the PC as a portion of itself.

The language FL_1 PR has for its alphabet: $\sim$, $\lor$, ., and $\supset$; the *term variables* x, y, z, with or without positive integral subscripts; the *functional variables* b, d, h, $b(x)$, $b(x, y)$, $b(x, y, z)$, ..., where each letter can have a positive integral subscript; (,), $\exists$. A functional variable (f.v.) cannot have more than one occurrence of the same term variable in its bracketed part; *e.g.* although $d(x, y_1)$ and h are f.v.s, $b(x, x)$, $h(y_1, y_1)$ and $d(x, y, x)$ are not f.v.s. F.v.s with a bracketed portion are said to have *attached term variables*. F.v.s with no attached term variables are intended to represent propositions: they have the role of p.v.s.

We shall use b, d, and h, with or without positive integral subscripts, as variables for the well-formed formulae of FL_1PR (and of FL_1LT, when that is introduced). Similarly, we shall use x, y, and z, with or without positive integral subscripts, to represent the term variables x, y, z,

[1] The terminology of "free" and "bound" variables is due to Hilbert (1922), cited in **2·08**, and to Hilbert and Ackermann: *Grundzüge der theoretischen Logik*. The older terminology was of "real" and "apparent" variables; this was due to Peano: *Formulaire de Mathématiques II (I)* p. 23, Turin, 1897.

etc. Although an expression such as $b(x, y)$ stands for a p.f. in which there are precisely two term variables each of which has at least one free occurrence, an expression such as b (x, y) is not restricted to denoting a well-formed formula in FL_1PR which contains free occurrences of precisely two variables; what it denotes may contain no free variables or more than two free variables. The purpose of such an expression with attached metalinguistic term variables is only to permit a more compact and precise formulation of rules of deduction, postulates, and epitheorems. The meaning of an expression such as b (x, y) is this: (i) b (x, y) stands for any well-formed formula in FL_1PR ($FL_1ŁT$); (ii) *if* there are free occurrences of (what is denoted by) x and y in (what is denoted by) b (x, y), then b (x_1, y_1) denotes precisely the same as (what is denoted by) b (x, y) except that an occurrence of (what is denoted by) x_1 replaces each *free* occurrence, if any, of (what is denoted by) x and an occurrence of (what is denoted by) y_1 replaces each free occurrence, if any, of (what is denoted by) y. For example, let x denote x and let b (x) denote

(3·051) $\qquad [(\exists x) b (x, y)] \supset [(y) d (x, y)];$

then if y denotes y, b (y) denotes

(3·052) $\qquad [(\exists x) b (x, y)] \supset [(y) d (y, y)].$

Again, let x denote x and let y denote y, and let b (x, y) denote

(3·053) $\quad [(\exists x) (y) (b (x) \supset d (y))] \supset [(\exists y) h (x, y)];$

then if x_1 denotes y and y_1 denotes x, b (x_1, y_1) denotes

(3·054) $\quad [(\exists x) (y) (b (x) \supset d (y))] \supset [(\exists y) h (y, y)].$

We can now enunciate the rules of formation for FL_1PR; a well-formed formula in FL_1PR will be called a *functional schema* (f.s.). (i) F.v.s are f.s.s if they are surrounded by a pair of round brackets; (ii) for all integral $n \geq 1$, if b $(x_1, x_2, \ldots, x_n)$ denotes a f.v. and $y_1, y_2, \ldots, y_n$ denote n term variables (which are not necessarily different from one another, nor need y_i be different from x_i), then b $(y_1, y_2, \ldots, y_n)$ is (denotes) a f.s. if it is surrounded by a pair of round brackets; (iii) an expression consisting of $\sim$ followed on the right by a f.s. is a f.s. if it is surrounded by a pair of round brackets; (iv) an expression consisting of **V**, ., or $\supset$ between two f.s.s is a f.s. if it is surrounded by a pair of round brackets; (v) an expression consisting of a (Peano-Russell) q.e. followed on the right by a f.s. is a f.s. if it is surrounded by a pair of round brackets; (vi) (i) to (v) give the only f.s.s in FL_1PR. As in the previous chapter we shall, for practical reasons, omit a large number of brackets that are strictly required when presenting an expression as a f.s.

The language FL_1LT has for its alphabet: N, A, K, and C; x, y, z, etc.; b, d, h, etc., bx, bxy, $bxyz$, etc. As exercises for the reader we leave the enunciation of formation rules of FL_1LT and of formation rules for the metalanguages FL_2PR and FL_2LT.

3·06 An Axiom Schemata System for the Functional Calculus (FCT)

The deductive system that we proceed to establish, for the FC, is essentially, from the formal point of view, the same as PCT, with the addition of two axiom schemata and two rules of deduction. However, the metalinguistic schemata variables in the new formulation of the earlier axiom schemata (2·161) to (2·1610) have now to be regarded as denoting f.s.s not p.s.s. The axiom schemata system that we are here concerned with will be labelled "FCT". The axiom schemata are:

(3·061) b $\supset$ (d $\supset$ b) $CbCdb$

(3·062) [b $\supset$ (d $\supset$ h)] $\supset$ [(b $\supset$ d) $\supset$ (b $\supset$ h)]
                                $CCbCdhCCbdCbh$

(3·063)	b ⊃ (b ∨ d)	$CbAbd$
(3·064)	d ⊃ (b ∨ d)	$CdAbd$
(3·065)	[b ⊃ h] ⊃ [(d ⊃ h) ⊃ ((b ∨ d) ⊃ h)]	
		$CCbhCCdhCAbdh$
(3·066)	(b.d) ⊃ b	$CKbdb$
(3·067)	(b.d) ⊃ d	$CKbdd$
(3·068)	[h ⊃ b] ⊃ [(h ⊃ d) ⊃ (h ⊃ (b.d))]	
		$CChbCChdChKbd$
(3·069)	∼ b ⊃ (b ⊃ d)	$CNbCbd$
(3·0610)	(∼ b ⊃ b) ⊃ b	$CCNbbb$
(3·0611)	[(x) b (x)] ⊃ [b (y)]	$CPxbxby$
(3·0612)	b (y) ⊃ [(∃ x) b (x)]	$CbySxbx.$

In (3·0611) and (3·0612) y must be free for x in b (x), that is no free occurrence of the term variable denoted by x can be in the scope of a q.e. containing an occurrence of the term variable denoted by y. Thus, if x denotes x and b (x) denotes $(y) b (x, y)$, then

(3·0613) $[(x) (y) b (x, y)] ⊃ [(y) b (y, y)]$

is not an axiom of the type (3·0611), because y is not free for x in $(y) b (x, y)$: x occurs freely in the scope of (y). On the other hand, if x denotes z and b (x) denotes $b (z, y)$, then

(3·0614) $[(z) b (z, y)] ⊃ [b (x, y)]$

and

(3·0615) $[(z) b (z, y)] ⊃ [b (y, y)]$

are both axioms of the type (3·0611), for x is free for z in $b (z, y)$ and y is free for z in $b (z, y)$.

The rules of deduction of FCT are:

Rule of Modus Ponens: If the f.s.s (denoted by) b and b ⊃ d [Cbd] are steps in a proof, then it is legitimate to affirm the f.s. (denoted by) d as a subsequent step in the proof.

Rule of Universal Quantifier Introduction: If the f.s. d ⊃ b (x) [*C*dbx], where the term variable x has no free occurrences in d, occurs as a step in a proof, then it is legitimate to affirm the f.s. d ⊃ (x) b (x) [*Cd*P*xbx*] as a subsequent step in the proof. (We have, in accordance with standard usage, omitted repeating the phrase "denoted by". We shall leave it henceforth to the reader, except occasionally, to insert this and analogous phrases.)

Rule of Particular Quantifier Introduction: If the f.s. b (x) ⊃ d [*C*bxd], where x has no free occurrences in d, occurs as a step in a proof, then it is legitimate to affirm the f.s. [(∃ x) b (x)] ⊃ d [*CS*xbxd] as a subsequent step in the proof.[1]

It is clear that any epitheorem for PCT will have a valid analogue in FCT if and only if the PCT demonstration did not depend upon the whole body of postulates and rule as being the only ones in the system, for which the epitheorem was to hold; for FCT contains whatever PCT contains—and more. For example, the PCT epitheorem s ⊢ s ∨ t can, apart from differences of notation, be obtained in FCT:

(3·0616) b°

(3·0617) b ⊃ (b ∨ d)

(3·0618) b ∨ d

References.—17: axs (3·063). 18: 16, 17, MP.

On the other hand, those PCT epitheorems whose demonstrations do involve the whole apparatus—postulates and rule—of the system will not automatically be valid for FCT since in FCT there are additional cases to be considered—two extra postulates and two extra rules—whose

---

[1] The two quantifier rules and the schemata (3·0611) and (3·0612) have their ultimate source in the axiomatic d.s. for the FC of Whitehead and Russell: *Principia Mathematica I.* They define the particular in terms of the universal quantifier:

$$(\exists x) \, b \, (x) =_{df} \sim (x) \sim b \, (x).$$

nature might make an essential difference, so that the PCT epitheorem is not a (valid) FCT epitheorem. In any case, if the demonstration of the epitheorem does depend on the whole apparatus, the demonstration within PCT will be inadequate as a demonstration for the FCT version of the formula. Hence, in particular, the Deduction Theorem, the Consistency Theorems and the Completeness Theorems for PCT cannot, without further consideration of the additional cases that arise from the extension of PCT to FCT, be taken to have valid analogues in FCT.

EXERCISES

E3·6·1. Establish the analogues in FCT of: (2·171); (2·1718); E2·17·59 to E2·17·71.

E3·6·2. Construct a categorical proof of $[(x) b (x). \sim (x) b (x)] \supset d$.

E3·6·3. Construct a categorical proof of $[\sim \sim (x) b (x)] \supset b (x)$.

*E3·6·4. (i) If b (1, n) ⊢ d, then d is said to *depend* on b_i ($i = 1, 2, \ldots, n$) if and only if it is not the case that b (1, $i - 1$), b ($i + 1, n$) ⊢ d. (ii) If b (1, n) ⊢ d, then y is said to be *held constant* for b_n if and only if either (a) y has no free occurrences in b_n, or (b) neither the rule of universal quantifier introduction nor the rule of particular quantifier introduction is used in the deduction of d from b (1, n). Demonstrate:

The Deduction Theorem for FCT:[1] If b (1, n) ⊢ d with the free term variables held constant for b_n, then b (1, $n - 1$) ⊢ b ⊃ d (Cb_nd). (First construct an argument strictly analogous to that in 2·18 up to the listing of the alternatives (a), (b), (c), and (d) there; secondly, consider the two additional cases that arise from the two extra rules in FCT: (e) univ. quant. introd., (f) part. quant. introd.; thirdly, consider (e) in relation to the two possibilities that the step of the form h ⊃ b (x) which produces d does, or does not, depend on b (x); and fourthly, consider (f) in relation to the two possibilities that the step of the form b (x) ⊃ h which produces d does, or does not, depend on b (x).)

E3·6·5. Show that (x) b (x) ⊃ (∃ x) b (x) is categorically provable.

E3·6·6. Establish the analogues in FCT of: E2·18·72 to E2·18·81; E2·18·88 to E2·18·93.

---

[1] The Deduction Theorem for the FC was first established by Herbrand: *Recherches sur la Théorie de la Démonstration*.

3·07 The Suppositional Method of Proof

It is easy to formulate p.s.s and f.s.s which are known on general, epitheoretic grounds to be categorically provable and which are yet such that the actual construction of categorical proofs of them involves the expenditure of inordinate difficulty and labour; cf. E2·13·58. This disadvantage of the postulational method in logic is to a great extent overcome by that other kind of d.s. which was briefly referred to in 2·08: a deductive system without postulates and with only rules of deduction. This kind of d.s. we shall call a *suppositional* d.s. and the method of deduction employed therein we shall call the *suppositional method.*[1]

A[2] proof in a suppositional d.s. has two parts, a proof structure and an appended list of references. The proof structure contains a number of formulae and it is constituted by these formulae in such a way that, subject to qualifications to be mentioned later, every step that is not a hypothesis (supposition) has to be a consequence of at least one preceding step in accordance with certain prescribed rules of deduction. In the list of references are cited the rules of deduction that serve to justify the presence of the non-suppositional steps in the proof structure.

In our arrangement of proof structures there are always several sections, which can be of order 1, order 2, and so on finitely. There can be only one section of order 1 but any finite number of sections for each of the higher

[1] The name "suppositional method" was proposed by Nidditch: *I.F.L.M.* The usual name is "natural deduction", (the German equivalent of) this name being introduced by Gentzen, G. (1909-45): "Untersuchungen über logische Schliessen I", *Math. Z.*, 1934-5, **39**, 176-210.

[2] The set-up described in this and the following paragraphs was introduced by Nidditch: *I.F.L.M.* This work was influenced by Fitch, F. B. (1908-): *Symbolic Logic, An Introduction* (New York, 1952). One convenient advance in *I.F.L.M.* was the introduction of the section of order 1; another was the restriction to a single supposition in sections of order $n \geq 2$.

orders. The section of order 1 cannot have a supposition. Any section of higher order can but need not have a supposition; if it does have a supposition, it can have only one. This restriction to a single supposition is not a limitation on what can be proved, for if one wished to adopt m f.s.s b_1 to b_m ($m \geq 2$) as suppositions, one can adopt instead the single supposition consisting of the conjunction of all the b_i. We shall indicate suppositions as previously we indicated hypotheses, by placing a small superscript circle to the right of the formula being supposed.

By definition, a formula is a categorical theorem (or theorem schema) in a suppositional d.s. if and only if there is a proof whose proof structure contains the formula as a step in the section of order 1. In practice the problem of constructing a suppositional method categorical proof is to determine, having placed the formula to be proved at the foot of the section of order 1 of a blank proof structure, how the blank can be so filled in that the formula can legitimately remain where it is because it is a consequence of justifiable, preceding steps by virtue of the rules of deduction.

Our arrangement for suppositional method proofs is to put the proof structure first and to append the list of references underneath. The general character of such a proof is illustrated by the following example, which is a categorical proof of $((b \supset d) . \sim d) \supset \sim b$ [$CKCbdNdNb$], since this f.s. is a step in the section of order 1.

The proof structure in this example has nine steps, which are numbered consecutively, the numbers being placed to the left of the vertical line marking the section of order 1. The structure contains three sections, one of each of the orders 1, 2, and 3. The section of order 1 has a single step, (3·079). The section of order 2 has four steps, (3·071), (3·072), (3·073), and (3·078). The section of order 3 has four steps, (3·074), (3·075), (3·076), and

(3·077). All the steps in each section are joined by a vertical line on their left.

(3·071)	$(b \supset d) . \sim d°$	$KCbdNd°$
(3·072)	$b \supset d$	Cbd
(3·073)	$\sim d$	Nd
(3·074)	$b°$	$b°$
(3·075)	$b \supset d$	Cbd
(3·076)	d	d
(3·077)	$\sim d$	Nd
(3·078)	$\sim b$	Nb
(3·079)	$((b \supset d) . \sim d) \supset \sim b$	$CKCbdNdNb$

References.—2: 1, con ex. 3: 1, con ex. 5: 2, tf. 6: 4, 5, imp ex. 7: 3, tf. 8: 6, 7, neg in. 9: 1, 8, imp in.

If S_1 and S_2 denote any two section of a proof structure, then S_2 is said to be *within* S_1 and S_1 is said, correlatively, to *contain* S_2 if and only if no part of the vertical line for S_2 goes above or below the vertical line for S_1.

It is a requirement for the formation of proof structures that if S is any section of order n ($n \geq 2$), then S must be within a section of order $n - 1$. Thus in our example above, the vertical line for the section of order 3 extends neither above nor below the vertical line for the section of order 2, and the latter line extends neither above nor below the vertical line for the section of order 1. It is an immediate consequence of the requirement mentioned that in any proof structure each section of order n ($n \geq 2$) must be within at least one section of each of the orders $n - i$ ($i = 1, 2, \ldots, n - 1$), and, in particular, the section of order 1 must contain all the sections of higher order.

Turning briefly to the references in our example, (3·072) is justified by the Rule of Conjunction Expulsion ("con ex", for short) applied to (3·071); (3·073) is justified on the same grounds; (3·075) is justified by the Rule of

Transference ("tf", for short) applied to (3·072); (3·076) is justified by the Rule of Implication Expulsion ("imp ex", for short) applied to (3·074) and (3·075); (3·077) is justified by the Rule of Transference applied to ·(3·073); (3·078) is justified by the Rule of Negation Introduction ("neg in", for short) applied to (3·076) and (3·077); and (3·079) is justified by the Rule of Implication Introduction ("imp in", for short) applied to (3·071) and (3·078). These rules and the others belonging to the suppositional method version of FCT will be formulated in **3·08.**

3·08 The Suppositional Method Version of FCT (SFCT)

Two approaches to the body of rules for a suppositional d.s. for the FC are possible. On the first approach, the rules are devised in complete independence of any postulational d.s. for the FC. This allows a suppositional d.s. for the FC to be constructed initially, instead of a postulational d.s. for the FC having to be constructed first. The disadvantage of this approach is that there is a consequent difficulty in demonstrating the consistency and completeness of the rules employed. Indeed, on this approach the difficulty in establishing such epitheorems is very great. On the second approach, the rules of the suppositional d.s. for the FC are treated directly in relation to some antecedently constructed postulational d.s.; they are treated as derived from the latter. With this approach the demonstrations of consistency and completeness for the suppositional d.s. are fairly simple, provided of course that the corresponding epitheorems for the basic postulational d.s. have been established. Because of these epitheoretic advantages we shall adopt the second approach. The postulational d.s. FCT forms the basis of our suppositional d.s. for the FC, which we shall label "SFCT".

The rules of deduction of SFCT are fifteen in number. In this section we shall give only those (eleven) rules which do not involve quantifiers.

(i) *Rule of Alternation Introduction*.—If b is (denotes) any step in a section of order n ($n \geq 1$) of a proof structure, then each of b ∨ d [Abd] and d ∨ b [Adb] may be asserted as subsequent steps in the section of order n containing b. The reference for a step that is asserted on the grounds of this rule consists of the proof number of b, followed by "alt in".

The two forms of this rule are derived from the FCT epitheorems

(3·081)   b $(1, m)$, b ⊢ b ∨ d   b $(1, m)$, b ⊢ Abd
and

(3·082)   b $(1, m)$, b ⊢ d ∨ b   b $(1, m)$, b ⊢ Adb.

These epitheorems are direct consequences of (3·063) and (3·064). They can be established by using MP. In (3·081) and (3·082), as always, b $(1, m)$ may be vacuous.

(ii) *Rule of Alternation Expulsion*.—If b ∨ d [Abd] is a step in a section of order n ($n \geq 1$) of a proof structure, then, if there are two sections of order $n + 1$ such that b is a supposition in one and h is another step therein, and d is a supposition in the other, and (the same) h is another step therein, then h may be asserted as a subsequent step in the original section of order n, *i.e.* in the section containing b ∨ d [Abd]. The reference for a step that is asserted on the grounds of this rule consists of the proof number of b ∨ d [Abd], followed by the proof numbers of h in the b° section and then in the d° section, followed by "alt ex".

This rule is derived from the FCT epitheorem

(3·083)   if b $(1, m)$ ⊢ b ∨ d (Abd) and b ⊢ h and d ⊢ h, then b $(1, m)$ ⊢ h.

This epitheorem is easily established by using the FCT version of the Deduction Theorem and (3·065).

(iii) *Rule of Conjunction Introduction.*—If b and d are any steps in the same section of order n ($n \geq 1$) of a proof structure, then b . d [Kbd] may be asserted as a subsequent step in the same section. The reference for a step that is asserted on the grounds of this rule consists of the proof numbers of b and of d in that order, followed by "con in".

This rule is derived from the FCT epitheorem

(3·084)   if b $(1, m)$ ⊢ b and b $(1, m)$ ⊢ d, then
b $(1, m)$ ⊢ b . d (Kbd).

This epitheorem can be established by means of the FCT version of the Deduction Theorem and (3·068).

(iv) *Rule of Conjunction Expulsion.*—If b . d [Kbd] is a step in a section of order n ($n \geq 1$) of a proof structure, then each of b and d may be asserted as subsequent steps in that same section. The reference for a step that is asserted on the grounds of this rule consists of the proof number of b . d [Kbd], followed by "con ex".

The two forms of this rule are derived from the FCT epitheorems

(3·085)   if b $(1, m)$ ⊢ b . d (Kbd), then b $(1, m)$ ⊢b

and

(3·086)   if b $(1, m)$ ⊢ b . d (Kbd), then b $(1, m)$ ⊢ d.

These epitheorems follow from (3·066) and (3·067).

(v) *Rule of Implication Introduction.*—If b is a suppositional step in a section of order n ($n \geq 2$) of a proof structure, and d is any other step in the same section, then b ⊃ d [Cbd] may be asserted as a subsequent step in the containing section of order $n - 1$. The reference for a step that is asserted on the grounds of this rule consists of the proof number of b° and then of d, followed by "imp in".

This rule is derived from the FCT version of the Deduction Theorem.

(vi) *Rule of Implication Expulsion.*—If b is a step in a section of order $n (n \geq 1)$ of a proof structure, and b ⊃ d [Cbd] is another step in the same section, then d may be asserted as a subsequent step in the same section. The reference for a step that is asserted on the grounds of this rule consists of the proof numbers of b and then of b ⊃ d [Cbd], followed by "imp ex".

This rule is derived from the FCT epitheorem
(3·087) if b (1, m) ⊢ b and b (1, m) ⊢ b ⊃ d (Cbd), then b (1, m) ⊢ d. This epitheorem is established by means of Modus Ponens: (*a*) b (1, m)°; (*b*) b—given as yielded by (*a*); (*c*) b ⊃ d—given as yielded by (*a*); (*d*) d — (*b*), (*c*), MP ("b (1, m)°" means: b_1°; b_2°; ...; b_m°.)

(vii) *Rule of Negation Introduction.*—If b is a suppositional step in a section of order $n (n \geq 2)$ of a proof structure, and both d and ∼ d [Nd] are steps in that section, then ∼ b [Nb] may be asserted as a subsequent step in the containing section of order $n - 1$. The reference for a step that is asserted on the grounds of this rule consists of the proof number of d and then of ∼ d [Nd], followed by "neg in".

This rule is derived from the FCT epitheorem
(3·088) if b (1, m), b ⊢ d, and b (1, m), b ⊢ ∼ d (Nd), then b (1, m) ⊢ ∼ b (Nb).
Cf. E2·18·90 and E2·18·91.

(viii) *Rule of Negation Expulsion.*—If b and ∼ b [Nb] are two steps in the same section of order $n (n \geq 1)$ of a proof structure, then d may be asserted as a subsequent step in the same section. The reference for a step that is asserted on the grounds of this rule consists of the proof number of b and then of ∼ b [Nb], followed by "neg ex".

This rule is derived from the FCT epitheorem

(3·089) if b (1, m) ⊢ b and b (1, m) ⊢ ∼ b (Nb), then b (1, m) ⊢ d.

This epitheorem can be established easily by use of (3·069).

(ix) *Rule of Repetition.*—If b is a step in a section of order n ($n \geq 1$) of a proof structure, then b may be asserted as a subsequent step in the same section. The reference for a step that is asserted on the grounds of this rule consists of the proof number of the original b, followed by "re".

This rule is derived from the FCT epitheorems

(3·0810) if b (1, m) ⊢ b, then b (1, m) ⊢ b; and b ⊢ b.

(x) *Rule of Transference.*—If b is a step in a section of order n ($n \geq 1$) of a proof structure, then b may be asserted as a subsequent step in any section of order $n + i$ ($i = 1, 2, 3, \ldots$) that is contained within the original section. The reference for a step that is asserted on the grounds of this rule consists of the proof number of the original b, followed by "tf".

This rule is derived from the FCT epitheorem

(3·0811) if b (1, i) ⊢ b, then b (1, i), d (1, j) ⊢ b.

(xi) *Rule of Double-Negation Expulsion.*—If ∼ ∼ b [NNb] is a step in a section of order n ($n \geq 1$) of a proof structure, then b may be asserted as a subsequent step in the same section. The reference for a step that is asserted on the grounds of this rule consists of the proof number of ∼ ∼ b [NNb], followed by "negneg ex".

This rule is derived from the FCT epitheorem

(3·0812) b (1, m), ∼ ∼ b ⊢ b   b (1, m), NNb ⊢ b.

Cf. the first example in **2·17**.

EXERCISES

Give the references to accompany the proof structures E3·8·7 to E3·8·14. The proof structures thus completed constitute categorical proof schemata of (3·061) to (3·0610).

E3·8·7.
1. | b°
2. | | d°
3. | | b
4. | d ⊃ b
5. | b ⊃ (d ⊃ b)

E3·8·8.
1. | b°
2. | b ∨ d
3. | d ∨ b
4. | b ⊃ (b ∨ d)
5. | b ⊃ (d ∨ b)

E3·8·9.
1. | b ⊃ (d ⊃ h)°
2. | | b ⊃ d°
3. | | | b°
4. | | | b ⊃ d
5. | | | d
6. | | | b ⊃ (d ⊃ h)
7. | | | d ⊃ h
8. | | | h
9. | | b ⊃ h
10. | (b ⊃ d) ⊃ (b ⊃ h)
11. | [b ⊃ (d ⊃ h)] ⊃ [(b ⊃ d) ⊃ (b ⊃ h)]

E3·8·10.
1. | h ⊃ b°
2. | | h ⊃ d°
3. | | | h°
4. | | | h ⊃ b
5. | | | b
6. | | | h ⊃ d
7. | | | d
8. | | | b.d
9. | | h ⊃ (b.d)
10. | (h ⊃ d) ⊃ (h ⊃ (b.d))
11. | [h ⊃ b] ⊃ [(h ⊃ d) ⊃ (h ⊃ (b.d))]

E3·8·11.
1. | b.d°
2. | b
3. | d
4. | (b.d) ⊃ b
5. | (b.d) ⊃ d

E3·8·12.
1. | ∼ b°
2. | | b°
3. | | ∼ b
4. | | d
5. | b ⊃ d
6. | ∼ b ⊃ (b ⊃ d)

E3·8·13.
1.   b ⊃ h°
2.   d ⊃ h°
3.   b **V** d°
4.   b°
5.   b ⊃ h
6.   h
7.   d°
8.   d ⊃ h
9.   h
10.   h
11.   (b **V** d) ⊃ h
12. (d ⊃ h) ⊃ ((b **V** d) ⊃ h)
13. [b ⊃ h] ⊃ [(d ⊃ h) ⊃ ((b **V** d) ⊃ h)]

E3·8·14.
1.   ∼ b ⊃ b°
2.   ∼ b°
3.   ∼ b ⊃ b
4.   b
5.   ∼ ∼ b
6.   b
7. (∼ b ⊃ b) ⊃ b

3·09 Intuitionist Logic

In FCT the so-called *law of the excluded middle* or *tertium non datur* is categorically provable: for every f.s. b

$$(3·091) \qquad \vdash b \text{ V} \sim b \qquad \qquad \vdash AbNb.$$

There is a school of mathematicians, founded by the Dutch mathematician Brouwer, who hold that (3·091) does not, in general, express a rationally acceptable assertion. Very briefly, this is because it is not rational to claim that something has some property unless it can actually be shown that it has. According to Brouwer the *tertium non datur* commits one to holding that whatever formula *b* is given, say in relation to any particular d.s. for which it is well-formed, one can actually show that within that d.s. the formula given is categorically provable or that its negation is categorically provable; but it is not the case that human beings, as they are at present constituted, have the capacity for thus promptly settling the question of the categorical provability of any given formula. And every mathematician would agree with him on this point even if they would not agree with the inference Brouwer draws from it. There are famous formulae of mathematics for which, as yet, neither categorical proof nor disproof are actually possible. An example of such a formula is Goldbach's Hypothesis: Every positive even integer greater than 2 is the sum of two prime numbers. Brouwer and his followers call themselves *Intuitionists*, for reasons into which we cannot here enter. The ordinary mathematician thinks of mathematical truth as existing apart from human constructions; for him a mathematical proposition actually *is* true or actually *is* false quite independently of whether or not it has been made so through human endeavour. The Intuitionists hold that the mathematician should not be committed, and rationally cannot be committed, to the acceptance of this metaphysical notion of an abstract realm of truth. In mathematics we cannot know and so we cannot make rational claims about merely abstract existence. For all we know mathematical entities, unlike physical objects, have no existence apart from the human mind. It is, therefore, nonsense to claim the existence of mathematical facts before these have been constructed by human beings.[1]

The logic associated with Intuitionist mathematics is called *Intuitionist logic*.[2] It is the same as the ordinary logic, which the ordinary mathematician accepts, but for the one important difference that it does not allow the *tertium non datur* to be a categorical theorem. The ordinary logic, in which the *tertium non datur* is categorically provable, is sometimes called *Classical logic*. FCT is a

[1] Cf. Brouwer, L. E. J. (1881-): *Over de grondslagen der wiskunde*, (Amsterdam, 1907); and numerous subsequent papers of his listed in Heyting, A.: *Intuitionism, An Introduction*, 123-5 (Amsterdam, 1956).

[2] The first postulational d.s. for an Intuitionist logic (PC) was given by Heyting: Sitzungsber. preuss. Akad. Wiss. Berlin, 42-56 (1930).

system of Classical logic. PCT is a Classical system for the PC. If axiom schema (2·0610) be eliminated from PCT and

(3·092)   (s ⊃ ∼ s) ⊃ ∼ s   *CC*s*N*s*N*s

be added instead, the rule of deduction remaining unaltered, then the resulting system for the PC is an Intuitionist one.[1] It is Intuitionistically complete, and consistent. This Intuitionist system for the PC may be labelled "PCIT". Similarly, if axiom schema (3·0610) be eliminated from FCT and

(3·093)   (b ⊃ ∼ b) ⊃ ∼ b   *CC*b*N*b*N*b

be added instead, the rule of deduction remaining unaltered, then the resulting system for the FC is an Intuitionist one. It is Intuitionistically complete, and consistent. This Intuitionist system for the FC may be labelled "FCIT".

SFCT is a Classical system, being equivalent to FCT in that every categorical theorem in the one is also a categorical theorem in the other. A suppositional method version of FCIT—SFCIT—is obtainable from SFCT by merely omitting the rule of double-negation expulsion. In our illustrations, steps and in particular categorical theorems (or theorem schemata) which are not Intuitionistically valid will be marked by a pair of closing inverted commas on their right.

3·10 Examples of Deductions in SFCT and SFCIT

(3·101)		b°			b°
(3·102)			d°			d°
(3·103)			b			b
(3·104)			b.d			*K*bd
(3·105)		d ⊃ b			*C*db
(3·106)		d ⊃ (b.d)			*C*d*K*bd
(3·107)	[b] ⊃ [d ⊃ b]			*C*b*C*db
(3·108)	[b] ⊃ [d ⊃ (b.d)]			*C*b*C*d*K*bd

References.—3: 1, tf.   4: 3, 2, con in.   5: 2, 3, imp in.
6: 2, 4, imp in.   7: 1, 5, imp in.   8: 1, 6, imp in.

(3·109)	$\sim$ b°	Nb°
(3·1010)	b°	b°
(3·1011)	$\sim$ b	Nb
(3·1012)	d	d
(3·1013)	b $\supset$ d	Cbd
(3·1014)	[$\sim$ b] $\supset$ [b $\supset$ d]	$CNbC$bd

References.—11: 9, tf.   12: 10, 11, neg ex.   13: 10,
12, imp in.   14: 9, 13, imp in.

(3·1015)	b°	b°
(3·1016)	$\sim$ b°	Nb°
(3·1017)	b	b
(3·1018)	$\sim$ $\sim$ b	NNb
(3·1019)	[b] $\supset$ [$\sim$ $\sim$ b]	$Cb NN$b

References.—17: 15, tf.   18: 17, 16, neg in.   19: 15,
18, imp in.

(3·1020)	$\sim$ (b $\vee$ $\sim$ b)°	$NAbN$b°
(3·1021)	b°	b°
(3·1022)	b $\vee$ $\sim$ b	AbNb
(3·1023)	$\sim$ (b $\vee$ $\sim$ b)	$NAbN$b
(3·1024)	$\sim$ b	Nb
(3·1025)	b $\vee$ $\sim$ b	AbNb
(3·1026)	$\sim$ $\sim$ (b $\vee$ $\sim$ b)	$NNAbN$b
(3·1027)	b $\vee$ $\sim$ b''	AbNb''

References.—22: 21, alt in.   23: 20, tf.   24: 22, 23,
neg in.   25: 24, alt in.   26: 25, 20, neg in.   27: 26,
negneg ex.

(3·1028)   b.(b ⊃ d)°   KbCbd°
(3·1029)   b   b
(3·1030)   b ⊃ d   Cbd
(3·1031)   d   d
(3·1032)   [b.(b ⊃ d)] ⊃ [d]   CKbCbdd

References.—29: 28, con ex.   30: 28, con ex.   31: 29, 30, imp ex.   32: 28, 31, imp in.

(3·1033)   ∼ d ⊃ ∼ b°   CNdNb°
(3·1034)   b°   b°
(3·1035)   ∼ d°   Nd°
(3·1036)   ∼ d ⊃ ∼ b   CNdNb
(3·1037)   ∼ b   Nb
(3·1038)   b   b
(3·1039)   ∼ ∼ d   NNd
(3·1040)   d"   d"
(3·1041)   b ⊃ d   Cbd
(3·1042)   [∼ d ⊃ ∼ b] ⊃ [b ⊃ d]"   CCNdNbCbd"

References.—36: 33, tf.   37: 35, 36, imp ex.   38: 34, tf. 39: 38, 37, neg in.   40: 39, negneg ex.   41: 34, 40, imp in.   42: 33, 41, imp in.

(3·1043)   b.(d ∨ h)°   KbAdh°
(3·1044)   b   b
(3·1045)   d ∨ h   Adh
(3·1046)   d°   d°
(3·1047)   b   b
(3·1048)   b.d   Kbd
(3·1049)   (b.d) ∨ (b.h)   AKbdKbh
(3·1050)   h°   h°
(3·1051)   b   b
(3·1052)   b.h   Kbh
(3·1053)   (b.d) ∨ (b.h)   AKbdKbh
(3·1054)   (b.d) ∨ (b.h)   AKbdKbh
(3·1055)   [b.(d ∨ h)] ⊃ [(b.d) ∨ (b.h)]   CKbAdhAKbdKbh

References.—44: 43, con ex. 45: 43, con ex. 47: 44, tf. 48: 47, 46, con in. 49: 48, alt in. 51: 44, tf. 52: 51, 50, con in. 53: 52, alt in. 54: 45, 49, 53, alt ex. 55: 43, 54 imp in.

EXERCISES

Construct categorical proofs of E3·10·15 to E3·10·47 by the suppositional method. Indicate, as in the text, which are obtained in a non-Intuitionist way.

E3·10·15. b ⊃ b.

E3·10·16. (∼ b ⊃ b) ⊃ b.

E3·10·17. [b ⊃ (d ⊃ h)] ⊃ [(b ⊃ d) ⊃ (b ⊃ h)].

E3·10·18. (b ⊃ ∼ b) ⊃ ∼ b.

E3·10·19. [b ⊃ d] ⊃ [(b ⊃ ∼ d) ⊃ ∼ d].

E3·10·20. [(b ∨ d) ⊃ h] ⊃ [b ⊃ h].

E3·10·21. CCbdCCdhCbh.

E3·10·22. CANbdCbd.

E3·10·23. CCbdCNdNb.

E3·10·24. CCbdNKNdb.

E3·10·25. CCbCdhCdCbh.

E3·10·26. CCbdCbChd.

E3·10·27. CNAbdKNbNd.

E3·10·28. CKNbNdNAbd.

E3·10·29. CNKbAdhNAKbdKbh.

E3·10·30. CKbAdNdb.

E3·10·31. CKbNbKKbNbd.

E3·10·32. CNdCAbdb.

E3·10·33. CNAbNbKNbNNb.

E3·10·34. CNKbdANbNd.

E3·10·35. CANbNdNKbd.

E3·10·36. CANNbNNdNNKbd.

*E3·10·37. **Glivenko's Theorem**:[1] If s ⊢ t in PCT, then ∼ ∼ s ⊢ ∼ ∼ t in PCIT; and if ∼ s, t ⊢ ∼ u in PCT, then ∼ s, ∼ ∼ t ⊢ ∼ u in PCIT.

E3·10·38. If s contains no connectives except negation or conjunction (alternation), and ⊢ s in PCT, then s contains signs of both negation and conjunction (alternation).

---

[1] Glivenko, V. (1891-1940): "Sur quelques points de la logique de M. Brouwer", Acad. Roy. Belgique, *Bulletins de la classe des sciences* (5), 1929, **15**, 183-8.

*E3·10·39. **Gödel's Theorem:**[1] If s has no connectives except negation and conjunction, and ⊢ s in **PCT**, then ⊢ s in **PCIT**.

3·11 The Consistency of FCT

In view of E3·6·5, it is usual to interpret a d.s. for the FC as presupposing the existence of at least one actual object. This interpretation is used in devising a procedure to test the validity of f.s.s by means of valuation tables similar to those presented in Chapter Two, and especially in devising a procedure to confirm the consistency of the d.s.[2]

Here we shall adopt the simplest procedure. We shall regard the term variables as being able to range over a domain of a single object only. This object can remain unnamed. It will be best to explain the procedure for testing validity of f.s.s by considering an example. Consider, then, the f.s.

$$(3·111) \qquad [(x)(b(x). \sim d)] \supset [d \supset (\exists y) \sim b(y)].$$

Now the p.f. denoted by $b(x)$ becomes a true proposition, or it becomes a false proposition, when a name of the one object denoted by x is substituted for each occurrence of the object variable in it. Hence, $b(x)$ can be assigned the t.v. truth if the first alternative is realised, and can be assigned the t.v. falsity if the second alternative is realised. In the light of the earlier explanations concerning f.v.s with resultant attached term variables[3] and the fact that our present domain contains a single object, it is clear that $b(y)$ takes the t.v. truth (falsity) if and only if $b(x)$ takes the t.v. truth (falsity). In view of our interpreting the term variables as having only a single possible value, it is permissible to interpret $(x) b(x)$ as being true (false) if

---

[1] Gödel, K. (1906-): "Zum intuitionistischon Aussagenkalkul", Akad. Wiss. Wien, *Math.-naturwiss. Klasse, Anzeiger*, 1932, **69**, 65-6.

[2] The first demonstration of the consistency of a d.s. for the FC was given by Hilbert and Ackermann: *Grundzüge der theoretischen Logik*.

[3] *I.e.* attached term variables that result from a process of substituting; cf. pp. 70-1.

and only if $b(x)$ is true (false); and to interpret $(\exists x) b(x)$ in exactly the same way.

In evaluating a f.s. the truth table definitions of connectives are adopted, and each constituent f.v. that is without attached term variables is regarded as being a p.v. in the sense that it can be assigned the numbers 0 and 1; these numbers can be thought of as representing t.v.s.

The valuation table for (3·111) is as follows, where the subscripts have been inserted to enable the reader to understand how the values given have been arrived at:

$$[(x)(b(x) \quad . \quad \sim d)] \quad \supset \quad [d \quad \supset \quad (\exists y) \sim b(y)]$$

(3·112)

1_5	0_2	1_4	1_3	0_1	0_9	0_1	1_8	1_7	1_6	0_2
0_5	0_2	0_4	0_3	1_1	0_9	1_1	0_8	1_7	1_6	0_2
1_5	1_2	1_4	1_3	0_1	0_9	0_1	0_8	0_7	0_6	1_2
1_5	1_2	1_4	0_3	1_1	0_9	1_1	0_8	0_7	0_6	1_2

It is seen that the principal column in (3·112) has only 0's. The f.s. (3·111) is said to be *1-identical* or *valid in a domain of 1 object*. If the term variables were allowed to range over a domain of k objects ($k = 1, 2, 3, \ldots$), (x) b (x) being assigned the value 0 (1) if b (x) is assigned the value 0 (1) for (not) every one of the k objects, and $(\exists x) b(x)$ being assigned the value 0 (1) if b (x) is assigned the value 0 (1) for at least one (for none) of the k objects, then if the principal column of the valuation table for (3·111) contained only 0's, (3·111) would be said to be *k-identical*, or *valid in a domain of k objects*.[1]

(3·113) **The 1-identity Theorem for FCT:** if b denotes a f.s. of FCT and $\vdash$ b, then b is 1-identical.

Demonstration: We proceed by course-of-values induction on the length k ($k = 1, 2, \ldots$) of the categorical proof of b. (We shall omit "denoted by", etc.)

[1] The concept of k-identity is due to Hilbert and Bernays: *Grundlagen der Mathematik I*.

If $\vdash_1$ b, then b must be an axiom. Axioms of the form (3·061) to (3·0610) have already been found to be tautologous; cf. E2·18·86. Hence they are 1-identical.

With respect to an axiom of the form (3·0611), either the value assigned to b (x) is 0 or it is 1. If the former, then the value assignable to (x) b (x) is 0 and the value assignable to b (y) is 0. Hence the value assignable to the axiom is 0. If the value assigned to b (x) is 1, then the value assignable to (x) b (x) is 1 and the value assignable to b (y) is 1. Hence, by the truth table definition of ⊃, the value to be assigned to the axiom is 0. Thus, an axiom of the form (3·111) is 1-identical.

With respect to an axiom of the form (3·0612), either the value assigned to b (x) is 0 or it is 1. If the former, then both b (y) and (∃ x) b (x) receive the value 0, so the whole axiom receives the value 0. If the value assigned to b (x) is 1, then both b (y) and (∃ x) b (x) receive the value 1, so the whole axiom receives the value 0. Thus, an axiom of the form (3·0612) is 1-identical.

Next, we suppose the validity of the assertion that for all b,

(3·114) if $\vdash_{k \leq m}$b, then b is 1-identical,

and aim to show that, for all b,

(3·115) if $\vdash_{m+1}$b, then b is 1-identical

is consequently also a valid assertion. We adopt the antecedent in (3·115) and aim to obtain the consequent therein.

Since *ex hypothesi* $\vdash_{m+1}$ b, then there is a categorical proof of b in $m + 1$ steps. Either (i) b occurs before the $(m + 1)$ st step or (ii) it does not occur until the $(m + 1)$ st step. If (i), then the validity of (3·115) would be established, by virtue of (3·114). If (ii), then there are four possibilities.

(*a*) b is an axiom. Then, as we have already seen, b must be 1-identical.

(*b*) b is a consequence by MP of two preceding steps. These preceding steps will each occur before the $(m + 1)$ st step, and so, by virtue of (3·114) and cf. E2·18·87, b will be 1-identical.

(*c*) b is a consequence of one preceding step by the rule of universal quantifier introduction. Then b is of the form d $\supset$ (x) h (x) and the preceding step is of the form d $\supset$ h (x). By virtue of (3·114) d $\supset$ h (x) is 1-identical. Therefore, using Q in a way similar to that explained in 2·20, either (1) Q (h (x)) = Q (d) = 0, or (2) Q (h (x)) = 0 and Q (d) = 1, or (3) Q (h (x)) = Q (d) = 1. If (1), then Q ((x) h (x)) = 0, so, since Q (d) = 0, Q (b) = 0. If (2), then Q ((x) h (x)) = 0, and so, since Q (d) = 1, Q (b) = 0. If (3), then Q ((x) h (x)) = 1, and so, since Q (d) = 1, Q (b) = 0. Accordingly, b is 1-identical if it follows by the rule of universal quantifier introduction.

(*d*) b is a consequence by the rule of particular quantifier introduction. Then b is of the form ($\exists$ x) h (x) $\supset$ d and the preceding step is of the form h (x) $\supset$ d. By virtue of (3·114) h (x) $\supset$ d is 1-identical. Therefore, either (1) Q (h (x)) = Q (d) = 0, or (2) Q (h (x)) = 1 and Q (d) = 0, or (3) Q (h (x)) = Q (d) = 1. But in each of these three cases Q (b) = 0. Consequently, b is 1-identical if it is a consequence by the rule of particular quantifier introduction.

By the principle of course-of-values induction, the demonstration of (3·113) is accomplished.

(3·116) **The Simple-consistency Theorem for FCT:** It is not the case that there is some f.s. denoted by b such that both $\vdash$ b and $\vdash \sim$ b [$\vdash$ Nb].

Demonstration: This is exactly analogous to the demonstration of Theorem (2·194).

(3·117) **The Absolute Consistency Theorem for FCT:** FCT is absolutely consistent.

Demonstration: First demonstrate, in an exactly analogous way to the demonstration of Theorem (2·195), that FCT is simply-consistent if and only if it is absolutely consistent, and then reason exactly analogously to the demonstration of Theorem (2·196).

Since (3·093) is tautologous, and so 1-identical, FCIT is simply-consistent and absolutely consistent.

It can be shown that FCT is complete. It is complete both in the sense that every k-identical f.s. $(k \geq 2)$ is categorically provable, and in being absolutely complete. ?
However, the demonstration of these theorems, due originally for the Whitehead-Russell system to Gödel, is highly complicated and advanced and cannot be given here.[1]

3·12 The Suppositional Method Version of FCT: Quantifier Rules

A section of a proof structure is said to be "general with respect to x" if and only if firstly there is at least one step in the section which contains some free occurrence of x, and secondly, no previous step in a section of lower order in the proof structure is placed in that section or in any section of higher order that is within it if the step contains some free occurrence of x. (Such a phrase as "free occurrence of x" means, as usual "free occurrence of what is denoted at the FL_1 level by x".)

(xii) *Rule of Universal Quantifier Introduction.*—If b $(x_1, x_2, \ldots, x_m)$ $[bx_1 x_2 \ldots x_m]$ is a step in a section of order n $(n \geq 2)$ of a proof structure, this section being without a supposition and general with respect to $x_1, x_2, \ldots, x_m$, then $(x_1)(x_2)\ldots(x_m)$ b $(x_1, x_2, \ldots, x_m)$ $[Px_1x_2\ldots x_m bx_1x_2\ldots x_m]$ may be asserted as a subsequent step in the containing section of order $n - 1$. The

---

[1] Gödel: "Die Vollständigkeit der Axiome des logischen Funktionenkalküls", *Monatsh. f. Math. u. Physik*, 1930, **37**, 349-60.

reference for a step that is justified on the grounds of this rule consists of the proof number of the f.v. with m attached term variables, followed by "uq in".

This rule is derived from the FCT epitheorem

$(3\cdot121)$ $b(x_1, x_2, \ldots, x_m) \vdash (x_1)(x_2)\ldots(x_m) b(x_1, x_2, \ldots x_m)$. For $m = 1$, the epitheorem $(3\cdot121)$ can be justified as follows, where the d in the formulation of the FCT rule of universal quantifier introduction is taken as an axiom (and is without free occurences of x).

$(3\cdot122)$ $b(x)^\circ$

$(3\cdot123)$ $b(x) \supset (d \supset b(x))$—axs $(3\cdot061)$

$(3\cdot124)$ $d \supset b(x)$　　　　　　—2, 3, MP

$(3\cdot125)$ $d \supset (x) b(x)$　　　　—4, universal quantifier introduction.

$(3\cdot126)$ d　　　　　　　　　—given as axiom

$(3\cdot127)$ $(x) b(x)$　　　　　　—6, 5, MP

(xiii) *Rule of Universal Quantifier Expulsion.* If $(x_1)(x_2)\ldots(x_m) b(x_1, x_2, \ldots, x_m)$ $[Px_1x_2\ldots x_m bx_1x_2\ldots x_m]$ is a step in a section of order n $(n \geq 1)$ of a proof structure, then if y_i is free for x_i in $b(x_1, x_2, \ldots, x_m)$ $[bx_1x_2\ldots x_m]$, $b(y_1, y_2, \ldots, y_m)$ $[by_1y_2\ldots y_m]$ may be asserted as a subsequent step in the same section. The reference for a step that is justified on the grounds of this rule consists in the proof number of what is denoted by the original quantified f.s., followed by "uq ex".

This rule is derived from the FCT epitheorem

$(3\cdot128)$ $(x_1)(x_2)\ldots(x_m) b(x_1, x_2, \ldots, x_m) \vdash b(y_1, y_2, \ldots, y_m)$, where y_i is free for x_i in $b(x_1, x_2, \ldots, x_m)$. This epitheorem can be demonstrated on the basis of axiom schema $(3\cdot0611)$; in the case when $m = 1$, $(3\cdot128)$ is justified directly by $(3\cdot0611)$.

(xiv) *Rule of Particular Quantifier Introduction.*—If $b(y_1, y_2, \ldots, y_m)$ $[by_1y_2\ldots y_m]$ is a step in a section of order n $(n \geq 1)$ of a proof structure, then, if y_i is free for x_i in b $(x_1, x_2, \ldots, x_m)$, $(\exists x_1)(\exists x_2)\ldots(\exists x_m)$ b $(x_1, x_2, \ldots, x_m)[Sx_1x_2\ldots x_m bx_1x_2\ldots x_m]$ may be asserted as a subsequent step in the same section. The reference for a step that is asserted on the grounds of this rule consists of the proof number of b $(y_1, y_2, \ldots, y_m)$ $[by_1y_2\ldots y_m]$, followed by "pq in".

This rule is derived from the FCT epitheorem

$(3\cdot129)$ b $(y_1, y_2, \ldots, y_m)$ $\vdash (\exists x_1)(\exists x_2)\ldots(\exists x_m)$ b $(x_1, x_2, \ldots, x_m)$, where y_i is free for x_i in b $(x_1, x_2, \ldots, x_m)$; this rule forms a generalisation of axiom schema $(3\cdot0612)$.

(xv) *Rule of Particular Quantifier Expulsion.* If $(\exists x_1)(\exists x_2)\ldots(\exists x_m)$ b $(x_1, x_2, \ldots, x_m)[Sx_1x_2\ldots x_m bx_1x_2\ldots x_m]$ is a step in a section of order n $(n \geq 1)$ of a proof structure, and a section of order $n + 1$ within that section is general with respect to $x_1, x_2, \ldots, x_m$ and contains b $(x_1, x_2, \ldots, x_m)$ $[bx_1x_2\ldots x_m]$ as supposition, then if this section of order $n + 1$ contains a step d which has no free occurrences of any x_i $(i = 1, 2, \ldots, m)$, d may be asserted as a subsequent step in the original section of order n. The reference for a step that is justified on the grounds of this rule consists of the proof numbers of what is denoted by the original quantified m.f.s. and by the d in the section of order $n + 1$, followed by "pq ex".

This rule is derived from the FCT epitheorem

$(3\cdot1210)$ if $(\exists x_1)(\exists x_2)\ldots(\exists x_m)$ b $(x_1, x_2, \ldots, x_m)$, b $(x_1, x_2, \ldots, x_m)$ $\vdash$ d, where d contains no free occurrences of any x_i and the free term variables are held constant for b $(x_1, x_2, \ldots, x_m)$, then $(\exists x_1)(\exists x_2)\ldots(\exists x_m)$ b $(x_1, x_2, \ldots, x_m)$ $\vdash$ d.

For $m = 1$, this epitheorem can be justified as follows, where we adopt the antecedent in $(3\cdot1210)$ and aim to obtain the consequent.

$(3\cdot1211)$ $(\exists x)$ b (x), b (x) $\vdash$ d

          —given by hypothesis

(3·1212) $(\exists x)\, b\,(x) \vdash b\,(x) \supset d$

—11, Deduction Theorem

(3·1213) $b\,(x) \supset d \vdash (\exists x)\, b\,(x) \supset d$

—12, rule of part. quant. int.

(3·1214) $(\exists x)\, b\,(x) \vdash (\exists x)\, b\,(x) \supset d$

—12, 13, transitivity of $\vdash$; cf. E2·17·63

(3·1215) $(\exists x)\, b\,(x)°$

(3·1216) $(\exists x)\, b\,(x) \supset d$

—deducible from 15, by 14

(3·1217) d   —15, 16, MP

Therefore

(3·1218) $(\exists x)\, b\,(x) \vdash d.$

The Intuitionist system SFCIT employs the rules (i) to (x) in **3·08**, together with the above four rules (xii) to (xv).[1]

EXERCISE

E3·12·40. Give full demonstrations of the FCT epitheorems (3·121), (3·128), (3·129), and (3·1210).

3·13 Further Examples of Deductions in SFCT and SFCIT

An occurrence of x at the top left of the vertical line for a section of a proof structure indicates that the section is general with respect to x.

(3·131) $(x)\, b\,(x)°$
(3·132) $b\,(x)$
(3·133) $(\exists x)\, b\,(x)$
(3·134) $(x)\, b\,(x) \supset (\exists x)\, b\,(x)$

References.—2: 1, uq ex. 3: 2, pq in. 4: 1, 3, imp in.

[1] The first suppositional d.s. for the FC and for the FCI was given by Gentzen: *Math. Z.*, 1934-5, **39**, 176-210. A similar approach was followed by Jaskowski, S. (*c.* 1902-) "On the Rules of Suppositions in Formal Logic", *Studia Logica* 1, Warsaw, 1934. Neither Gentzen nor Jaskowski developed an axiom schema system nor did either explicitly derive his rules from a postulational d.s. Neglecting the schemata aspect, the present treatment stems from that in Fitch: *Symbolic Logic, An Introduction*; and from Nidditch: *I.F.L.M.*

(3·135) |(∃ x) (y) b (x, y)°
(3·136)   x|(y) b (x, y)°
(3·137)   y |(y) b (x, y)
(3·138) |b (x, y)
(3·139) |(∃ x) b (x, y)
(3·1310) |(y) (∃ x) b (x, y)
(3·1311) |(y) (∃ x) b (x, y)
(3·1312) |(∃ x) (y) b (x, y) ⊃ (y) (∃ x) b (x, y)

References.—7: 6, tf. 8: 7, uq ex. 9: 8, pq in.
10: 9, uq in. 11: 5, 10, pq ex. 12: 5, 11, imp in.

(3·1313) |(∃ x) b (x)°
(3·1314) |(x) ∼ b (x)°
(3·1315) |(∃ x) b (x)
(3·1316)   x|b (x)°
(3·1317) |(x) ∼ b (x)
(3·1318) |∼ b (x)
(3·1319) |∼ (x) ∼ b (x)
(3·1320) |∼ (x) ∼ b (x)
(3·1321) |∼ (x) ∼ b (x)
(3·1322) |(∃ x) b (x) ⊃ ∼ (x) ∼ b (x)

References.—15: 13, tf. 17: 14, tf. 18: 17, uq ex.
19: 16, 18, neg ex. 20: 15, 19, pq ex. 21: 14, 20,
neg in. 22: 13, 21, imp in.

(3·1323) |∼ (∃ x) b (x)°
(3·1324)   x|∼ (∃ x) b (x)
(3·1325) |b (x)°
(3·1326) |(∃ x) b (x)
(3·1327) |∼ (∃ x) b (x)
(3·1328) |∼ b (x)
(3·1329) |(x) ∼ b (x)
(3·1330) |∼ (∃ x) b (x) ⊃ (x) ∼ b (x)

References.—24: 23, tf. 26: 25, pq in. 27: 23, tf.
28: 26, 27, neg in. 29: 28, uq in. 30: 23, 29, imp in.

(3·1331) |NSxyNbxy°
(3·1332)   xy|NSxyNbxy
(3·1333) |Nbxy°
(3·1334) |SxyNbxy
(3·1335) |NSxyNbxy
(3·1336) |NNbxy
(3·1337) |bxy"
(3·1338) |PxyNNbxy
(3·1339) |Pxybxy
(3·1340) CNSxyNbxyPxyNNbxy
(3·1341) CNSxyNbxyPxybxy"
(3·1342) |NPxybxy°
(3·1343) |NSxyNbxy°
(3·1344) |CNSxyNbxyPxybxy"
(3·1345) |Pxybxy
(3·1346) |NPxybxy
(3·1347) |NNSxyNbxy
(3·1348) |SxyNbxy"
(3·1349) CNPxybxySxyNbxy"

References.—32: 31, tf. 34: 33, pq in. 35: 32, tf.
36: 34, 35, neg in. 37: 36, negneg ex. 38: 36, uq in.
39: 37, uq in. 40: 31, 38, imp in. 41: 31, 39, imp in.
44: 41, tf. 45: 43, 44, imp ex. 46: 42, tf. 47: 45, 46,
neg in. 48: 47, negneg ex. 49: 42, 48, imp in.

(3·1350) |SxNbx°
(3·1351)   x|Nbx°
(3·1352) |Pxbx°
(3·1353) |bx
(3·1354) |Nbx
(3·1355) |NPxbx
(3·1356) |NPxbx
(3·1357) CSxNbxNPxbx

References.—53: 52, uq ex. 54: 51, tf. 55: 53, 54, neg in. 56: 50, 55, pq ex. 57: 50, 56, imp in.[1]

EXERCISES

Construct categorical proofs by the suppositional method, of E3·13·41 to E3·13·53. Indicate which steps and theorems (theorem schemata) are obtained in a non-Intuitionist way. (The attached metalinguistic term variables are superfluous, strictly.)

E3·13·41. (x) [b (x). d (x)] ⊃ [(x) b (x). (x) d (x)].

E3·13·42. (x) [b (x) **V** d (x)] ⊃ [(x) b (x) **V** (x) d (x)].

E3·13·43. (∃ x) [b (x). d (x)] ⊃ [(∃ x) b (x). (∃ x) d (x)]. Is the converse valid?

E3·13·44. (∃ x) [b (x) **V** d (x)] ⊃ [(∃ x) b (x) **V** (∃ x) d (x)]. Is the converse valid?

E3·13·45. (x) (y) b (x, y) ⊃ (y) (x) b (x, y).

E3·13·46. (∃ x) (∃ y) b (x, y) ⊃ (∃ y) (∃ x) b (x, y).

E3·13·47. [(x) (b (x) ⊃ d)] ⊃ [(∃ x) b (x) ⊃ d], if x is not free in d.

E3·13·48. [(x) (b (x) ⊃ d (x))] ⊃ [(∃ x) b (x) ⊃ (∃ x) d (x)].

E3·13·49. (x) [b (x) ⊃ d (x)] ⊃ [(x) b (x) ⊃ d (x)].

E3·13·50. ∼ (x) (y) (z) b (x, y, z) ⊃ (∃x) (∃y) (∃z) ∼ b (x, y, z).

E3·13·51. *CNNP*xbx*P*xNNbx.

E3·13·52. *CCP*xbx*S*xdx*S*xCbxdx.

E3·13·53. *CC*bS*x*dx*S*xCbdx, if x is not free in b.

E3·13·54. Construct valuation tables for theorems of the form E3·13·47 to E3·13·53 and confirm that the f.s.s are 1-identical.

E3·13·55. Give an example of a f.s. that is 1-identical and is not categorically provable in FCT. (Hence FCT is not 1-identically complete, although it is absolutely complete.)

---

[1] For details concerning many other systems associated with the PC and the FC than those considered in this and the previous chapter, the reader may consult Church: *Introduction to Mathematical Logic I*, (Princeton, 1956), which uses the Peano-Russell notation (with some modifications); and Prior, A. N. (1914-): *Formal Logic* (Oxford, 1955), which uses the Łukasiewicz-Tarski notation. Unlike Prior's book, Church's gives detailed epitheoretic treatments; but Prior, unlike Church, deals also with Modal Logic. For this subject, see also: Lewis, C. I. (1883-1947) and Langford, C. H. (1895-): *Symbolic Logic* (New York, 1932); Parry, W. T. (1908-): "Modalities in the *Survey* system of strict implication", *J. Symbolic Logic*, 1939, **4**, 137-54; and Lemmon, E. J. (1930-): "New foundations for Lewis modal systems", *J. Symbolic Logic*, 1957, **22**, 176-86.

CHAPTER FOUR

BOOLEAN ALGEBRA AND SET THEORY

4·01 Introduction

In this chapter we begin by explaining the nature of
Boolean Algebra. Two axiomatic systems for Boolean
Algebra, both due to Huntington, are given. The notions
of an interpretation and of a model of a formal d.s. are
introduced. In terms of models the axioms of the second
axiomatic d.s. for Boolean Algebra are shown to be
independent and to be simply-consistent. A d.s. for
Boolean Algebra can be interpreted propositionally, and
this propositional interpretation is investigated further.
This leads to the consideration of Boolean polynomials
and of their normal form, which in turn provides another
decision procedure, different from that of the truth-table
method, for testing whether or not a p.s. is valid.

We then proceed to sketch the elements of general Set
Theory in an informal way. Among the elements included
are the notion of function and the notion of an indexed
family of sets. We also deal, briefly, with cardinal numbers
and the paradoxes of Set Theory.

4·02 Huntington's First Axiomatic System for Boolean Algebra (BAH₁)

Let x, y, and z denote any regions of a particular square;
if x and y are any such regions, then let x_y denote the
smallest region which includes both x and y; let x_y
denote the region common to x and y; let $çx$ denote the
region consisting of the whole square apart from x; let
u be the whole square and let $\grave{u}$ be the null region of the

square, that is a region consisting of no part whatever of the square; and finally, let $x = y$ be the formula to the effect that the region denoted by x is identically the same as the region denoted by y.

Again, let x, y, and z denote any of the numbers 1, 2, 3, 5, 6, 10, 15, 30; if x and y are any such numbers, then let x_y denote the least common multiple of x and y (*e.g.* 3_5 is 15); let x_y denote the greatest common factor of x and y (*e.g.* 10_15 is 5); let $çx$ denote the quotient $30/x$ (*e.g.* $ç10$ is 3); let u be 30 and let $ù$ be 1; and let $x = y$ mean that the numbers x and y are the same.

For both the cases described in the two preceding paragraphs, the following ten formulae (4·021) to (4·0210) are satisfied; the " W " that occurs in them being interpreted for the first case as representing the totality of all the regions of the square, and being interpreted for the second case as the totality whose sole members are the numbers 1, 2, 3, 5, 6, 10, 15, and 30. Except for (4·023), (4·024), (4·029), and (4·0210), for all x, y, and z, if x, y, and z are members of W, then:

(4·021) x_y is a member of W;

(4·022) x_y is a member of W;

(4·023)   There is some member $ù$ of W such that $x\_ù = x$ for every x that is a member of W;

(4·024)   There is some member u of W such that $x\_u = x$ for every x that is a member of W;

(4·025) $x\_y = y\_x$;

(4·026) $x\_y = y\_x$;

(4·027) $x\_(y\_z) = (x\_y)\_(x\_z)$;

(4·028) $x\_(y\_z) = (x\_y)\_(x\_z)$;

(4·029)   For each member x of W there is some member $çx$ of W such that $x\_çx = u$ and such that $x\_çx = ù$;

(4·0210) *W* contains at least two distinct members, that is
there is some *x* and some *y* such that *x* and *y*
are both members of *W* and it is not the case
that *x* = *y*.

The formulae (4·021) to (4·0210) are axioms of a type of
theory called *Boolean Algebra* ("BA" for short) that are
due to Huntington.[1] We shall label the d.s. to which these
axioms belong "BAH$_1$". As commonly in mathematics
BAH$_1$ makes tacit use of rules or theorems belonging to
the FC, and of the standard properties of equality (=).
These standard properties are four in number. Firstly,
equality is reflexive: for all *x*, *x* = *x*. Secondly, equality
is symmetrical: for all *x* and *y*, if *x* = *y* then *y* = *x*.
Thirdly, equality is transitive: for all *x*, *y*, and *z*, if *x* = *y*
and *y* = *z*, then *x* = *z*. Fourthly—and this is a rule of
deduction, whereas the previous three are axioms—
if x = y has been established as a theorem, then
b (x) = b (y), where b represents an expression built up
out of object variables, *u* and *ù* by the use of $\smile$, $\frown$, or ç,
may be asserted as a theorem too, cf. **4·03**. Examples of
categorical theorems in BAH$_1$ are (4·0211) to (4·0221)
below. Except for (4·0213), (4·0214), and (4·0219), for
all *x*, *y*, and *z* of *W*:

(4·0211) $x \smile x = x$;

(4·0212) $x \frown x = x$;

(4·0213) There is a single member *ù* of *W* such that for
all *x* of *W*, $x \smile ù = x$;

(4·0214) There is a single member *u* of *W* such that for
all *x* of *W* $x \frown u = x$;

(4·0215) $x \smile u = u$;

(4·0216) $x \frown ù = ù$;

(4·0217) $x \smile (x \frown y) = x$;

[1] Huntington, E. V. (1874-1952): "Sets of independent postulates for the algebra of logic", *Trans. Amer. Math. Soc.*, 1904, **5**, 288-309.

(4·0218) $x_-(x_-y) = x$;

(4·0219) For each member x of W there is a single member $çx$ of W such that $x_-çx = u$ and such that $x_-çx = \dot{u}$;

(4·0220) $(x_-y)_-z = x_-(y_-z)$;

(4·0221) $(x_-y)_-z = x_-(y_-z)$;

(4·0222) If $x_-y = x_-z$ and $x_-y = x_-z$, then $y = z$;

(4·0223) $ççx = x$.

If the expressions occurring in the postulates of a d.s. are assigned certain meanings outside the d.s., as the expressions in (4·021) to (4·0210) are assigned meanings in the first two paragraphs of this section, then if the objects (such as the regions of a square or the positive factors of 30) introduced by this assignment satisfy the postulates, the totality of the objects is said to be a *model*[1] of the d.s.   The totality of the regions of a square is a model of BAH_1, as is also the totality of the positive factors of 30. Each model of an axiomatic d.s. for BA is said to be a *Boolean algebra*.   The totality of the regions of a square and the totality of the positive factors of 30 are Boolean algebras.   Each axiomatic d.s. for BA is a Boolean algebra schema; such a system is not itself a Boolean algebra, but it is the form or pattern of actual Boolean algebras.[2]

In the postulates themselves of the various postulational d.s.s we have so far described in this book there is no mention of what the objects are that the d.s.s are supposed to be about.   PCWR is supposed to be about—to be the theory of—propositions, although the term "proposition" is not expressed in the axioms.   Similarly, FCT is supposed

[1] The notion of model and the first use of it for showing consistency and independence of axioms are due to Hilbert: *Die Grundlagen der Geometrie*, following Peano.   Cf. footnotes in **9·04**.

[2] With a few exceptions, the concepts and fundamental laws of BA are due to Boole, G. (1815-64): *The Mathematical Analysis of Logic* (Cambridge, 1847); *The Laws of Thought* (Cambridge, 1854).

to be ultimately about quantified or unquantified formulae, although there was no explicit indication of this in the postulates themselves. In these two cases and in those of the other postulational d.s.s presented in the second and third chapters, there are "intended interpretations" of the systems. In each case the intended interpretation of the system was elucidated before the formalism was set out, in order that the reader might understand what underlay and motivated the system.

Now of course the notion of intention is a psychological, not a logical one. It could well happen that a postulational d.s. is constructed to be the theory of a certain subject-matter and of just this, while there are in fact other subject-matters as well as this which the d.s. serves to cover. In such an eventuality one can properly speak of the author's "intended interpretation" because there is *the* intended interpretation by the author, although additional interpretations are possible. In short, the author has a particular model in mind, whereas there are other totalities of objects which satisfy the postulates. But, on the other hand, it can also happen that an author of a postulational d.s. intends to cover several subject-matters at once by a single theory. It will here not be appropriate to speak of the author's "intended interpretation" because the author does not have a single interpretation in mind; he envisages several models of his system.

Now it had been recognised by workers in BA, before the first postulational d.s. for BA was constructed, that the theory is open to two interpretations. One interpretation is in terms of classes and the other is in terms of propositions. It was subsequently recognised that yet other interpretations are possible. As a result, when Huntington put forward (his original version of what we have called) BAH₁, he put it forward as a purely abstract system that was not tied, psychologically or logically, to any specific subject-matter.

It was realised that there are not merely several, but potentially infinitely many models of the system. However, it has been most usual and fruitful to regard an axiomatic d.s. for BA as either a Calculus of Classes or as a Calculus of Propositions.

If BAH_1 is viewed as a Calculus of Classes (Sets, Collections, Totalities), then: (i) x, y, and z denote classes; (ii) W denotes a totality of classes; (iii) $x_{-}y$ denotes the union-class of x and y, *i.e.* the class whose members are all the objects that are members of x or of y or of both[1]; (iv) $x_{-}y$ denotes the intersection-class of x and y, *i.e.* the class whose members are all the objects that are members of both x and y; (v) $ù$ denotes a null class, *i.e.* a class without any members (of the universe of discourse) at all; (vi) u denotes the universe of discourse, *i.e.* the class whose members are all the objects that are members of the classes belonging to W^2; (vii) $çx$ denotes the complement of x, *i.e.* the class whose members are all the objects that are members of u except for those that are members of x; (viii) $x = y$ is a formula that affirms the identity of x and y, *i.e.* that x and y have the very same membership. For example, let u be the class whose members are the integers 1 to 6, x be the class whose members are the integers 1, 2 and 3, and let y be the class whose members are the integers 2, 3, and 4; then $x_{-}y$ is the class whose members are 1, 2, 3, and 4, $x_{-}y$ is the class whose members are 2 and 3, and $çx$ is the class whose members are 4, 5, and 6.

If BAH_1 is viewed as a Calculus of Propositions, then: (i) x, y, and z become p.v.s; (ii) W represents a class of propositions; (iii) $x_{-}y$ represents the alternation

---

[1] In Boole, the union operator was restricted to classes without common membership. The very important advance of removing this restriction so that the operator can apply to classes with common members is due to Jevons, W. S. (1835-1882): *Pure Logic*, (London, 1864).

[2] This notion is due to De Morgan: "On the Structure of the Syllogism . . .", *Trans. Camb. Phil. Soc.*, 1849 (read 1846), 8; and to Boole: *The Laws of Thought*, p. 42.

(disjunction) of x and y, and so has the same sense as $x \vee y$; (iv) x_y represents the conjunction of x and y, and so has the same sense as $x.y$; (v) $\dot{u}$ denotes a fixed false proposition; (vi) u represents a fixed true proposition; (vii) $çx$ represents the negation of x, and so has the same sense as $\sim x$; (viii) $x = y$ represents the affirmation that x and y are equivalent—that x and y imply one another— and so has the same sense as $x \equiv y$ [Exy]; but also (ix), for each x of W, $x = \dot{u}$ (i.e. x is false) or $x = u$ (i.e. x is true), so that, in the last resort, $W = \{\dot{u}, u\}$.

The axioms (4·021) to (4·0210) of BAH₁ are pair-wise consistent, that is none of them is the negation of any of the others, if and only if the model provided by the totality of the positive factors of 30 is free from literal or metaphorical contradiction. (We mention metaphorical contradiction because only formulae, presumably, can literally contradict one another.) If the axioms were inconsistent, that inconsistency would be reflected somewhere in the model, and conversely. Since it is straightforward, though admittedly laborious, to check that the model referred to is free from contradiction (cf. **4·03**), it follows that (4·021) to (4·0210) are pair-wise consistent. Further, the three informally stated axioms relating to $=$, to the effect that $=$ is a reflexive, symmetrical and transitive relation, and the rules of the FC and of the substitution of equals for equals are also fulfilled within the model. Consequently,

(4·0224) **The Simple-Consistency Theorem for BAH₁:** BAH₁ is simply-consistent.

EXERCISES

*E4·2·1. Demonstrate (4·0211) to (4·0219), and (4·0222) and (4·0223) as theorems in BAH₁.

*E4·2·2. Demonstrate in BAH₁ that $x\_y = ç(çx\_çy)$; that $ç(x\_y) = çx\_çy$.

---

[1] $ç(x\_y) = çx\_çy$ and $ç(x\_y) = çx\_çy$, as theorems for classes, are due to De Morgan, A. (1806-71): *Formal Logic* (London, 1847); they are often called *De Morgan's Laws*.

*E4·2·3.   Demonstrate (4·0220) and (4·0221) as theorems in BAH₁.

E4·2·4.   Let us introduce into BAH₁ the definition: For all x and y of W, $x < y$ if and only if $x\_y = y$. Formulate a rule of proof whereby this definition can be used in BAH₁.

E4·2·5.   Within the arithmetical model describe in **4·02**, what does $<$ signify? What does it signify within the regions-of-a-square model?

Demonstrate E4·2·6 to E4·2·11 as theorems in the form of BAH₁ as modified by E4·2·4.

E4·2·6. $x < y$ if and only if $x\_y = x$.

E4·2·7. $x < x$.

E4·2·8.   If $x < y$ and $y < x$, then $x = y$.

E4·2·9.   If $x < y$ and $y < z$, then $x < z$.

E4·2·10. $x < (x\_y)$.

E4·2·11. $(x\_y) < x$.

E4·2·12.   **Sheffer's Theorem:**[1] The totality of 2^n positive integers that are all the factors of a positive integer u which contains no square factor (*i.e.* no factor x such that x equals y^2 for some integer y) except 1, is a Boolean algebra.

4·03 Another Huntington System for Boolean Algebra (BAH₂): Independence of Axioms

The formulae (4·031) to (4·035) below constitute a more economical axiomatic basis for Boolean Algebra than the axioms of BAH₁. These new formulae are a version of the axiomatic basis of another d.s. for BA that is due to Huntington.[2] We shall label this system "BAH₂". Except for (4·032), for all x, y, and z, if x, y, and z are members of W, then:

(4·031) x_y is a member of W;

(4·032)   For each member x of W there is some member çx of W;

(4·033) $x\_y = y\_x$;

---

[1] Sheffer: Review of C. I. Lewis's *A Survey of Symbolic Logic*, *Amer. Math. Monthly*, 1920, **27**, 310, footnote.
[2] Huntington: "New sets of independent postulates for the algebra of logic", *Trans. Amer. Math. Soc.*, 1933, **35**, 274-304.

(4·034) $(x\_y)\_z = x\_(y\_z)$;

(4·035) $\varsigma(\varsigma x\_\varsigma y)\_\varsigma(\varsigma x\_y) = x$.

To these axioms are to be added the "logical" axioms of equality (4·036) to (4·038). For all x, y, and z of W:

(4·036) $x = x$;

(4·037) If $x = y$, then $y = x$;

(4·038) If $x = y$ and $y = z$, then $x = z$.

To the inferential apparatus provided by the FC is to be added the following:

Rule of Boolean Substitution.—Let v_1 and v_2 denote any elements of W. If $v_1 = v_2$ has been established as a step in a deduction, then one is entitled to assert $b(v_1, x, y, z, \ldots) = b(v_2, x, y, z, \ldots)$ as a subsequent step in the deduction; $b(v_1, x, y, z, \ldots)$ denoting any element of W, that is built up from occurrences of one or more among v_1, x, y, z, $\ldots$ by successive applications of $\_$ and ς, and $b(v_2, x, y, z, \ldots)$ being identical with $b(v_2, x, y, z, \ldots)$ except that each occurrence of v_1 has been replaced by an occurrence of v_2.

An obvious and striking difference between BAH$_1$ and BAH$_2$ is that $\_$, $\grave{u}$, and u are not explicitly dealt with in the latter system. However, BAH$_2$ can be made to deal explicitly with those things by introducing the definitions, for all x and y that are members of W: $x\_y \leftrightarrow \varsigma(\varsigma x\_\varsigma y)$; $\grave{u} \leftrightarrow \varsigma(x\_\varsigma x)$; and $u \leftrightarrow x\_\varsigma x$. We shall in what follows disregard these definitions since they do not, in principle, add to the scope of BAH$_2$. As we remarked earlier, in **2·09**, definitions in a d.s. are theoretically dispensable. For an epitheory their presence only brings unnecessary and better avoided complications.

Let W represent the totality whose members are the positive factors of 30; let x_y represent the least common multiple of x and y that belong to W, and let ςx represent the quotient $30/x$ for each member x of W. Then W is a model of BAH_2, that is to say its members satisfy the axioms of this d.s. For consider first (4·031). Each of "1_1", "1_2", "1_3". "1_5", "1_6", "1_10", "1_15", and "1_30" denotes a member of W, for these expressions denote in turn 1, 2, 3, 5, 6, 10, 15, and 30, which are (the sole) members of W. Similarly, each of "2_1", "2_2", "2_3", "2_5", "2_6", "2_10", "12_15", and "2_30" denotes a member of W, for these expressions denote in turn 2, 2, 6, 10, 6, 10, 30, and 30, which are members of W. The remaining six groups of cases "3_1", "3_2", etc., "5_1", "5_2", etc., "6_1", "6_2", etc., "10_1", "10_2", etc., "15_1", "15_2", etc., and "30_1", "30_2", etc., are analogously dealt with. Consider next (4·032). Each of "ç1", "ç2", "ç3", "ç5", "ç6", "ç10", "ç15", and "ç30" denotes a member of W, for these expressions denote in turn 30, 15, 10, 6, 5, 3, 2, and 1, which are members of W. Consider next (4·033). In confirming that the present W satisfies (4·031) one incidentally obtains results that show this W also to satisfy (4·033). For example, $3\_6 = 6$ and $6\_3 = 6$, and $2\_10 = 10$ and $10\_2 = 10$; and similarly for the remaining 34 cases. Consider next (4·034). Here there are 512 $(= 8 \times 8 \times 8)$ cases to check; e.g. $(1\_1)\_4 = 1\_4 = 4$ and $1\_(1\_4) = 1\_4 = 4$, and $(3\_5)\_10 = 15\_10 = 30$ and $3\_(5\_10) = 3\_10 = 30$. Consider finally (4·035). Here as in (4·031) there are 64 cases to check; e.g.

$$ç\,(ç6\_ç30)\_ç\,(ç6\_30) = ç\,(5\_1)\_ç\,(5\_30) = ç5\_ç30 = 6\_1 = 6.$$

As was pointed out in **4·02**, if there exists a model of an axiomatic d.s. and this model is consistent, then the d.s. itself is consistent. Thus, in view of the work sketched in the preceding paragraph, we have shown

(4·039) **The Simple-Consistency Theorem for BAH_2:** BAH_2 is simply-consistent.

Although it is not logically obligatory, yet it is usually regarded as desirable that the axioms of an axiomatic d.s. be independent of one another, that is, roughly, that each of the axioms contribute something new to the system and that none of the axioms be superfluous, being provable categorically from the remaining axioms. We shall now give a more strict description of independence. It has already been seen that a model of an axiomatic d.s. S is a totality of objects which satisfy (fulfil, make true) the axioms of S. An axiomatic d.s. S is said to be *satisfiable* if and only if there exists some (consistent) model of S. If A is an axiom of S, we use "(S — A) + not-A" to denote the axiomatic d.s. in which the axioms are all the axioms of S except A, together with the negation of A.

By definition, if S is an axiomatic d.s. and A is one of its axioms, then A is an independent axiom of S if and only if both S and (S — A) + not-A are satisfiable.

In practice, then, the procedure to be adopted to demonstrate that the axioms A_1, A_2, ..., A_n of an axiomatic d.s. S are each independent axioms of S is to construct n models M_1, M_2, ..., M_n of (S — A_1) + not-A_1, (S — A_2) + not-A_2, ..., (S — A_n) + not-A_n respectively, together with a model of S. In particular, if we want to show that the axioms (4·031) to (4·035) of BAH$_2$ are independent axioms of BAH$_2$, we should show, firstly, that BAH$_2$ is satisfiable; we should show, secondly, that the set of axioms consisting of (4·032) to (4·035) together with

(4·0310) It is not the case that, for every x and y that are members of W, x_y is a member of W

is satisfiable; we should show, thirdly, that the set of axioms consisting of (4·031) and (4·033) to (4·035) together with

(4·0311) It is not the case that, for every x that is a member of W, çx is a member of W

is satisfiable; and so on. We shall now carry out this programme for BAH_2.

We have already, in demonstrating (4·039), shown that BAH_2 is satisfiable. BAH_2 is satisfied by the totality of the positive factors of 30.

Let W have 0 and 1 as its sole members, and let $\smile$ and ç be determined as follows: $0\smile0 = 0$; $1\smile1 = 1$; $0\smile1 = 2$; $1\smile0 = 2$; ç$0 = 1$; ç$1 = 0$. It will be found on examination that each of the axioms (4·032) to (4·035) is verified, but that (4·031) is falsified (and so (4·0310) is verified) for $0\smile1$ and $1\smile0$ are not members of W.

Let W have 0 and 1 as its sole members, and let $\smile$ and ç be determined as follows: $0\smile0 = 0$; $0\smile1 = 1$; $1\smile0 = 1$; $1\smile1 = 1$; ç$0 = 2$; ç$1 = 2$. It will be found on examination that each of the axioms (4·031) and (4·033) to (4·035) is verified, but that (4·032) is falsified (and so (4·0311) is verified) for ç0 and ç1 are not members of W.

Let W have 0, 1, 2, 3, 4, and 5 as its sole members, and let $\smile$ and ç be determined as follows: (a) (i) $x\smile x = x$ for all x of W; (ii) $0\smile x = x\smile0 = x$ for all x of W; (iii) $1\smile x = x\smile1 = 1$ for all $x \geq 1$ of W; (iv) $2\smile3 = 3\smile2 = 2\smile4 = 4\smile2 = 1$, $2\smile5 = 2$, $5\smile2 = 5$; (v) $3\smile4 = 3$, $3\smile5 = 5\smile3 = 1$, $4\smile3 = 4$; (vi) $4\smile5 = 5\smile4 = 1$; (b) (i) ç$x = x - 1$ for each x of W that is an odd number; (ii) ç$x = x + 1$ for each x of W that is not an odd number. E.g. ç$1 = 0$ by (b) (i) and ç$4 = 5$ by (b) (ii). It will be found on examination that each of the axioms (4·031), (4·032), (4·034), and (4·035) is verified, but that (4·033) is falsified for $2\smile5 \neq 5\smile2$ and $3\smile4 \neq 4\smile3$.

Let W have 0, 1, 2, and 3 as its sole members, and let $\smile$ and ç be determined as follows: (a) (i) $x\smile x = x$ for all x of W; (ii) $0\smile x = x\smile0 = x$ for all x of W; (iii) $1\smile2 = 2\smile1 = 2$, $1\smile3 = 3\smile1 = 0$; (iv) $2\smile3 = 3\smile2 = 1$; (b) (i) ç$x = x - 1$ for each x of W that is an odd number; (ii) ç$x = x + 1$ for each x of W that is not an odd number.

It will be found on examination that each of the axioms (4·031) to (4·033), and (4·035), is verified, but that (4·034) is falsified for *e.g.* $(2\_1)\_3 = 2\_3 = 1$ whereas $2\_(1\_3) = 2\_0 = 2$.

Finally, let W have 0, 1, 2, 3, 4, and 5 as its sole members, and let $\_$ and ς be determined as follows: (*a*) (i) $x\_x = x$ for all x of W; (ii) $0\_x = x\_0 = x$ for all x of W; (iii) $1\_x = x\_1 = 1$ for all x of W; (iv) for all x and y of W, if $y \geq 2$ and $x > y$, then $y\_x = x\_y = 1$; (*b*) (i) $\varsigma x = x - 1$ for each x of W that is an odd number; (ii) $\varsigma x = x + 1$ for each x of W that is not an odd number. It will be found on examination that each of the axioms (4·031) to (4·034) is verified, but that (4·035) is falsified for *e.g.* $\varsigma (\varsigma 2\_\varsigma 4)\_\varsigma (\varsigma 2\_4) = \varsigma (3\_5)\_\varsigma (3\_4) = \varsigma 1\_\varsigma 1 = 0\_0 = 0 \neq 2$.

Thus we have shown

(4·0312)   **The Independence Theorem for BAH$_2$:** Each of the axioms (4·031) to (4·035) of BAH$_2$ is an independent axiom of BAH$_2$.[1]

EXERCISES

Demonstrate E4·3·13 to E4·3·17 as theorems in BAH$_2$.

*E4·3·13. $\varsigma\varsigma x = x$.

*E4·3·14. $\varsigma (x\_x)\_x = x\_\varsigma x$.

*E4·3·15. $\varsigma x\_(y\_x) = x\_\varsigma x$.

*E4·3·16. $\varsigma (x\_y)\_(y\_x) = x\_\varsigma x$.

*E4·3·17. $\varsigma (\varsigma x\_y)\_(\varsigma (z\_x)\_(z\_y)) = x\_\varsigma x$.

*E4·3·18.   An axiomatic d.s. S is said to be *complete* if and only if (i) S is simply-consistent and (ii) it is not the case that there is some well-formed formula b in the language used in S such that if b is added as an axiom in S, then b is an independent axiom of $S + b$. Demonstrate, by using E4·3·14 to E4·3·17 and Post's Completeness Theorem for PCWR (cf. E2·20·107), or otherwise:

---

[1] This epitheorem of BAH$_2$ and the particular methods we have used to demonstrate it are due to Huntington: *Trans. Amer. Math. Soc.*, 1933, **35**, 274-304.

The Completeness Theorem for BAH$_2$: BAH$_2$ is complete.

E4·3·19. An axiomatic d.s. S is said to be *categorical*[1] if and only if any two models M$_1$ and M$_2$ of S are *isomorphic*, that is (i) each member of M$_1$ can be made to correspond with a single member of M$_2$ and conversely, and (ii) $f(x, y, z, \ldots) = f(x', y', z', \ldots)$ for each operator f used in S, x' being the member of M$_2$ that corresponds with x of M$_1$, and similarly for y' and z'; e.g. in BAH$_2$ there are two operators, ⌣ and ç, the former being a 2-place and the latter a 1-place operator. Is BAH$_2$ categorical?

E4·3·20. Write out the axioms of BAH$_1$ and of BAH$_2$ in a bracket-free manner.

E4·3·21. Show that if b (denotes what) is categorically provable in BAH$_2$, then b (denotes what) is categorically provable in BAH$_1$.

*E4·3·22. Show that if b is categorically provable in BAH$_1$, then b is categorically provable in BAH$_2$ (to which have been added the definitions of ⌣, $\dot{u}$, and u mentioned in the text in 4·03).[2]

E4·3·23. **Schröder's Duality Theorem:**[3] If b is a categorically provable equation of BAH$_1$, then b', which is identical with b except that each occurrence of "⌣" in b has been changed into an occurrence of "⌢", and similarly each occurrence of "⌢", "$\dot{u}$", and "u" in b has been changed into an occurrence of "⌣", "u", and "$\dot{u}$" respectively in b', is a categorically provable equation of BAH$_1$. (By virtue of E4·3·22, this epitheorem is also valid for BAH$_2$.)

4·04 Canonical Forms of Boolean Polynomials

In this section it will be more convenient pedagogically to base our considerations upon BAH$_1$ rather than upon BAH$_2$.

In view of the fact that the operators ⌣ and ⌢ are commutative and associative, we may for practical purposes disregard bracketing of terms joined together by ⌣ or by ⌢. For instance, "çx⌢y⌢z" will be used instead of either of the

---

[1] Notion and term due to Veblen, O. (1880-). "A system of axioms for geometry", *Trans. Amer. Math. Soc.*, 1904, **5**, 343-84.

[2] Huntington: *Trans. Amer. Math. Soc.*, 1933, **35**, 274-304.

[3] Schröder, E. (1841-1902): *Vorlesungen über die Algebra der Logik I* (Leipzig, 1890).

particular forms "$(çx\smile y)\frown z$" and "$çx\frown(y\frown z)$" which we know to be synonymous. But of course brackets cannot be omitted from such an expression as "$x\frown(y\frown z)$" since in general "$x\frown(y\frown z)$" is not synonymous with "$(x\smile y)\frown z$".

A Boolean polynomial in n variables ($n = 1, 2, 3, \ldots$) is an expression built up out of the object variables x, y, and z (with or without subscripts) through the use of cups ($\smile$), caps ($\frown$) or cedillas (ç); if $n = 1$, a single occurrence of a single variable is also counted as a Boolean polynomial. Thus

(4·041) x

is a Boolean polynomial in 1 variable;

(4·042) $x\frown(y\smile çx)$

is a Boolean polynomial in 2 variables; and

(4·043) $(x\frown x)\frown ç(y\frown z)$

is a Boolean polynomial in 3 variables. Letting x_i ($i = 1, 2, 3, \ldots$) denote object variables, we shall use "$p(x_1, x_2, x_3, \ldots)$" to represent a Boolean polynomial in the variables $x_1, x_2, x_3, \ldots$. For example, $p(x)$ is any Boolean polynomial in the single variable x and $p(x, y, z)$ is any Boolean polynomial in the three variables x, y, and z. Hence $p(x_1, x_2, x_3, \ldots)$ denotes Boolean polynomial schemata.

With respect to any given Boolean polynomial in n variables, a *minimal* Boolean polynomial is one that consists of caps between an occurrence of each of the n variables; some or all of these variables might but need not be prefixed by a cedilla. And such a minimal Boolean polynomial (m.B.p.) will be said to be *canonical* if and only if the variables occurring in it do so in a prescribed order. The order we prescribe is: alphabetical order, and if two variables (like x_1 and x_2) have the same alphabetical order, then in the order of their subscripts, the variable without subscripts having precedence. With respect to (4·043)

(4·044) $x_-çy_-çz$

is a canonical minimal Boolean polynomial (c.m.B.p.), and so are

(4·045) $çx_-y_-z$

and

(4·046) x_-y_-z.

However, $ç(x_-y)_-z$, x_-y_-z, and $y_-(x_-z)$ are not m.B.p.s. at all, and $y_-çx_-z$ and z_-y_-x are m.B.p.s. but they are not c.m.B.p.s. since the variables do not occur in the prescribed order.

A Boolean polynomial is said to be the *canonical* (or *normal*) *transform* of $p(x_1, x_2, x_3, \ldots)$ if and only if it consists of cups between c.m.B.p.s., none of the latter being duplicated. Since, by (4·0211), $x_-x = x$, it follows by the Rule of Substitution that (4·043) is equal to

(4·047) $x_-ç(y_-z)$,

and it follows from E4·2·2 that (4·047) is equal to

(4·048) $x_-çy_-çz$,

so that (4·043) is equal to (4·048). (4·048) is the canonical transform of (4·043). Consider, again, (4·042). Since, by (4·024), x is equal to x_-u and by (4·029) u equals $y_-çy$, it follows that (4·042) is equal to

(4·049) $(x_-(y_-çy))_-(y_-çx)$,

and by using successively (4·028) and (4·025), (4·049) is equal to

(4·0410) $(x_-y)_-(x_-çy)_-(çx_-y)$.

(4·0410) is the canonical transform of (4·042).

It can be shown that every Boolean polynomial has either a canonical transform or is equal to $\grave{u}$.

Compare

(4·0411) $(x_-y)_-(x_-çy)_-(çx_-y)_-(çx_-çy)$

with

(4·0412) $(p \cdot q) \lor (p \cdot \sim q) \lor (\sim p \cdot q) \lor (\sim p \cdot \sim q)$.

It is clear that (4·0412) is tautologous, for all the possible combinations of t.v.s for p and q are covered by the alternatives contained, and consequently one of these alternatives is bound to take the t.v. truth. Analogously, (4·0411) can be shown to equal u; for, by applying (4·028), (4·0411) becomes

(4·0413) $(x_\smile(y_\smile\varsigma y))_\smile(\varsigma x_\smile(y_\smile\varsigma y))$,

and this becomes

(4·0414) $x_\smile\varsigma x$

by applying (4·029) and (4·024); and finally (4·0414) becomes simply u by applying (4·029) again. This example illustrates the general theorem that a Boolean polynomial in n variables can be interpreted as a t.p.s. if and only if the polynomial has a canonical transform which contains 2^n c.m.B.p.s.[1]

EXERCISES

E4·4·24. Show that every Boolean polynomial is either equal to u or has a canonical transform.

E4·4·25. Show that a Boolean polynomial in n variables is tautologous if and only if it has a canonical transform which contains 2^n c.m.B.p.s.

For each of E4·4·26 to E4·4·32 (i) obtain a canonical transform; (ii) thereby determine whether the given Boolean polynomial is tautologous; (iii) check by changing the symbols into the corresponding ones of L_1PR and either constructing full truth tables or using the indirect truth table method.

E4·4·26. $x_\smile(x_\smile\varsigma y)$.

E4·4·27. $\varsigma(\varsigma y_\smile x)_\smile x$.

E4·4·28. $\varsigma((\varsigma x_\smile y)_\smile\varsigma x)_\smile\varsigma y$.

E4·4·29. $\varsigma((\varsigma x_\smile y)_\smile\varsigma y)_\smile\varsigma x$.

---

[1] This theorem and the notion of canonical transform is due to the labours of Boole and Schröder in their already cited works, and to the labours of Whitehead: *Universal Algebra* (Cambridge, 1898). For the general theory of Boolean Algebra, cf. Birkhoff, G. (1911-): *Lattice Theory*, second edition (New York, 1948). An excellent introductory treatment is in Bennett, A. A. (1888-) and Baylis, C. A. (1902-): *Formal Logic* (New York, 1939).

E4·4·30. $((x_\smile y)_\frown (x_\smile çy))_\frown (x_\smile y_\smile z)$.

E4·4·31. $ç(x_\smile(y_\smile z))_\frown (x_\smile y)_\frown (x_\smile z)$.

E4·4·32. $x_\frown çx_\smile y_\smile z$.

E4·4·33. Show that if a Boolean polynomial has a canonical transform, it has a unique one, apart from the order of its c.m.B.p.s.

E4·4·34. A *maximal* Boolean polynomial is defined exactly as a minimal, except that "cup" and "cap" are interchanged. Show that every Boolean polynomial is either equal to *ù* or is equal to a Boolean polynomial consisting of caps between canonical maximal Boolean polynomials, none of which are duplicated. (Such a resultant expression is said to be a *conjunctive* canonical transform, whereas that type considered in the text is a *disjunctive* one.)

E4·4·35. How many distinct (unequal) Boolean polynomials are denoted by (a) $p(x)$, (b) $p(x, y)$, (c) $p(x, y, z)$?

4·05 Sets, Set Membership, Set Inclusion, Set Equality

The notion of a collection, class or totality of objects is a familiar one. In conformity with current usage in mathematics we shall usually employ the term "set" for this notion in general. The letters "s", "t", "w" and "e" will be used as variables for sets (French "ensemble", German "Menge").

In order to state that something x is a member of the set s, one writes

(4·051) $x \in s$.[1]

In order to affirm that x is not a member of s one writes

(4·052) $x \notin s$,

or uses one of the logical symbols for negation.

There are two ways of specifying or defining any particular set. One way is to list all its members. In such a case one uses the curly brackets {} and encloses the list of members within them.[2] Thus, the set of positive integers less than 10 is {1, 2, 3, 4, 5, 6, 7, 8, 9}. The

---

[1] Notation due to Peano: *Notations de logique mathématique*.

[2] Notation due to Cantor, G. (1845-1918): "Beiträge zur Begründung der transfiniten Mengenlehre", *Math. Ann.*, 1895, **46**, 481-512.

ellipsis " ... " is allowed to occur within the curly brackets provided one can tell what the intervening objects are whose places are occupied by the ellipsis. {1, 2, 3, 4, 5, ..., 100} is the set of positive integers from 1 to 100. This mode of defining a set is excluded if the set has an infinite number of members, as has the set of all the positive integers, or if the set has for its members objects which are not known to be its members, as the set of all the digits that occur at least 25 times consecutively somewhere in the decimal expansion of π. The second and incomparably more usual way of defining a set is by the enunciation of a property or complex of properties whose possession serves as a necessary and sufficient condition for an object to be a member of the set. For such a definition of a set it is usual to use as the framework {: }. For instance, "{x : x is a prime number}" is an expression for the set of prime numbers; this expression may be read "the set of all the x's such that (:) x is a prime number". The property definition of a set is of the form

$$\{x_1, x_2, \ldots : b\,(x_1, x_2, \ldots)\}.$$

A set of theoretic importance is the set with no elements at all. This is called the *null* or the *empty* set. It is denoted by the symbol $\emptyset$.[1] Accordingly, for no x is it the case that $x \in \emptyset$.

The set of all the positive integers is included in the set of all the integers. Each member of the former set is a member of the latter set. If a set s is included in a set t, s is said to be a *subset* of t, and to express that s and t are so related one writes

(4·053) $s \subseteq t$.

In order to affirm that s is not a subset of t one writes

(4·054) $s \nsubseteq t$

[1] This notion derives ultimately from Boole: *The Mathematical Analysis of Logic*, who considered an empty class (denoted by "0") as a class with no members in the "universe of discourse".

or uses one of the logical symbols for negation. If $s \subseteq t$, it can but need not happen that also $t \subseteq s$. If both $s \subseteq t$ and $t \subseteq s$, so that s and t have exactly the same membership, then s and t are said to be *equal* and one can write

(4·055) $s = t$.

If, on the other hand, $s \subseteq t$ and $t \nsubseteq s$, then s is said to be a *proper subset* of t, and one writes

(4·056) $s \subset t$.

The negation of (4·055) and (4·056) is expressed either by the stroke (/) through the set-theoretic symbol or by use of one of the logical symbols for negation.

We shall now give formal definitions of $s \subseteq t$, $s \subset t$, $s = t$, and $\emptyset$; we use the symbol $\equiv [E]$ for mutual implication.

(4·057) $(s)(t) [(s \subseteq t) \equiv (x)(x \in s \supset x \in t)]$
$$PstEs \subseteq tPxCx \in sx \in t.$$

(4·058) $(s)(t) [(s \subset t) \equiv (s \subseteq t . \sim t \subseteq s)]$
$$PstEs \subset tKs \subseteq tNt \subseteq s.$$

(4·059) $(s)(t) [(s \equiv t) \equiv (x)(x \in s \equiv x \in t)]$
$$PstEs = tPxEs \in sx \in t.$$

(4·0510) $(x) [x \in \emptyset \equiv \sim (s)(s = s)]$
$$PxEx \in \emptyset NPss = s.$$

In Chapter Three, fifteen rules for SFCT were formulated. We want to be able to use this apparatus in deductions outside the FC as well as within it; hence we lay down that in the statements of the rules the occurrences of "b", "d", and "h" are to represent also any actual formulae or formula schemata in any language used for reasoning, and the occurrences of "x" and "y", etc., are to represent also any actual objects or object schemata (in particular, object variables). We shall henceforth employ "b", "d", "h", "x", "y", etc., in this extended way. At this stage we shall add three rules to the rules (i) to (xv) already given.

(xvi) *Rule of Definition Introduction.*—If b has been specified as being a definition, then an occurrence of b may be inserted in any section of any order of a proof structure. The reference for a step that is asserted on the grounds of this rule consists of the number assigned to b in our text numbering, followed by "df in".

(xvii) *Rule of Mutual Implication Introduction.*—If b is a supposition in a section of order n of a proof structure ($n \geq 2$) and d is another step in that section, and d is a supposition in a subsequent section of the same order n and b is another step in that section, then b $\equiv$ d [Ebd] may be asserted as a subsequent step in the section of order $n - 1$ containing these two sections (if there is such a section). The reference for a step that is asserted on the grounds of this rule consists of the proof numbers of b° and d, d° and b in that order, followed by "mutimp in".

(xviii) *Rule of Mutual Implication Expulsion.*—If b $\equiv$ d [Ebd] and b (d) denote steps that occur in the same section of order n ($n \geq 1$) of a proof structure, then d (b) may be asserted as a subsequent step in the same section. The reference for a step that is asserted on the grounds of this rule consists of the proof numbers of b (d) and b $\equiv$ d [Ebd] in that order, followed by "mutimp ex".

Now, by means of the suppositional method of proof we shall establish $(s)(s \subseteq s)$, $(s)(s = s)$, and $(s)(\emptyset \subseteq s)$ as categorical theorems of Set Theory. It is of logical importance to notice, in passing, that many of the steps obtained in the deduction are obtained from previous steps that contain free variables and so these previous steps are not propositions or p.s.s but propositional forms or schemata of such, (4·0514), (4·0516), (4·0517), and (4·0518) are examples. As we remarked when introducing the Functional Calculus, this point is often overlooked. Rules of inference or proof for mathematics must be formulated in terms of formulae instead of in terms of propositions.

(4·0511)	$s\|(s)\,(t)\,[(s \subseteq t) \equiv (x)\,(x \in s \supset x \in t)]$
(4·0512)	$(s)\,(t)\,[(s = t) \equiv (x)\,(x \in s \equiv x \in t)]$
(4·0513)	$x\| \quad \|x \in s°$
(4·0514)	$\|x \in s$
(4·0515)	$\|x \in s°$
(4·0516)	$\|x \in s$
(4·0517)	$x \in s \supset x \in s$
(4·0518)	$x \in s \equiv x \in s$
(4·0519)	$(x)\,(x \in s \supset x \in s)$
(4·0520)	$(x)\,(x \in s \equiv x \in s)$
(4·0521)	$(s \subseteq s) \equiv (x)\,(x \in s \supset x \in s)$
(4·0522)	$(s = s) \equiv (x)\,(x \in s \equiv x \in s)$
(4·0523)	$s \subseteq s$
(4·0524)	$s = s$
(4·0525)	$(s)\,(s \subseteq s)$
(4·0526)	$(s)\,(s = s)$
(4·0527)	$s\| \quad x\| \quad \|x \in \emptyset°$
(4·0528)	$(x)\,(x \in \emptyset \equiv \sim (s)\,(s = s))$
(4·0529)	$x \in \emptyset \equiv \sim (s)\,(s = s)$
(4·0530)	$\sim (s)\,(s = s)$
(4·0531)	$(s)\,(s = s)$
(4·0532)	$x \in s$
(4·0533)	$x \in \emptyset \supset x \in s$
(4·0534)	$(x)\,(x \in \emptyset \supset x \in s)$
(4·0535)	$(s)\,(t)\,[(s \subseteq t) \equiv (x)\,(x \in s \supset x \in t)$
(4·0536)	$(\emptyset \subseteq s) \equiv (x)\,(x \in \emptyset \supset x \in s)$
(4·0537)	$\emptyset \subseteq s$
(4·0538)	$(s)\,(\emptyset \subseteq s)$

References.—11: (4·057), df in. 12: (4·059), df in. 14: 13, re. 16: 15, re. 17: 15, 16, imp in. 18: 13, 14, 15, 16, mutimp in. 19: 17, uq in. 20: 18, uq in. 21: 11, uq ex. 22: 12, uq ex. 23: 19, 21, mutimp ex.

24: 20, 22, mutimp ex. 25: 23, uq in. 26: 24, uq in. 28: (4·0510), df in. 29: 28, uq ex. 30: 27, 29, mutimp ex. 31: 26, tf. 32: 31, 30, neg ex. 33: 27, 32, imp in. 34: 33, uq in. 35: (4·057), df in. 36: 35, uq ex. 37: 34, 36, mutimp ex. 38: 37, uq in.

EXERCISES

E4·5·36. Formulate, for the suppositional method, a Rule of Theorem Introduction, which will allow a categorical theorem that has already been proved by the suppositional method to be inserted as a step in any section of any order of a proof structure. This will be regarded as rule (xix) in our body of rules.

E4·5·37. Show that rules (xvii), (xviii), and (xix) are derivable rules, that is that any step in a proof structure that is obtained by means of them is ultimately obtainable without them.

Give suppositional method proofs of E4·5·38 to E4·5·47.

E4·5·38. $PstwCKs \subseteq tt \subseteq ws \subseteq w$.

E4·5·39. $PstwCKs \subset tt \subset ws \subset w$.

E4·5·40. $PstwCKKs \subseteq tt \subseteq ww \subseteq sKKs = ts = wt = w$.

E4·5·41. $PstCs = tt = s$.

E4·5·42. $PstwCKs = tt = ws = w$.

E4·5·43. $PstCs \subset tSxKx \in tNx \in s$.

E4·5·44. How many subsets has $\{x\}$?

E4·5·45. How many subsets has $\{x, y\}$?

E4·5·46. How many subsets has $\{x, y, z\}$?

E4·5·47. How many subsets has $\{x_1, x_2, x_3, \ldots, x_n\}$?

4·06 Union, Intersection, Subtraction, and Complementation of Sets

The union-set of s and t is the set of all the objects that are either members of s or members of t or members of both s and t. This union-set is denoted by "s_t". Thus, for all s and t,

(4·061) $s\_t \leftrightarrow \{x : x \in s \lor x \in t\}$ $\_st \leftrightarrow \{x : Ax \in sx \in t\}$,

or, what comes to the same thing,

(4·062) $(s)(t)(x)[(x \in s \smile t) \equiv (x \in s \lor x \in t)$

$PstxEx \in \smile stAx \in sx \in t.$[1]

For example, $\{1, 2, 3, 4\} \smile \{3, 4, 5, 6, 7\}$ is equal to $\{1, 2, 3, 4, 5, 6, 7\}$, and $\{0\} \smile \{x : x$ is a positive integer$\}$ is equal to the set of all the non-negative integers.

Since $\lor$ [A] is a commutative and associative operator—$b \lor d \equiv d \lor b$, and $(b \lor d) \lor h \equiv b \lor (d \lor h)$—it follows that $\smile$ too is a commutative and associative operator:

(4·063) $(s)(t)(s \smile t = t \smile s)$ $Pst \smile st = \smile ts$;

(4·064) $(s)(t)(w)[(s \smile t) \smile w = s \smile (t \smile w)]$ $Pstw \smile \smile stw = \smile s \smile tw.$

By virtue of (4·063) and (4·064) brackets can be omitted from an expression for a union-set; the members of $s_1 \smile s_2 \smile s_3 \smile \ldots \smile s_n$ are all the objects that are members of at least one s_i $(i = 1, 2, 3, \ldots, n)$. For instance

(4·065) $\{1\} \smile \{3, 4\} \smile \{1, 2, 3, 5\} \smile \{6\} = \{1, 2, 3, 4, 5, 6\}.$

The intersection-set of s and t is the set of all the objects that are members of both s and t. This intersection-set is denoted by "$s \frown t$".[2]   Thus, for all s and t,

(4·066) $s \frown t \leftrightarrow \{x : x \in s . x \in t\}$ $\frown st \leftrightarrow \{x : Kx \in sx \in t\}$,

or, what comes to the same thing,

(4·067) $(s)(t)(x)[(x \in s \frown t) \equiv (x \in s . x \in t)]$

$PstxEx \in \frown stKx \in sx \in t.$

---

[1] The reader will notice that sometimes the sign "$\leftrightarrow$" and sometimes the signs "E" and "$\equiv$" are used in definitions; different logicians have different opinions on this point.   We here use whichever seems most convenient.   However, it is necessary to notice that, if a definition such as (4·061) occurs as a step in a proof structure by rule (xvi), then an additional rule—a rule of definition expulsion—will be needed to enable the content of the definition to be used.   This new rule will be to the effect: if b (x) $\leftrightarrow$ d (x) and b (x) (or d (x)) are steps in the same section of a proof structure, then it is legitimate to affirm d (x) (or b (x)) as a subsequent step in the same section.

[2] The modern use of the signs $\smile$ and $\frown$ is due to Peano: *Notations de logique mathématique*, who used them for alternation and conjunction (formulary operators analogous to the set-theoretic ones). As set-theoretic symbols they were first used extensively by Whitehead and Russell: *Principia Mathematica I*. The signs had earlier been used, arithmetically, by Leibniz, G. W. (1646-1716): *De Arte Combinatoria* (Leipzig, 1666).

For example, $\{1, 2, 3, 4\}_\frown\{3, 4, 5, 6, 7\}$ is equal to $\{3, 4\}$ and $\{0\}_\frown\{x : x$ is a positive integer$\}$ is (equal to) the null set $\emptyset$.

Since $[K]$ is a commutative and associative operator, it follows that $_\frown$ too is a commutative and associative operator:

(4·068) $(s) (t) (s_\frown t = t_\frown s)$ $Pst_\frown st = _\frown ts$;

(4·069) $(s) (t) (w) [(s_\frown t)_\frown w = s)_\frown t_\frown w)$

$$Pstw_{\frown\frown}stw = _\frown s_\frown tw.$$

By virtue of (4·068) and (4·069) brackets can be omitted from an expression for an intersection-set; the members of $s_1_\frown s_2_\frown s_3_\frown\ldots_\frown s_n$ are all the objects that are members of every s_i ($i = 1, 2, 3, \ldots, n$). For instance

(4·0610) $\{1\}_\frown\{1, 2\}_\frown\{1, 2, 3\}_\frown\{1, 2, 3, 4\} = \{1\}$.

Since conjunction is distributive over alternation and conversely, that is

(4·0611) $[b.(d \vee h)] \equiv [(b.d) \vee (b.h)]$ $EKbAdhAKbdKbh$

and

(4·0612) $[b \vee (d.h)] \equiv [(b \vee d).(b \vee h)]$

$$EAbKdhKAbdAbh,$$

it follows that intersection is distributive over union and conversely:

(4·0613) $(s) (t) (w) [s_\frown(t_\frown w) = (s_\frown t)_\frown(s_\frown w)]$

$$Pstw_\frown s_\frown tw = _{\frown\frown}st_\frown sw;$$

(4·0614) $(s) (t) (w) [s_\frown(t_\frown w) \equiv (s_\frown t)_\frown(s_\frown w)]$

$$Pstw_\frown s_\frown tw = _{\frown\frown}st_\frown sw.$$

Similarly, it can be demonstrated more generally that

(4·0615) $s_\frown(t_1_\frown t_2_\frown\ldots_\frown t_n) = (s_\frown t_1)_\frown(s_\frown t_2)_\frown\ldots_\frown(s_\frown t_n)$;

(4·0616) $s_\frown(t_1_\frown t_2_\frown\ldots_\frown t_n) = (s_\frown t_1)_\frown(s_\frown t_2)_\frown\ldots_\frown(s_\frown t_n)$.

The subtraction-set or the difference of s and t is the set of all the objects that are members of s and are not members of t. This difference is denoted by "$s - t$". Thus, for all s and t,

(4·0617) $s - t \leftrightarrow \{x : x \in s . \sim x \in t\}$
$$- st = \{x : Kx \in sNx \in t\},$$

or, what comes to the same thing,

(4·0618) $(s)(t)(x)[(x \in s - t) \equiv (x \in s . \sim x \in t)]$
$$PstxEx \in - stKx \in sNx \in t.$$

For example, $\{1, 2, 3, 4\} - \{3, 4, 5, 6, 7\}$ is equal to $\{1, 2\}$ and $\{3, 4, 5, 6, 7\} - \{1, 2, 3, 4\}$ is equal to $\{5, 6, 7\}$. These cases show that subtraction is not a commutative operator. Nor is it associative, as is shown by the following counterexample:

$$(\{1, 2, 3, 4\} - \{1, 2, 3\}) - \{1, 2\} = \{4\} - \{1, 2\} = \{4\},$$

whereas

$$\{1, 2, 3, 4\} - (\{1, 2, 3\} - \{1, 2\}) = \{1, 2, 3, 4\} - \{3\}$$
$$= \{1, 2, 4\}.$$

Suppose that each of the sets s_1, s_2, ... is a subset of a fixed set 1. Then $1 - s_i$ is called the *complement* of s_i and may be denoted more compactly by "$çs_i$". For instance, let $N (N^{\geq})$ be the set of all the positive (non-negative) integers $1, 2, 3, \ldots (0, 1, 2, 3, \ldots)$; and for each i of $N (N^{\geq})$ let N_i $(N_i^{\geq})$ be the set of all the positive (non-negative) integers from 1 (0) to i, so that *e.g.* $N_5 = \{1, 2, 3, 4, 5\}$, and $N_5^{\geq} = \{0, 1, 2, 3, 4, 5\}$. For each i of N, $N_i \subseteq N$. $çN_5$ has all the natural numbers greater than 5 for its members: $çN_5 = \{x : x \in N . x > 5\}$. More generally,
(4·0619) $çN_i = \{x : x \in N . x > i\}$.

In the older literature the fixed set 1 is called the *universe of discourse*. In more recent literature it is called the *basic space* or the *basic set*. We shall use this last name. We employ the symbol "1" for two reasons.[1]   In the first place, it conforms with the widespread

---

[1] Symbol introduced by Nidditch: *I.F.L.M.* In the older literature the usual symbol, originally introduced by Boole: *The Mathematical Analysis of Logic*, is "1".

adoption of "$\emptyset$" for the null set. In the second place, in BA $\varsigma\dot{u} = u$ and $\varsigma u = \dot{u}$. If "$\emptyset$" replaces "$\dot{u}$" and "1" replaces "u", we have $\varsigma\,\emptyset = 1$ and $\varsigma 1 = \emptyset$. Now in the propositional interpretation of BA, $\emptyset$ will denote a fixed false proposition and 1 will denote a fixed true proposition. This fits in neatly with our use of "0" and "1" for truth and falsity respectively in Chapter Two; for, remembering that the stroke symbol / functions as a negation sign, as in $\neq$ and $\nsubseteq$, "$\emptyset$" can be read as the negation of a fixed true proposition (and so as a fixed false proposition) and "1" can be read as the negation of a fixed false proposition (and so as a fixed true proposition).

EXERCISES

E4·6·48. What are the members of the union-set, and of the intersection-set, of $\{1, 2, 5\}$ and $\{2, 3, 4, 5\}$?

E4·6·49. To what set is the union-set, and the intersection-set, of $\{4, 5\}$, $\{2, 3\}$, and $\{2, 3, 4, 5\}$ equal?

E4·6·50. What are the members of $\mathbf{N}_{10} - \mathbf{N}_5$?

Give suppositional method proofs of E4·6·51 to E4·6·57.

E4·6·51. (i) $(s)\,(\emptyset\_s = s)$; (ii) $(s)\,(\emptyset\_s = \emptyset)$.

E4·6·52. (i) $(s)\,(1\_s = s)$; (ii) $(s)\,(1\_s = 1)$.

E4·6·53. $(s)\,(t)\,[(s\_t = t) \equiv (s \subseteq t)]$.

E4·6·54. $(s)\,(t)\,[(s\_t = s) \equiv (s \subseteq t)]$.

E4·6·55. (i) $(s)\,(t)\,[s\_(s\_t) = s]$; (ii) $(s)\,(t)\,[s\_(s\_t) = s]$.

E4·6·56. $(s)\,(t)\,[s = (s\_t)\_(s - t)]$.

E4·6·57. $(s)\,(t)\,(w)\,[(s - t) - w = (s - t) - (t\ \ w)]$.

Demonstrate E4·6·58 to E4·6·66. In E4·6·61 and thereafter it is to be assumed that all the sets concerned are subsets of a fixed set 1.

E4·6·58. If $s\_t = s\_w$ and $s\_t = s\_w$, then $t = w$.

E4·6·59. $s\_t\_w = (s - t)\_(t - w)\_(w - s)\_(s\_t\_w)$.

E4·6·60. $s_1\_s_2\ldots\_s_n =$
$(s_1 - s_2)\_(s_2 - s_3)\_\ldots\_(s_{n-1} - s_n)\_(s_n - s_1)\_(s_1\_s_2\_\ldots\_s_n)$.

E4·6·61. (i) $s - t = s\_\varsigma t$; (ii) $s\_\varsigma s = \emptyset$.

E4·6·62. (i) $\varsigma\,(s - t) = \varsigma s\_t$; (ii) $s - t = \varsigma\,(\varsigma s\_t)$.

E4·6·63. (i) $\varsigma\varsigma s = s$; (ii) $s = (s\_t)\_(s\_\varsigma t)$.

E4·6·64. (i) $\varsigma\,(s\_t) = \varsigma s\_\varsigma t$; (ii) $\varsigma\,(s\_t) = \varsigma s\_\varsigma t$.

E4·6·65. $\varsigma\,(s_1\_s_2\_\ldots\_s_n) = \varsigma s_1\_\varsigma s_2\_\ldots\_\varsigma s_n$.

E4·6·66. $\varsigma\,(s_1\_s_2\_\ldots\_s_n) = \varsigma s_1\_\varsigma s_2\_\ldots\_\varsigma s_n$.

4·07 Systems of Sets: Modules, Rings, Fields

By the *absolute difference, modular difference* or *symmetric difference* of s and t is meant the set whose members are all the objects that are either members of s but not of t, or are members of t and not of s.[1] The symmetric difference of s and t is denoted by "$s + t$". Thus,

$$(4·071) \quad s + t \leftrightarrow \{x : (x \in s. \sim x \in t) \lor (\sim x \in s . x \in t)\}$$
$$+ st \leftrightarrow \{x : AKx \in sNx \in tKNx \in sx \in t\}.$$

It will now be convenient to introduce another formula connective, that for exclusive alternation. This connective will be symbolised in the Peano-Russell notation by "$\lor\!\!\!\!-$"; in the Łukasiewicz-Tarski notation the corresponding symbol is "J". By definition, then,

$$(4·072) \quad [b \lor\!\!\!\!- d] \leftrightarrow [(b . \sim d) \lor (\sim b.d)]$$
$$Jbd \leftrightarrow AKbNdKNbd.$$

In terms of exclusive alternation we can give a compact definition of symmetric difference:

$$(4·073) \quad (s)(t)(x) [(x \in s + t) \equiv (x \in s \lor\!\!\!\!- x \in t)]$$
$$PstxEx \in + stJx \in sx \in t.$$

For example, $\{1, 2, 3\} + \{3, 4, 5, 6\} = \{1, 2, 4, 5, 6\}$, and $\{4, 16, 25\} + \{4, 36, 49\} = \{16, 25, 36, 49\}$, and $N_8 + N_{10} = \{9, 10\}$.

Since $\lor\!\!\!\!- [J]$ is a commutative and associative operator, it follows that $+$ is also a commutative and associative operator:

$$(4·074) \quad (s)(t)(s + t = t + s) \qquad Pst + st = + ts;$$
$$(4·075) \quad (s)(t)(w) [(s + t) + w = s + (t + w)]$$
$$Pstw + + stw = + s + tw.$$

Since J is not distributive over A or over K, it follows that $+$ is not distributive over $\smile$ or over $\frown$; and since A is not

[1] Notion introduced by Daniell, P. J. (1889-1946): "The modular difference of classes", *Bull. Amer. Math. Soc.*, 1916, **23**, 446-50.

distributive over *J*, it follows that ⌣ is not distributive over +. On the other hand, *K* is distributive over *J*: *EKbJdhJKbdKbh* is tautologous. Therefore

(4·076) (*s*) (*t*) (*w*) [*s*⌣(*t* + *w*) = (*s*⌣*t*) + (*s*⌣*w*)]

$$Pstw \smile s + tw = + \smile st \smile sw.$$

A set is said to be a *family of sets* if and only if all its members are themselves sets. We shall use the Greek letters α, β, γ as variables for families of sets. For instance, {**N**₁, **N**₂} is a family of sets; it has two members, **N**₁ and **N**₂. It should be noticed that although 1 ∈ **N**₁ (and 1 ∈ **N**₂), it is not the case that 1 ∈ {**N**₁, **N**₂}.

A set is said to be *closed* under a 1 (2) place operator if the result produced by that operator on any 1 (2) member(s) of the set is itself a member of the set. *E.g.* a BA *W* (which, be it remembered, is a totality, a set) is closed under the 1 place operator ç and under the 2 place operator ⌣; cf. (4·032) and (4·031).

Now a non-empty family of sets is a *module of sets* if and only if it is closed under symmetric subtraction +. If we want briefly to say that x is a module of sets, we do so by the expression "xéms". Hence, by definition,

(4·077) *PaCNa* = ∅*Eaéms PstCKs* ∈ α*t* ∈ α + *st* ∈ α.

It follows directly from the definition that

(4·078) (α) [aéms ⊃ ∅ ∈ α] *PaCa*éms∅ ∈ α;

for since α is a module of sets, it is a non-empty family of sets, and so contains at least one member *s*; but being a module of sets, *s* + *s* ∈ α, and since *s* + *s* = ∅, ∅ ⊂ u.

A non-empty family of sets is said to be a *ring of sets* if and only if it is closed under union ⌣ and subtraction —. If we want briefly to say that x is a ring of sets, we do so by the expression "xérs". Hence, by definition,

(4·079) *PaCNa* = ∅*Eaérs PstCKs* ∈ α*t* ∈ α*K*⌣*st* ∈ α — *st* ∈ α.

If α is a ring of sets, then it is also closed under $\smallsmile$ and $+$, for

$$(4 \cdot 0710) \quad (s)(t)[s \smallfrown t = s - ((s \smallfrown t) - t)]$$
$$Pst \smallfrown st = -s - \smallfrown stt,$$

and

$$(4 \cdot 0711) \quad (s)(t)[s + t = (s - t) \smallsmile (t - s)]$$
$$Pst + st = \smallsmile - st - ts.$$

So again, if α is a ring of sets, $\emptyset \in \alpha$.

A non-empty family of sets is said to be a *field of sets* if and only if it is a Boolean algebra.[1]

EXERCISES

E4·7·67.   Show that $\{\emptyset\}$ is a ring of sets.

E4·7·68.   Show that if Us is a family of sets that consists of all the subsets of s, then $\{Us\}$ is a ring of sets.

E4·7·69.   Show that a ring of sets is a Boolean algebra if and only if there is some member t of the ring such that for all s of the ring, $s \smallfrown t = t$. (This t is of course our 1, or u.)

E4·7·70.   A non-empty set s is said to be a *partly ordered set* if and only if there exists a relation $\leq$ between any members x and y of s such that: (i) for all x of s, $x \leq x$; (ii) for all x and y of s, if $x \leq y$ and $y \leq x$, then $x = y$; and (iii) for all x, y, and z, of s, if $x \leq y$ and $y \leq z$, then $x \leq z$.[2] (The symbol $\leq$ may be read "precedes.") (*a*) Show that every non-empty family of sets is a partly ordered set (by equating $\leq$ and $\subseteq$). (*b*) Show that **N** is a partly ordered set, by interpreting "$\leq$" as meaning the same as "is a factor of".

E4·7·71.   Show that every non-empty subset of a partly ordered set is a partly ordered set.

---

[1] The algebraic notions of ring and field were introduced into Set Theory by Hausdorff, F. (1868-1942): *Grundzüge der Mengenlehre*, Zweite Ausgabe (Leipzig, 1927). The first full demonstration that systems of sets can have structures identical with the structures of algebraic rings and fields (and related algebraic systems) was given by Stone, M. H. (1903-): "Subsumption of the theory of Boolean algebras under the theory of rings", *Proc. Nat. Acad. Sci.*, 1935, **21**, 103-5; "The theory of representations for Boolean algebras", *Trans. Amer. Math. Soc.*, 1936, **40**, 37-111.

[2] Hausdorff: *Grundzüge der Mengenlehre*, Erste Ausgabe (Leipzig, 1914).

E4·7·72. A non-empty set s is said to be a *simply*, or a *linearly*, or a *chainwise*, *ordered set*, or simply a *chain*, if and only if (i) it is a partly ordered set and (ii) for each x and y of s: $(x \leq y) \, \mathbf{V} \, (y \leq x) \, [Ax \leq yy \leq x]$.[1]   (a) Show that if x and y are members of a chain and $x \neq y$, then $(x \leq y) \, \mathbf{W} \, (y \leq x)$.   (b) Show that $\mathbf{N}$ is a chain. (c) Show that a subset of a chain is a chain.   (d) Show that a chain s of n members (where $n \in \mathbf{N}$) has a unique member x such that for all y of s: $x \leq y$; and has a unique member z such that for all y of s: $y \leq z$. (Such a x and z may be called respectively the initial and final members of s.)

E4·7·73. A non-empty set s is said to be a *well-ordered set* if and only if (i) it is a partly ordered set and (ii) every non-empty subset of s has an initial member.[1] Show that $\mathbf{N}$ is a well-ordered set.

E4·7·74. Show that every well-ordered finite set is a chain.

E4·7·75. A set s is said to be of *order type* ω if and only if (i) it is a chain, (ii) if $x \in s$, then $\{y : y \leq x\}$ is finite, and (iii) s has no final member.   Show that $\mathbf{N}$ is of order type ω.[2]

*E4·7·76. Show that the axioms of partial ordering (treating (i), (ii)- and (iii) of E4·7·70 as axioms) are simply-consistent, independent, and non-categorical.

*E4·7·77. Show that the axioms of linear ordering are simply, consistent, independent and non-categorical.

4·08 Ordered Pairs and Relations

If x and y denote any objects whatever, then the ordered pair (x, y) [$\&xy$] is the pair of objects x and y in that order. Similarly, the ordered pair (y, x) [$\&yx$] is the pair of objects y and x in that order.   When plotting a graph the point say $(3, 5)$ is different from the point $(5, 3)$; the point $(3, 5)$ is the point with x-coordinate 3 and y-coordinate 5, whereas the point $(5, 3)$ is the point with x-coordinate 5 and y-coordinate 3; $(3, 5)$ and $(5, 3)$ are ordered pairs, the first component of a pair indicating the x-coordinate of

---

[1] Huntington: "The continuum as a type of order", *Ann. of Math.*, 1905, **6**, 151-84.   Earlier work in *e.g.* Russell: *Principles of Mathematics*.

[2] Cantor: "Ueber unendliche lineare Punktmannigfaltigkeiten", *Math. Ann.*, 1883, **21**, 545-91, especially 548.

the point corresponding to the ordered pair, and the second component indicating the y-coordinate of that point. Thus, although $\{3, 5\} = \{5, 3\}$, it is not the case that $(3, 5) = (5, 3)$. Two ordered pairs (x_1, x_2) and (y_1, y_2) are equal $(=)$ if and only if $x_1 = y_1$ and $x_2 = y_2$; in particular, then, $(x, y) = (y, x)$ if and only if $x = y$.

Consider the family $\{\{x\}, \{x, y\}\}$. This is equal to the family $\{\{y\}, \{y, x\}\}$ if and only if $x = y$. Hence $\{\{x\}, \{x, y\}\}$ can be regarded as the same as (x, y). In fact one can define ordered pairs in such purely set-theoretic terms:

$$(4\cdot081) \quad (x, y) \leftrightarrow \{\{x\}, \{x, y\}\} \qquad \&xy \leftrightarrow \{\{x\}, \{x, y\}\}.$$

Thus an ordered pair is merely a family of sets.[1]

The *Cartesian product*[2] of s and t is the set of all the ordered pairs (x, y) such that $x \in s$ and $y \in t$. It is denoted by "$s \times t$". Thus,

$$(4\cdot082) \quad s \times t \leftrightarrow \{(x, y) : x \in s . y \in t\}$$
$$\times st = \{\&xy : Kx \in sy \in t\},$$

or, what comes to the same thing,

$$(4\cdot083) \quad (s)(t)(z) [(z \in (s \times t))$$
$$\equiv (\exists x)(\exists y)(z = (x, y) . (x \in s . y \in t))]$$
$$PstzEz \in \times stSxyKz = \&xyKx \in sy \in t.$$

For example, the members of $\{2, 3, 4\} \times \{5, 6, 7, 8\}$ are $(2, 5)$, $(2, 6)$, $(2, 7)$, $(2, 8)$, $(3, 5)$, $(3, 6)$, $(3, 7)$, $(3, 8)$, $(4, 5)$, $(4, 6)$, $(4, 7)$, $(4, 8)$; and the members of $\{5, 6, 7, 8\} \times \{2, 3, 4\}$ are $(5, 2)$, $(5, 3)$, $(5, 4)$, $(6, 2)$, $(6, 3)$, $(6, 4)$, $(7, 2)$, $(7, 3)$, $(7, 4)$, $(8, 2)$, $(8, 3)$, $(8, 4)$. This example shows that the set-theoretic multiplication operator $\times$ is not commutative. Again, this operator is not associative; for *e.g.*

---

[1] Kuratowski, C. (1896-): "Sur la notion de l'ordre dans la Théorie des Ensembles", *Fund Math.*, 1920, **2**, 161-71.

[2] The notion is in Cantor: *Math. Ann.*, 1895, **46**, 481-512. The terminology is due to Hausdorff: *Grundzüge der Mengenlehre*, Erste Ausgabe.

$(\{1, 2\} \times \{3\}) \times \{4\} = \{(1, 3), (2, 3)\} \times \{4\} = \{((1, 3), 4),$
$((2, 3), 4)\}$, whereas

$$\{1, 2\} \times (\{3\} \times \{4\}) = \{1, 2\} \times \{3, 4\}$$
$$= \{(1, 3), (1, 4), (2, 3), (2, 4)\}.$$

A set all of whose members are ordered pairs is said to be a *relation*. "xérel" expresses that x is a relation. By definition,

(4·084) $(s) [(sérel) \equiv (z) \{(z \in s) \supset (\exists x)(\exists y)(z = (x, y))\}]$
$PsEsérel\ PzCz \in sSxyz = \&xy.$

If s is a relation, then its members are ordered pairs (x, y).[1] Obviously the set whose members are all the ordered pairs (y, x) is also a relation. This set is called the *inverse relation* to s, and it may be denoted by "s^{-1}". By definition,

(4·085) $(s) [(sérel) \supset (x)(y)((x, y) \in s^{-1} \equiv (y, x) \in s)]$
$PsCsérelPxyE\&xy \in {}^{-1}s\&yx \in s.$

For example, the inverse relation to $\{(1, 2), (3, 5), (-6, 8)\}$ is $\{(2, 1), (5, 3), (8, -6)\}$.

In the ordered pair (x, y) x is called the *first component* and y is called the *second component*. If s is a relation, then the set of all the first components of the ordered pairs belonging to s is called the *first projection* of s, and is denoted by "p_1s"; and the set of all the second components of the ordered pairs belonging to s is called the *second projection* of s, and is denoted by "p_2s". For example,

$p_1 \{(2, 3), (2, 7), (4, 5)\} = \{2, 4\}$ and
$$p_2 \{(2, 3), (2, 7), (4, 5)\} = \{3, 5, 7\}.$$

It is obvious that the first projection of a relation is equal to the second projection of the inverse relation, and that

[1] The definition of relations as sets (of the things related, the relata) is due to Wiener, N. (1894-): "Studies in synthetic logic", *Proc. Camb. Phil. Soc.*, 1914-16, **18**, 14-28.

the second projection of a relation is equal to the first projection of the inverse relation.

By definition, then,

(4·086) (s) $[(\text{sérel}) \supset \{[(x)(x \in p_1 s \equiv (\exists y)((x, y) \in s))]\}]$
$$P s C s \text{érel} P x E x \in p_1 s S y \& x y \in s;$$

(4·087) (s) $[(\text{sérel}) \supset \{(y)(y \in p_2 s \equiv (\exists x)(x, y) \in s))\}]$
$$P s C s \text{érel} P y E y \in p_2 s S x \& x y \in s.$$

Something that is ordinarily regarded as being a relation, say equality among sets, is set-theoretically treated as the set of all the ordered pairs whose components have this relation between them; thus $s = t$ if and only if (s, t) is a member of the relation (set of ordered pairs) definable as: $\{(e, w) : e$ and w have the same membership$\}$. Or consider the case of the relation (in the ordinary sense) of being a factor of, among the positive integers; $i \mid j$ (i is a factor of j, i and j positive integers) if and only if (i, j) is a member of the relation (set of ordered pairs) definable as: $\{(m, m_1) : (\exists n)(m_1 = m \times n)\}$ where m, m_1 and n denote positive integers.

A relation s is said to be *reflexive* if and only if $x \in p_1 s$ implies $(x, x) \in s$. Clearly, equality among sets and being a factor of, among the positive integers, are reflexive relations; for $(s)(s = s)$ and $(i)(i \mid i)$.

A relation s is said to be *symmetrical* if and only if $(x, y) \in s$ implies $(y, x) \in s$; consequently, s is symmetrical if and only if $s = s^{-1}$. The relation of equality among sets is symmetrical; but the relation of being a factor of, among the positive integers, is not symmetrical, since *e.g.* $3 \mid 6$ but it is not the case that $6 \mid 3$.

A relation s is said to be *transitive* if and only if $(x, y) \in s$ and $(y, z) \in s$ jointly imply $(x, z) \in s$. Among these, the relation of equality and the relation of being a proper subset of, are transitive relations.

A relation s is said to be an *equivalence relation* if and only if s is reflexive, symmetrical, and transitive.[1] The relation of equality among sets, *i.e.* where the members of the first and second projections are sets, is an equivalence relation. The logical relation $\equiv [E]$ is also an equivalence relation, among formulae[2].

EXERCISES

E4·8·78. What are the members of (a) $\{1, 2\} \times \{1, 2\}$; (b) $\{1\} \times \{1, 2, 3\}$; (c) $\{1, 2, 3\} \times \{1, 2\}$; (d) $\emptyset \times \{1, 2\}$?

E4·8·79. Show that $s \times t = \emptyset$ if and only if $s = \emptyset$ or $t = \emptyset$ (or both).

E4·8·80. Show that $s \times t = w \times e$ if and only if $s = w$ and $t = e$.

E4·8·81. Show that $(s\_t) \times w = (s \times w)\_(t \times w)$.

E4·8·82. Show by constructing a counter-example that in general it is not the case that $(s \times t)\_w = (s\_w) \times (t\_w)$.

E4·8·83. From (4·081) show (a) that $(x, y) = (y, x)$ if and only if $x = y$, and (b) that $(x_1, y_1) = (x_2, y_2)$ if and only if $x_1 = x_2$ and $y_1 = y_2$.

E4·8·84. Demonstrate that if s is a relation, then $s^{-1-1} = s$.

E4·8·85. Formulate fully, for the suppositional method of proof, a *Rule of Set-theoretic Substitution*, according to which if $x = y$ and $b(x)$, then $b(y)$. (Rule (xx.)

E4·8·86. Give a suppositional method proof of $PsCs\text{érel}^{-1}s\text{érel}$.

E4·8·87. Give a suppositional method proof of
$$PsCs\text{érel}Kp_1^{-1}s = p_2sp_2^{-1} = p_1s.$$

E4·8·88. If a set t is partitioned into n non-empty subsets $s_1, s_2, \ldots, s_n$ which have no members in common, then if "$x \equiv y$" means that x and y belong to the same subset of t show that $\equiv$ is an equivalence relation. (The sets s_i are called *equivalence classes*.)

E4·8·89. Two integers i and j are said to be *congruent modulo m* (m an integer) if and only if $m \mid (i - j)$; symbolically, "$i \equiv j \,(\mathrm{mod}\; m)$". Show that if $i \equiv j \,(\mathrm{mod}\; m)$, then i and j leave the same remainders (possibly zero) on division by m.

---

[1] The current use of "reflexive", "symmetrical", "transitive", and "equivalence" relations is due to Russell: *Principles of Mathematics*; but, *e.g.* "transitive" had been employed earlier by Peirce.

[2] For further details concerning the Logic of Relations and of Functions, see Whitehead and Russell: *Principia Mathematica I*; and, for a more recent treatment, Rosser, J. B.: *Logic for Mathematicians* (New York, 1953), especially Chapter X.

E4·8·90.   Show that if and only if m is a prime number does it
follow from $a\,b \equiv 0 \pmod{m}$ that either $a \equiv 0 \pmod{m}$
or $b \equiv 0 \pmod{m}$.

4·09 Functions and One-One Correspondences

Various definitions of function are possible. We shall
adopt the simplest. According to this, a function is merely
a special kind of relation (set of ordered pairs). Therefore,
in the ultimate set-theoretic analysis, it is a family of sets,
cf. (4·081). We shall say that a relation s is a function
("$s$éf") if and only if each x of $p_1 s$ is associated with a
single y in s; that is, if and only if $(x, y) \in s$ and $(x, z) \in s$
jointly imply that y and z are identical.[1] For example,
the relations $\{(1, 2), (4, 6), (7, 8), (10, 12)\}$ and $\{(1, 1), (2, 4),
(3, 9), (4, 16)\}$ are functions, but the relation $\{(1, 1), (1, 2),
(4, 6), (5, 9)\}$ is not a function, for the second components
of $(1, 1)$ and $(1, 2)$ are not identical. By definition, then,

(4·091) $(s)\,[(s\text{éf}) \equiv$
$((s\text{érel}).(x)\,(y)\,(z)\,\{((x, y) \in s\,.\,(x, z) \in s) \supset (y = z)\})]$
$PsEs\text{éf}Ks\text{érel}PxyzCK\&xy \in s\&xz \in sy = z.$

If s is a function, then it is usual to call its first projection
the *domain* (*of definition*) of s, and to call its second projection the *range* (*of values*) of s. However, we shall
continue to use the p_1 and p_2 symbolism.

If s is a function, then the second component y of an
ordered pair (x, y) that is a member of s is said to be the
image or the *value* of x. The standard practice is to indicate
such a value by the symbol "$s\,(x)$"; in bracket-free notation
we shall employ "$\wedge sx$". It is important not to confuse
$s\,(x)$ with the function s itself. $s\,(x)$ is not a function
(except in special cases); it is a member of $p_2 s$, and hence
is never identical with s itself. By definition,

[1] Due to Moore, E. H. (1862-1932): *Introduction to a Form of
General Analysis* (New Haven, 1910). The terminology of function
was introduced by Leibniz.

(4·092) (s) [(séf) ⊃ {(x) (y) ((s (x) = y) ≡ ((x, y) ∈ s))}]
                    PsCséfPxyE ∧ sx = y&xy ∈ s.

In a function there is usually a regular connection between the members of the domain and those of the range. One is ordinarily interested only in those functions for which it is possible to devise a rule of association between x and $s(x)$, even if, as frequently happens, the rule has to be a complex one containing several conditions. Let us consider a simple example. The function {(1, 1), (2, 4), (3, 9), (4,16), (5, 2), (6, 36)} is a function each of whose members is of the form (x, x^2) and so might be called a *squaring function*. Again, the function {(0, 1), (1, 0)} might be called (*inter alia*) the *negation function*; we here interpret "0" and "1" as truth falsity respectively. In this function the rule governing the association between x of the domain and its value $N(x)$ is: $N(x)$ is equal to the remainder in $(x + 1)/2$. Let us consider a final simple example. The function {((0, 0), 1), ((0, 1), 0), ((1, 0), 0), ((1,1), 1)} might be called the *exclusive alternation function* if we interpret the "0" and "1" as truth and falsity respectively. In this function the rule governing the association between each (x, y) of the domain and its value $J((x, y))$ is: $J((x, y))$ is equal to the remainder in $(x + y + 1)/2$.

A function such as the negation function, for which no member of its domain is an ordered pair, is often called a *function of one variable*. A function such as the exclusive alternation function, for which each member of its domain is an ordered pair but no component of any of these ordered pairs is itself an ordered pair, is often called a *function of 2 variables*.

A function s is said to be a *one-one correspondence*[1] if and only if $(x, y) \in s$ and $(z, y) \in s$ jointly imply $x = z$.

---

[1] Term due to Russell: *Principles of Mathematics*.

In other words, a function is a one-one correspondence if and only if each member of the range is associated with a single member of the domain. For instance, the exclusive alternation function is not a one-one correspondence, for 0 is the value of $(0, 1)$ and of $(1, 0)$ (and 1 is the value of $(0, 0)$ and of $(1, 1)$); on the other hand, the squaring function mentioned in the penultimate paragraph is a one-one correspondence, for no member of the range is associated with more than a single member of the domain; but the different squaring function $\{(-1, 1), (1, 1), ((-2, 4), (2, 4)\}$ is not a one-one correspondence. The negation function is another elementary example of a one-one correspondence.

In our informal explanation of the nature of a one-one correspondence we have said that a function is a one-one correspondence if and only if each member of the range is associated with a single member of the domain. But this is equivalent to saying that a function s is a one-one correspondence if and only if the inverse relation s^{-1} is also a function. It is this version that we shall use in our definition of one-one correspondence. We employ "xéc" to express that x is a one-one correspondence. By definition,

$(4 \cdot 093)$ $(s) [(séc) \equiv (séf \cdot s^{-1}éf)]$ $PsEsécKséf^{-1}séf.$

If s is a function and s^{-1} is a function, then s^{-1} is called the *inverse function* to s.

EXERCISES

E4·9·91. Give a suppositional method proof of: $PsCséf^{-1-1}s = s$.

E4·9·92. Show that there is a one-one correspondence having **N** as domain and $\mathbf{N}_e$ (the set of the positive even integers) as range. What is the rule of association between n of **N** and its value?

E4·9·93. Show that if s has m members and t has n members (m and n positive integers), then (a) if $m = n$, there is a one-one correspondence having s as domain and t as range, and

(b) if there is a one-one correspondence having s as domain and t as range, then $m = n$.

E4·9·94. Show that if s has n members ($n \in$ N), then (a) s has fewer members than the family Us of all its subsets, (b) the family Us has a finite number of members, and (c) there is no one-one correspondence having s as domain and Us as range.

4·10 Indexed Families of Sets

A one-one correspondence is said to be an *indexed family of sets* if and only if the range of the correspondence is a family of sets. If t is the domain of an indexed family of sets, it is called the *set of indices* of the indexed family.[1] If a one-one correspondence has been established between {1, 2, 3} and a family α of sets s, (that is if one has constructed a one-one correspondence having {1, 2, 3} as domain and α as range), then the members of the correspondence—of the indexed family of sets—are the ordered pairs $(1, s)$, $(2, s)$, and $(3, s)$. The set that is the image of 1 (2, 3) is written usually as "s_1" ("s_2" and "s_3"). An indexed family of sets is called an *infinite sequence of sets* if and only if either (a) the set of indices of the indexed family is the set N of all the positive integers, or (b) the set of indices of the indexed family can be made the range of a one-one correspondence that has N as domain. For example, i denoting the members of N,

(4·101) $\{(1, \{1\}), (2, \{1, 2\}), \ldots, (i, \{1, 2, \ldots, i\}), \ldots\}$

is an infinite sequence of sets, for it is a one-one correspondence between N and the family having the sets N_i as its members. Again, i denoting the members of N and p_i denoting the ith prime among the positive integers in the natural ordering,

(4·102) $\{(x, y) : x = i.10 \text{ and } y = \{p_i\}\}$

[1] The terminology relating to and the fully generalised notion of an indexed family of sets are due to Bourbaki, N. (pseudonym): *Eléments de Mathématiques, Théorie des Ensembles* (*Fascicule de Résultats*), (Paris, 1939).

is an infinite sequence of sets, for it is a one-one corre-spondence between the positive multiples of 10 and the family having the sets $\{p_i\}$ as range; and the set whose members are the positive multiples of 10 can be made the range of a one-one correspondence that has $\mathbf{N}$ as domain, such a correspondence being constructable in accordance with the rule: associate i of $\mathbf{N}$ with the member $i.10$ of the set of positive multiples of 10; and finally the relation (4·102) is indeed a one-one correspondence, for the set of the positive prime numbers is, using the natural ordering of $\mathbf{N}$, of order type ω (cf. E4·7·75).

(That the set of positive prime numbers has no final member can be shown thus:[1] Suppose that the only positive primes were p_1, p_2, ..., p_n, these being in their natural order, so that p_n is the final member of the set. Let $a = (p_1 \times p_2 \times \ldots \times p_n) + 1$. For each i from 1 to n, it is not the case that $p_i \mid a$, for there is always a remainder of 1. Hence either a is itself an additional prime, which is greater than p_n, or there is at least one prime number p between p_n and a. Therefore, in either eventuality, p_n is not the final member of the set of positive prime numbers.)

If e is an indexed family of sets, t being its domain and a its range, then if s is a variable for the members of a, by definition:[2]

$$(4\cdot103) \quad \bigcup_{x\in t} s_x \leftrightarrow \{y : (\exists x)(x \in t . y \in s_x)\}$$
$$\bigcup_{x\in t} s_x \leftrightarrow \{y : SxKx \in ty \in s_x\};$$

$$(4\cdot104) \quad \bigcap_{x\in t} s_x \leftrightarrow \{y : (x)(x \in t \supset y \in s_x)\}$$
$$\bigcap_{x\in t} s_x \leftrightarrow \{y : PxCx \in ty \in s_x\}.$$

Consider, by way of example, the infinite sequence of sets

$$(4\cdot105) \quad \{(x, s) : x \in \mathbf{N} \text{ and } s = \{1, 2, 3, \ldots, x\}\}.$$

[1] Demonstration due to Euclid: *The Elements*, Book IX.

[2] The large cup and cap used in these definitions were introduced by Moore: *Introduction to a Form of General Analysis*. That part of the notation which consists in subscripting "x ∈ T", T the set of indices, is due to Bourbaki: *Eléments de Mathématiques, Théorie des Ensembles*.

The members of $\underset{x \in \mathbf{N}}{\cup} s_x$ are those objects which are members of at least one member of the range of (4·105); 1 is such an object for $1 \in \{1\}$; 2 is such an object for $2 \in \{1, 2\}$; generally, for each positive integer i, i is such an object for $i \in \{1, 2, 3, \ldots, i\}$. Hence, the members of $\underset{x \in \mathbf{N}}{\cup} s_x$ are all the positive integers, and so $\underset{x \in \mathbf{N}}{\cup} s_x = \mathbf{N}$. On the other hand, the members of $\underset{x \in \mathbf{N}}{\cap} s_x$ are those objects which are members of every member of the range of (4·105). 1 is the only such object, since, if i is an integer greater than 1, $i \notin \{1\}$. Thus, $\underset{x \in \mathbf{N}}{\cap} s_x = \{1\}$.

It is clear that $\cup$ and $\cap$ are simply generalised operators of the same kind fundamentally as the union operator $\smile$ and the intersection operator $\frown$; hence, these generalised operators are also called *union* and *intersection* respectively. Then $\underset{x \in t}{\cup} s_x$ is the union-set of the indexed family $\{(x, s) : x \in t$ and $s \in a\}$; and $\underset{x \in t}{\cap} s_x$ is the intersection-set of the indexed family $\{(x, s) : x \in t$ and $s \in a\}$. ("s_x" is just a more concise way of writing "(x, s)".)

If e is an indexed family of sets, t being the set of indices, then for each s of the range a of e it might happen that s is a subset of a basic set 1. If so,

$$(4 \cdot 106) \quad \underset{x \in t}{\cup} s_x \subseteq 1;$$

$$(4 \cdot 107) \quad \underset{x \in t}{\cap} s_x \subseteq 1.$$

We can define the complement ςw of any set w that is a subset of 1 as $\{y : y \in 1$ and $y \notin w\}$.

If $y \in \varsigma \underset{x \in t}{\cap} s_x$, then $y \notin \underset{x \in t}{\cap} s_x$. Therefore, for some x, $y \notin s_x$ and so $y \in \varsigma s_x$. Hence, $y \in \underset{x \in t}{\cup} \varsigma s_x$. Conversely, if $y \in \bigcup_{x \in t} \varsigma s_x$, then there is some x such that $y \in \varsigma s_x$. Thus there is at least one x for which $y \notin s_x$. Consequently, $y \notin \bigcap_{x \in t} s_x$. Accordingly, $y \in \varsigma \bigcap_{x \in t} s_x$. We have demonstrated that

$$(4\cdot108) \quad \varsigma \bigcap_{x \in t} s_x = \bigcup_{x \in t} \varsigma s_x.$$

Suppose $y \in \varsigma \bigcup_{x \in t} s_x$. Then $y \notin \bigcup_{x \in t} s_x$. Therefore there is no x of t such that $y \in s_x$. In other words, for every x of t, $y \notin s_x$, and so $y \in \varsigma s_x$. Hence $y \in \bigcap_{x \in t} \varsigma s_x$. Conversely, suppose $y \in \bigcap_{x \in t} \varsigma s_x$. Then $y \in \varsigma s_x$ for every x of t. Thus, for no x of t is $y \in s_x$, and so $y \notin \bigcup_{x \in t} s_x$. Therefore $y \in \varsigma \bigcup_{x \in t} s_x$.

We have demonstrated that

$$(4\cdot109) \quad \varsigma \bigcup_{x \in t} s_x = \bigcap_{x \in t} \varsigma s_x.$$

We shall now show that

$$(4\cdot1010) \quad \bigcup_{x \in \mathbf{N}_m} s_x = s_1 + (s_2 - s_1) + (s_3 - (s_2 - s_1)) + \ldots$$
$$+ \underbrace{(s_m - s_{m-1} - (\ldots - (s_2 - s_1)))\ldots)}_{m-1 \text{ brackets}}$$

Suppose $y \in \bigcup_{x \in \mathbf{N}_m} s_x$. Then for some x of $\mathbf{N}_m$, $y \in s_x$. If $y \in s_x$ for more than one x of the set of indices, let x' be the first member of this set (in its natural order) such that $y \in s_{x'}$. Then

$$(4\cdot1011) \quad y \in (s_{x'} - (s_{x'-1} - \ldots - (s_2 - s_1)))\ldots),$$

and so y is a member of the set denoted by the expression on the right-hand side of $(4\cdot1010)$. Conversely, suppose y is a member of this latter set. Then there is some x of $\mathbf{N}_m$

such that $y \in (s_x - (s_{x-1} - \ldots) \ldots;$ consequently $y \in s_x$ and so $y \in \bigcup\limits_{x \in \mathbf{N}_m} s_x$. Thus, (4·1010) is demonstrated.

Any two sets s and t are said to be *disjoint* if and only if $s \smallsmile t = \emptyset$. m sets s_i ($i = 1, 2, \ldots, m$) are said to be *pair-wise disjoint* if and only if $s_j \smallsmile s_k = \emptyset$ (where $j \in \mathbf{N}_m$ and $k \in \mathbf{N}_m$, $j \neq k$). (4·1010) shows that the union-set of m sets is equal to the symmetric difference of m pair-wise disjoint sets.

4·11 Cardinal Numbers and Set-Theoretic Paradoxes

The set s is said to be *finite* if and only if, for some non-negative integer m, s can be made the range of a one-one correspondence having $\mathbf{N}_m$ as domain. s is said to be *infinite* if and only if it is not finite. Obviously $\mathbf{N}$ is an infinite set.

It will be convenient to use the symbolism "$s \approx t$" to indicate that the sets s and t can be put in one-one correspondence. It is clear that $\approx$ is an equivalence relation.

A set s is said to be *countable* if and only if $\mathbf{N} \approx s$. The set $\mathbf{N}_e$ of all the positive even integers is countable: associate each i of $\mathbf{N}$ with the number $2i$ of $\mathbf{N}_e$. Similarly, the set $\mathbf{N}_o$ of all the positive odd integers is countable: associate each i of $\mathbf{N}$ with the number $2i - 1$ of $\mathbf{N}_o$. The set $\mathbf{Z}$ of all the integers (positive, negative, and zero) is countable: associate each even i of $\mathbf{N}$ with the number $i/2$ of $\mathbf{Z}$, and associate each odd i of $\mathbf{N}$ with the number $-((i - 1)/2)$ of $\mathbf{Z}$, as is illustrated in (4·111):

$$(4·111) \qquad
\begin{array}{ccccccccc}
1 & 2 & 3 & 4 & 5 & 6 & 7 & 8 & 9 \ldots \\
0 & 1 & -1 & 2 & -2 & 3 & -3 & 4 & -4 \ldots
\end{array}$$

The set $\mathbf{Z} - \mathbf{N}$ is the set of all the non-positive integers. The set $\mathbf{Z} - \mathbf{N}$ and the set $\mathbf{N}$ are disjoint, and each is countable since obviously $\mathbf{N} \approx \mathbf{N}$ and each i of $\mathbf{N}$ can be asociated with $-i + 1$ of $\mathbf{Z} - \mathbf{N}$. But we have also seen that the set $\mathbf{Z}$ of all the integers is countable. It follows that the union-set of two disjoint sets that are countable is itself countable, for $\mathbf{Z} = \mathbf{N} \cup (\mathbf{Z} - \mathbf{N})$. This result can easily be extended, by the use of course-of values induction, to show that the union-set of n pair-wise disjoint, countable sets ($n \in \mathbf{N}$) is itself countable. Consequently, by mathematical induction, the union-set of n countable sets (pairwise disjoint or not) is countable.

By definition, the *cardinal number* of a set s is the family $\bar{\bar{s}}$ of all the sets t such that $s \infty t$. (The double bar over "s" is intended to suggest the two processes of abstraction that lead to the formation of the family $\bar{\bar{s}}$; the first being the abstraction from the nature or content of the members of s, the second being the abstraction from the order in which the members of s occur if s is a set in which there is some kind of ordering.)

It is possible to define the non-negative integers as cardinal numbers, as follows. The family of all the sets s such that $\emptyset \infty s$ is the cardinal number 0; *i.e.* that family is denoted by "0". The family of all the sets s such that $\{\emptyset\} \infty s$ is the cardinal number 1. The family of all the sets s such that $\{\emptyset, \{\emptyset\}\} \infty s$ is the cardinal number 2. The family of all the sets s such that $\{\emptyset, \{\emptyset\}, \{\{\emptyset\}\}\} \infty s$ is the cardinal number 3. The subsequent positive integers can be similarly defined. Thus, on this approach, the non-negative integers are sets of sets. Accordingly, the set $\mathbf{N}$ of all the positive integers is a set of sets of sets.

The family of all the sets s such that $\mathbf{N} \infty s$ is the cardinal $\aleph_0$ (aleph-nought).

The non-negative integers are said to be *finite* cardinals (cardinal numbers); $\aleph_0$ is said to be a *transfinite* cardinal. A set s is said to *have* the cardinal $\bar{\bar{s}}$; so $\{1, 2, 3, 4\}$ has the cardinal 4 and $\mathbf{N}$ has the cardinal $\aleph_0$. Hence, s is *finite* if and only if s has the cardinal m ($m = 1, 2, 3, \ldots$) and s is *countable* if and only if s has the cardinal $\aleph_0$.

(4·112) **The Family of Subsets Theorem:** It is not possible for there to be a one-one correspondence between a non-empty set s and the family Us of all the subsets of s.

Demonstration: Let s be any non-empty set and let e be any function having s as its domain and a subset of Us as its range. (We have shown, cf. (4·0525), that every set is a subset of itself; therefore we are not excluding the possibility, by this description of e, that its range is Us itself.) We next define the set t as follows: $x \in t$ if and only if both $x \in s$ and $x \notin e(x)$. So t has for its members those objects that belong to s but which do not belong to the subsets of s which are their values in e. For example, the function $\{(1, \{1, 2\}), (2, \{3\}), (3, \emptyset)\}$ has $\{1, 2, 3\}$ as its domain and a subset of $U\{1, 2, 3\}$ as its range; the set corresponding to t for this case has 2 and 3 for its members, for $2 \notin \{3\}$ and $3 \notin \emptyset$; it does not have 1 for a member because $1 \in \{1, 2\}$. Either t is empty or t is not empty. If t is empty, then $t \subseteq s$, for $\emptyset$ is a subset of every set, cf. (4·0538). If t is not empty, then all its members are members of s, so again $t \subseteq s$. We shall show that in e there is no x of s with which t is associated; from which it will follow that the range of e is a proper subset of Us. Suppose that t were the value, in e, of some x of s. Either (a) $x \in t$ or (b) $x \notin t$. If (a), then $x \in e(x)$; but by the definition of t, if $x \in e(x)$, then $x \notin t$. Therefore if $x \in t$, then $x \notin t$. If (b), then $x \notin e(x)$, and so by the definition of t it follows that $x \in t$; again a contradiction. Since the supposition that t is the value, in e, of some x of s leads to a contradiction, the supposition must be denied. Therefore t is not a member of the range of e; this implies that the range of e is a proper subset of Us.[1]

---

[1] All the material of this section up to this point is based on Cantor: *Math. Ann.*, 1895, **46**, 485-512. For the general theory of Cardinal and Ordinal Numbers, cf. Sierpinski, W. (1882-): *Cardinal and Ordinal Numbers* (Warsaw, 1958).

There is said to be an *antinomy* or a *paradox* if and only if two contradictory formulae are both categorical theorems. Paradoxes are undesirable because they allow any formula whatever in the language of the theory to be a categorical theorem; a theory containing a paradox is simply-inconsistent.

Suppose that there is a legitimate totality which is the set X of all sets that are not members of themselves. By the *tertium non datur*, either $X \in X$ or $X \notin X$. If $X \in X$, then $X \notin X$ for by the definition of X only those sets are members of X which are not members of themselves. If $X \notin X$, then, by the definition of X, $X \in X$. So we have a paradox.[1] But cf. E4·11·101.

By definition: (i) $\bar{\bar{s}} < \bar{\bar{w}}$ if and only if $s \infty t$ where $t \subset w$; (ii) $\bar{\bar{s}} \leq \bar{\bar{w}}$ if and only if $\bar{\bar{s}} < \bar{\bar{w}}$ or $s \infty w$. It follows from the Family of Subsets Theorem that $\bar{\bar{s}} < \overline{\overline{\overline{Us}}}$.

Suppose that there is a legitimate totality which is the set Y of all sets. By the *tertium non datur*, either $\overline{\overline{Y}} < \overline{\overline{\overline{UY}}}$ or not-($\overline{\overline{Y}} < \overline{\overline{\overline{UY}}}$). If $\overline{\overline{Y}} < \overline{\overline{\overline{UY}}}$, then not-($\overline{\overline{Y}} < \overline{\overline{\overline{UY}}}$), for since Y is the set of all sets it follows that $UY \subseteq Y$; hence $\overline{\overline{UY}} \leq \overline{\overline{Y}}$. If it is not the case that $\overline{\overline{Y}} < \overline{\overline{\overline{UY}}}$, then the Family of Subsets Theorem is contradicted. So again we have a paradox.[2]

There are several ways that have been devised by mathematicians for eliminating these and the other paradoxes that have come to light. The most generally favoured way is to construct an axiomatic theory of sets which is so designed as to prevent any of the known paradoxes from

[1] Due to Russell and called "Russell's Paradox". Published in the postscript to Frege: *Grundgesetze der Arithmetik II* (Jena, 1903); also in *The Principles of Mathematics*, § 78.

[2] Due to Cantor and called "Cantor's Paradox". Cantor: *Gesammelte Abhandlungen mathematischen und philosophischen Inhalts*, herausgeg. von E. Zermelo (Berlin, 1932). This paradox was discovered by Cantor in 1899, although unpublished till 1932.

arising in it or from it. Many apparently satisfactory axiomatic systems of Set Theory have been constructed, but none has been shown positively to be simply-consistent. For such systems the reader must consult the literature.[1]

EXERCISES

Demonstrate E4·11·95 to E4·11·99,

E4·11·95. If $\bar{\bar{s}} = \bar{\bar{t}} = \aleph_0$, then $\overline{\overline{s\_t}} = \aleph_0$.

E4·11·96. If $\bar{\bar{s}}_1 = \bar{\bar{s}}_2 = \ldots = \bar{\bar{s}}_n = \aleph_0$, then $\overline{\overline{s_1 s_2 \_ \ldots \_ s_n}} = \aleph_0$.

E4·11·97. If each member s of the range of a one-one correspondence having $\mathbf{N}$ as domain has the cardinal $\aleph_0$, then $\overline{\overline{\bigcup_{x\in\mathbf{N}} s_x}} = \aleph_0$.

E4·11·98. The set $\mathbf{Q}$ of all the rational numbers m/n ($m \in \mathbf{Z}$, $n \in \mathbf{Z}$) has the cardinal $\aleph_0$. (Define an array in which the mth row ($m = 1, 2, 3, \ldots$) contains all the positive rationals m/n ($n = 1, 2, 3, \ldots$); then use E4·11·97. Next show that the set of non-positive rationals has the same cardinal as the set of positive rationals; then use E4·11·95.)

*E4·11·99. The family $\mathbf{UN}$ of all the subsets of $\mathbf{N}$ is infinite and is not countable. (This family is an example of an *uncountable* set. The family of all the sets s such that $\mathbf{UN} \infty s$ is denoted by "$2^{\aleph_0}$".)

E4·11·100. Demonstrate that, for any sets s and t,
$$JJ\,(\bar{\bar{s}} < \bar{\bar{t}})\,(\bar{\bar{s}} = \bar{\bar{t}})\,(\bar{\bar{t}} < \bar{\bar{s}}).$$

[1] Zermelo, E. (1871-1953): "Untersuchungen über die Grundlagen der Mengenlehre", *Math. Ann.*, 1908, **65**, 261-81. Russell: "Mathematical logic as based on the theory of types", *Amer. J. of Math.*, 1908, **30**, 222-62. Brouwer: "Begründung der Mengenlehre unabhängig vom logischen Satz vom ausgeschlossenen Dritten", *Verhandelingen Akad., Amsterdam*, 1918-19, **12**, Nos. 5 and 7; "Zur Begründung der intuitionistischen Mathematik", *Math. Ann.*, 1924, **93**, 244-58. Fraenkel, A. (1891-): "Untersuchungen über die Grundlagen der Mengenlehre", *Math. Z.*, 1925, **22**, 250-73. von Neumann: "Die Axiomatisierung der Mengenlehre", *Math. Z.*, 1928, **27**, 669-752. Quine, W. O. (1908-): *Mathematical Logic*, revised edition (Harvard, 1951). Fitch: *Symbolic Logic*, Kelley, J. L. (1916-): *General Topology* (Princeton, 1955). See also Bernays: *Axiomatic Set Theory* (Amsterdam, 1958); Fraenkel and Bar Hillel, Y. (1915-): *Foundations of Set Theory* (Amsterdam, 1958). The last three works, in particular, may be consulted for the General Theory of Sets.

E4·11·101. Show that the paradoxes described in **4·11** will, if the *tertium non datur* is not used, get no further than being formulae of the sort: "if *b*, then not-*b*, and if not-*b*, then b"—which is no inconsistency.

E4·11·102. A definition of a set *s* (a property *p*) and an object *x*— which might itself be a set—is said to be *impredicative*, if and only if (*a*) $x \in s$ (*x* has the property *p*) and (*b*) the definition of *x* depends on *s* (*p*).[1]   Impredicative definitions are clearly, in some respect, circular.   Show that the two paradoxes described in **4·11** involve impredicative definitions.

---

[1] Poincaré, H. (1854-1912): "Les mathématiques et la logique", *Rev. de Mét. et de Morale*, 1906, **14**, 294-317.

CHAPTER FIVE

OBSERVATION AND THE OPERATIONAL
PATTERN OF SCIENCE

5·01 Introduction

We begin by stressing the objective, empirical character of natural science; the ultimate test of the acceptability of scientific doctrines is not their conformity with received authoritarian edicts but their conformity with the facts of Nature as disclosed in experience. It is then pointed out that there are certain themes about scientific method in the writings of those who have pondered on this sort of procedure; these themes are described briefly in what we have called the "operational pattern" of science. This operational pattern consists of six stages, which are outlined in turn: the specialised selection of a group of phenomena for study; the conduct of observations and experiments to discover the detailed properties of these phenomena; the construction of scientific laws which embody the regularities found in the type of phenomena investigated by the observations and experiments; the conception and elaboration of theories to explain these scientific laws; the testing of these theories by further observations and experiments, so that their scope and validity can be gauged; and, finally, the continuance of both empirical and theoretical study of the phenomena and of related phenomena, with a view to finding out more facts about Nature and to enlarging and detailing the theoretical explanations. In the last section, the general nature of observation is taken up in more detail; it is stated that scientific observation is active, systematic, sequential, should be adequate, precise, and impartial, and that the observations should be suitably recorded.

5·02 Science, Experience and the Rejection of Authority

The aim of science is the discovery and communication of rational beliefs about Nature. Experience provides the ultimate test for all scientific beliefs, for a belief cannot rationally be held if it is known to conflict with the facts. The sort of experience relevant to science is that of the environment external to the individual observer; it is that of the environment common to all observers, at least potentially. The reason for this concentration on the common, external world is to eliminate the subjective which varies from individual to individual. Thus science becomes impersonal and objective; thereby is the opportunity for cooperative inquiry made possible. "L'art, c'est *moi*; la science, c'est *nous*."[1]

For science, all genuine knowledge of Nature is regarded as being knowledge of the existence and properties of things belonging to the universe in so far as these things display or can be made to display their existence and properties to our senses of sight, touch, hearing, taste, and smell. The final criterion of the trustworthiness of a belief about the existence or properties of natural objects is always the facts as disclosed to the senses of any competent observer.

During the Middle Ages the predominant mentality was authoritarian in character. In religion the books of the Bible were regarded as the Words of the omniscient God. In science, from the twelfth century onwards, the writings of Aristotle were treated in an analogous fashion. By and large, scientific questions were answered by examining Aristotle's lecture notes, not by studying the nature of things themselves. He was the authority and the truth of his utterances was not disputed. The truths of religion had been made known by God's revelation; the truths of science had been made known by Aristotle's reason. It was because of this that he was later sceptically described as "the God of scholastic knowledge".[2]

Even in the seventeenth century, Aristotle's opinions were still being put up as obstacles to scientific progress by those who had more reverence for antiquity and tradition than for the truth. Their conduct provoked Pascal, one of the

[1] Bernard, C. (1813-78): *Introduction à l'étude de la médicine expérimentale*, Part I, Chap. II, § IV (Paris, 1860).
[2] Montaigne, M. de (1533-92): *Essais* (first edition, Paris, 1580; final, revised edition 1595), Book II, Essay XII.

great mathematicians and scientists of the age, and also an apologist for Christianity, to remark: "The respect for the ancients has now reached such a point, in matters where it should not be so strong [viz. in science as against in theology] that oracles are made of all their thoughts and mysteries are made even out of their obscurities; the result is that nothing new can any more be proposed without danger [remember the trials of Galileo!] and the text of an author is sufficient to destroy the strongest reasons. . . . With the subjects which fall within the scope of the senses or reasoning, authority is useless; only the rational faculties can give rise to knowledge. . . . It is thus that geometry, arithmetic, music, physics, medicine, architecture, and all the sciences that are subject to reasoning and experience have to be increased in order to attain perfection. Let us limit this respect we have for the ancients. . . . Let us bear in mind that if they had remained so modest as not to dare to add anything to the knowledge that they had received and that if those of their time had made the same difficulties about receiving the innovations offered them, they would have deprived themselves and their posterity of the fruit of their discoveries. As the ancients used the discoveries bequeathed to them only as a means of making discoveries of their own, this fortunate boldness opening to them the way to great things, so we ought to take those discoveries we have received from them in the same manner, and, following their example, make those discoveries the means and not the end of our study, thus in imitating them trying to surpass them. . . . It is strange in what way their thoughts are revered. It is made a crime to contradict them and an outrage to add to them, as though they had left no more truths to be known".[1]

[1] Pascal, B. (1623-62): *Préface pour le traité du vide* (in the first collected edition, in five volumes, of Pascal's works, edited by Bossut, who called this unfinished piece "De l'autorité en matière de philosophie"), (The Hague, 1779).

Pascal's interest in physics was in the field of hydrostatics; the main problem he dealt with was whether it was possible for a vacuum to exist. The doctrine of Aristotle, traditionally accepted, was that Nature abhors a vacuum. Pascal held that this scientific question cannot rationally be settled by a text, but only by the observable facts; the appeal must be to Nature, not to a scripture. And the reason for this is easy to grasp. Any ordinary proposition about the world can, in principle, be either true or false. Initially we do not know which of these two possible truth-values the proposition has. Since the proposition is about certain putative facts, the obvious way to determine the truth-value rationally is to use one's senses to discover the nature of the facts. Galileo and other experimenters and observers had shown that textual authorities were unreliable, that the deliverances of "reason" unaided by sense could well be mistaken[1]. In any case, there was not the slightest good evidence for accepting *a priori* that Aristotle's physical doctrines were correct. The aim of science is rational belief. We must therefore subject our ideas to the pressure of the relevant sensible facts. We have to be critical; we have to be slow in judging until we have collected and evaluated the appropriate evidence.

5·03 The Operational Pattern of Science

There are certain common themes which occur in the discussions of those who have considered the general methods of science. Connecting these themes with one another, we can say that there is widespread agreement about the nature of the scientific method in the sense that there is widespread agreement about the existence and structure of an operational pattern in scientific research. It is this operational pattern that is the kernel of the scientific method; it is the form of science, the particular

[1] Galilei, Galileo (1564-1642): *Dialogo sopra i due massimi sistemi del Mondo* (Florence, 1632), available in English.

subject-matters of inquiry constituting the content. Although perhaps no part of science passes through the various stages, to be mentioned, entirely one at a time or in the exact order of the abstract scheme, yet, in the long run, the systematic, theoretico-empirical study of any related group of phenomena does tend to concentrate on each of these stages in turn. The operational pattern suggested by writers on scientific method corresponds satisfactorily enough with the realities of research to avoid gross distortion of the nature of scientific activity; there is bound to be some measure of over-simplification in the picture given because concretely science is so multifarious in character.

It is only retrospectively that the scientist can notice distinct phases in his treatment of a problem, and these phases are considered from a "logical" rather than from a historical standpoint. At any time in the midst of his researches the scientist has in mind a welter of empirical facts, well-established hypotheses, speculative ideas, and projects for further observational or theoretical investigation. Subsequently he can compile a neat report on his work that imposes order and light on the chaos and obscurity that prevailed in the actual scientific experience. There are two justifiable reasons for this logical embellishment of the historical processes. One is that the human factors, especially the states of mind of the scientist in the course of his work, are irrelevant to science as such, for what matters scientifically is empirical evidence and rational explanations of this, not the psychological history of how these were sought or obtained. The other reason is that for the efficient communication of ideas and data attention must be paid only to the impersonal, objective aspects of the research; the narrative would be confusing if the personal background and psychological concomitants of the inquiry were described.

The operational pattern of science is outlined in **5·04** to **5·09**.

5·04 Selection of Problems or Group of Phenomena for Study

In modern times science has assumed such vast complexity and proportions that it is no longer possible to be the master of more than one small part of it. As a result of the scientific progress that has been so marked a feature of the last century and a half it has grown beyond any one man's capacity to carry in his head more than a fragment of the multitudinous body of scientific data and theories. But original research, original contribution to knowledge, presupposes a thorough familiarity with the minutiae of facts and explanations that have been built up over the years by numerous workers in different lands. Accordingly, in order to promote the advancement of science, the scientist is forced to specialise.

However, there is also another side and sense of specialisation. We have learned the futility of trying to answer large questions about Nature without first obtaining a knowledge of particular facts and organising these in a connected series of explanations having testable consequences. It has been found fruitless to begin by asking questions of the type, What is Life? What is Matter? Satisfactory scientific answers to such questions cannot be given except after and on the basis of detailed investigations into the specific varieties of natural phenomena. The manner in which Galileo's treatment of motion differed from Aristotle's is well known: Galileo made experiments. And his experiments dealt with simple cases, exemplified by his rolling balls down inclined planes and his dropping objects of greatly different weights from the Tower of Pisa. Galileo specialised the problem of motion. His method was analytic, instead of being synthetic as the meta-physicians' had been. By commencing with elementary cases one creates better opportunities for becoming acquainted with the prime factors composing them, and for learning the possibilities of reducing the more complex cases to combinations of the initial, more simple ones. The scientist is obliged to be modest in his choice of questions, not allowing the ambition of human wishes to deter him from examining small-scale problems, which being so much more concrete, determinate and specific are much more likely to permit of definite answers that represent established, evidential knowledge; and this in turn provides a firm footing for further investigation and progress.

5·05 Observation and Experiment

By means of observation and experiment, facts pertinent to the problem or group of phenomena selected for study are discovered and recorded.

"The only facts which can ever become useful as grounds of physical enquiry," says Herschel, "are those which happen uniformly and invariably under the same circum-stances. This is evident: for if they have not this character they cannot be included in laws; they want that univer-sality which fits them to enter as elementary particles into the constitution of those universal axioms we aim at discovering. . . . Hence, whenever we notice a remarkable effect of any kind, our first question ought to be. Can it be reproduced? What are the circumstances under which it has happened? And will it always happen again if those circumstances, so far as we have been able to collect them, coexist?

"The circumstances, then, which accompany any observed fact, are main features in its observation, at least until it is ascertained by sufficient experience what circumstances have nothing to do with it, and might therefore have been left unobserved without sacrificing *the fact*."[1]

Observation can be of either naturally occurring or of experimentally produced events. The advantages of experimentation are chiefly three. The first is that by the artificial production of phenomena the scientist can study them at his own convenience and leisure, without having to wait on Nature which might, besides, not bring together in the ordinary course of events the circumstances necessary for the occurrence of that kind of phenomenon in which the scientist is interested. The second advantage of experimentation is that the phenomena can be reproduced time and again, which permits a closer and more continual study of them and allows the scientist's results to be checked and rechecked. The third advantage of experimentation is that through the artificial manufacturing of phenomena, these can, within limits, be studied on the scientist's own terms. The conditions under which the artificially occurring phenomena occur are well-defined; hence the effects of modifying these conditions can be readily observed. In these ways the experimenter can obtain a more rapid and deeper knowledge of the sufficient and necessary conditions governing the phenomena, and, in the case of measurable properties, of the quantitative relations that exist between them.

5·06 The Formulation of Laws

Science is concerned with generality, not with particularity. The data afforded by observations and experiments are valued only as a means, not as an end. They are valued because it is hoped that they will enable generalisations

---

[1] Herschel, J. F. W. (1792-1871): *Preliminary Discourse on the Study of Natural Philosophy*, p. 119, revised edition (London, 1846). (First edition, London, 1830.) By an "axiom" Herschel means an acceptable law of sufficient generality as to be capable of being used as a basis for the drawing of many, varied scientific deductions.

to be made about all the facts which are isomorphic to those actually experienced. The scientist deals with individual facts in order to discover the properties of the whole set of phenomena to which the individual facts belong; his interest is in sets of facts rather than in their members as such.

The data obtained from observations and experiments, then, are examined with the object of arriving at a knowledge about the total facts which the data can be regarded as illustrating. One aims at discovering a law or group of laws governing the sets of facts. The scientific formulae put forward as corresponding with Laws of Nature have to lead to correct predictions; they are entertained not merely as abstracts and brief chronicles of the past, but also as guides to the future. There are two reasons for the insistence that scientific formulae should enable predictions and correct predictions to be made. Unless there are empirically testable consequences, a formula about facts can rationally be neither supported nor subverted; if there can be no evidence for it or against it, it is useless, not to say a hindrance, for the attainment of rational beliefs about Nature. "The revolution that the method of experience has worked in the sciences," says Bernard, "consists in having replaced a scientific criterion for a personal authority. The character of the empirical method is to be self-contained, because its criterion— experience—is included in it. The only authority it recognises are facts; it rids itself of all personal authority. When Descartes said that one has to rely on evidence alone, or on what has been adequately demonstrated, that meant that there had to be no more recourse to authority, as in scholasticism, but reliance only on the facts well attested by experience."[1] The reason for demanding that

[1] Bernard: *Introduction à l'étude de la médicine expérimentale*; *loc. cit.*

correct predictions follow from a formula is that only in this way can one tell whether the formula is acceptable. If it leads always to correct predictions when strictly tested, then the observed facts conforming with these predictions provide good evidence that the formula is a legitimate hypothesis. They make its acceptance rationally justifiable until such time as contrary evidence appears. On the other hand, if a consequence of the formula is incompatible with observed facts, then one can promptly infer that the formula is false and does not correspond with a Law of Nature, by virtue of the logical principle embodied in the schema $((b \supset d) . \sim d) \supset \sim b$ [$CKCbdNdNb$].

Important aspects of the nature and functions of scientific laws are described in the following quotation from Herschel:

"It will now be asked how we are to proceed to analyse a composite phenomenon into simpler ones, and whether any general rules can be given for this important process? We answer, None; any more than . . . general rules can be laid down by the chemist for the analysis of substances of which all the ingredients are unknown. Such rules, could they be discovered, would include the whole of natural science; but we are very far, indeed, from being able to propound them. However, we are to recollect that the analysis of phenomena, philosophically [= scientifically] speaking, is principally useful, as it enables us to recognise, and mark for special investigation, those which appear to us simple; to set methodically about determining their laws, and thus to facilitate the work of raising up general axioms, or forms of words, which shall include the whole of them. . . . And what renders the power of doing this so eminently desirable is, that, in thus reasoning back from generals to particulars, the propositions at which we arrive apply to an immense multitude of combinations and cases, which were never individually contemplated in the mental process by which our axioms were first discovered; and that, consequently, when our reasonings are pushed to the utmost limit of particularity, their results appear in the form of *individual facts*, of which we might have had no knowledge from immediate experience; and thus we are not only furnished with the explanation of all known facts, but with the actual discovery of such as were before unknown. . . . To give [an] example: The law of gravitation is a physical axiom of a very high and universal kind, and has been raised by a succession of inductions and abstractions drawn from the observation of numerous facts and subordinate laws in the planetary system. When this law is taken for granted, and laid down as a basis of reasoning, and applied to the actual condition of our own planet, one of the consequences to which it leads is, that the earth, instead of being an exact sphere, must be compressed or flattened in the direction of its polar diameter, the one diameter being about thirty miles shorter than the other; and this conclusion, deduced at first by mere reasoning, has been since found to be true in fact. All astronomical predictions are examples of the same thing. . . .

"A law of nature, being the statement of what will happen in certain general contingencies, may be regarded as the announcement, in the same words, of a whole group or class of phenomena. Whenever, therefore, we perceive that two or more phenomena agree in so many or so remarkable points, as to lead us to regard them as forming a class or group, if we lay out of consideration, or *abstract*, all the circumstances in which they disagree, and then under this kind of mental convention, frame a definition or statement of one of them, in such words that it shall apply to them all, such statement will appear in the form of a general proposition, having so far at least the character of a law of nature. . . .

"We may therefore regard a law of nature either, first, as a general proposition, announcing, in abstract terms, a whole group of particular facts relating to the behaviour of natural agents in proposed circumstances; or, secondly, as a proposition announcing that a whole class of individuals agreeing in one character agree also in another. For example: in the case before us, ['doubly refracting substances exhibit periodical colours by exposure to polarized light'], the law arrived at includes, in its general announcement, among others, the particular facts, that rock crystal and saltpetre exhibit periodical colours; for these are both of them doubly refracting substances. Or, it may be regarded as announcing a relation between the two phenomena of double refraction, and the exhibition of periodical colours; which in the actual case is one of the most important, *viz.* the relation of *constant association*, inasmuch as it asserts that in whatever individual the one character is found, the other will invariably be found also. . . .

"There is still another light in which we may regard a law of the kind in question, viz. as a proposition asserting the mutual connection, or in some cases the entire identity, of two classes of individuals (whether individual objects or individual facts); and this is, perhaps, the simplest and most instructive way in which it can be conceived, and that which furnishes the readiest handle to further generalisations in the raising of yet higher axioms. . . .

"It is thus we perceive the high importance in physical science of just and accurate classification of particular facts, or individual objects, under general well considered heads or points of agreement (for which there are none better adapted than the simple phenomena themselves into which they can be analysed in the first instance); for by so doing each of such phenomena, or heads of classification, becomes not a particular but a general fact; and when we have amassed a great store of such *general facts*, they become the objects of another and higher species of classification, and are themselves included in laws which, as they dispose of groups, not individuals, have a far superior degree of generality, till at length, by continuing the process, we arrive at *axioms* of the highest degree of generality of which science is capable."[1]

5·07 The Construction of Theories

When a thorough knowledge of the laws governing a group of phenomena or type of phenomenon has been reached, there arises the desire to explain them. The precise nature of the explanation differs from case to case. However, often, though by no means always, the explanation consists, firstly, of an imaginative picture of certain entities, or kinds of entity, whose properties and resultant behaviour lead to the phenomena in question having the characters they are known from experience to possess; and consists, secondly, of a body of formulae that represent the fundamental features of the picture, and that imply the scientific laws whose explanation is being sought. The classical theory to explain the various laws relating to gases is the Kinetic Molecular Theory of Gases. In the picture associated with this theory gases are treated as composed of extremely small particles—molecules—which are highly elastic, between which the attractive, binding forces are negligible, which move randomly at high, though variable speeds, and which collide frequently with one another and with the walls of the gas container. The second part of the Kinetic Molecular Theory consists of a group of formulae (and of their implications) which express the ideas embodied in the picture, in mathematical terms; all the established gas laws, mathematically formulated, find a place in this group.

[1] Herschel: *Preliminary Discourse on the Study of Natural Philosophy*, pp. 96-102.

It has already been pointed out that scientific laws must have empirically testable consequences. For the same reasons as those mentioned previously, scientific theories too must have empirically testable consequences.

"We have seen," says Darwin, "that the members of the same [biological] class, independently of their habits of life, resemble each other in the general plan of their organisation. This resemblance is often expressed by the term 'unity of type'; or by saying that the several parts and organs in the different species are homologous. The whole subject is included under the general term of Morphology. This is one of the most interesting departments of Natural History, and may almost be said to be its very soul. What can be more curious than that the hand of a man, formed for grasping, that of the mole for digging, the leg of the horse, the paddle of the porpoise, and the wing of the bat, should all be constructed on the same general pattern, and should include similar bones, in the same relative positions? . . .

"Geoffrey St. Hilaire has strongly insisted on the high importance of relative position or connection in homologous parts; they may differ to almost any extent in form and size, and yet remain connected together in the same invariable order. We never find, for instance, the bones of the arm and forearm, or of the thigh and leg, transposed. Hence the same names can be given to the homologous bones in widely different animals. We see the same great law in the construction of the mouths of insects: what can be more different than the immensely long spiral proboscis of a sphinx-moth, the curious folded one of a bee or bug, and the great jaws of a beetle? yet all these organs, serving for such widely different purposes, are formed by infinitely numerous modifications of an upper lip, mandibles, and two pairs of maxillae. The same law governs the construction of the mouths and limbs of crustaceans. So it is with the flowers of plants."[1]

Thus far Darwin summarily depicts for us laws, found by observation, relating to the structure of animals and plants. He continues:

"Nothing can be more hopeless than to attempt to explain this similarity of pattern in members of the same class, by utility or by the doctrine of final causes. The hopelessness of the attempt has been expressly admitted by Owen in his most interesting work on the *Nature of Limbs*. On the ordinary view of the independent creation of each being, we can only say that so it is—that it has pleased the Creator to construct all the animals and plants in each great class on a uniform plan; but this is not a scientific explanation."[1]

In this way Darwin indicates the need for an explanation of the laws derived from observation, but rejects a metaphysical explanation, this being one that has no empirically testable consequences. Darwin proceeds to sketch his own theory:

"The explanation is to a large extent simple on the theory of the selection of successive slight modifications—each modification being profitable in some way to the modified form, but often affecting by correlation other parts of the organisation. In changes of this nature, there will be little or no tendency to alter the original pattern, or to transpose the parts. . . . If we suppose [here Darwin gives an illustration belonging to his picture] that an early progenitor—the arch-type, as it may be called—of all mammals, birds, and reptiles, had its limbs constructed on the existing general pattern, for whatever purpose they served, we can at once perceive the plain signification of the

[1] Darwin, C. (1809-82): *Of the Origin of Species by means of Natural Selection, or the Preservation of Favoured Races in the Struggle for Life*, Chap. XIV, section headed "Morphology" (London, 1859).

homologous construction of the limbs throughout the class. So with the mouths of insects, we have only to suppose that their common progenitor had an upper lip, mandibles, and two pairs of maxillae, these parts being perhaps very simple in form; and then natural selection will account for the infinite diversity in the structure and functions of the mouths of insects."[1]

5·08 The Testing of Theories

The picture associated with an explanation of a range of scientific laws may be called a *theoretical picture* and the body of formulae which constitutes the exact symbolic expression of the explanation may be called the *theoretical system*.

Some implications of the basic formulae of a theoretical system are already established laws. But many of the implications will not have been previously tested empirically because they are formulae that are logical consequences of the basic formulae of the theoretical system and are distinct from those laws which gave rise to the theory. These latter formulae are inductions from experience: they are general hypotheses about Nature that are put forward on the grounds of the evidence obtained by observation or experiment. Here the observations and experiments come first in time and the general hypotheses come after. The other formulae of a theoretical system, the hitherto empirically unestablished ones, are deductions from the basic formulae of the system; they are put forward on the grounds of the basic formulae, not on the grounds of observation or experiment. Since, however, they cannot be proposed with rationally justified confidence unless there are good empirical reasons for believing that the theory is a good one, the theory must, accordingly, be subjected to a detailed empirical scrutiny. It is to be

[1] Darwin: *Of the Origin of Species . . ., loc. cit.*

tested by comparing predictions of the formulae arrived at by deduction with relevant observable facts. In order to gain rational assurance of the correctness of a theory, it is necessary to attempt to falsify its predictions; that is to say, it is necessary to attempt to find facts which are incompatible with the theory. This requirement of seeking to refute a theory in order to justify it—if it stands up in spite of the strenuous efforts to knock it down—was first emphasised by Bernard: "When in science we have put forward an idea or a theory, we must not aim at preserving it by seeking everything that might support it and eschewing everything that might weaken it. On the contrary, we have to examine with the utmost care the facts that seem to upset it, because real progress always consists in changing an old theory which contains less facts for a new theory which contains more. This shows that one has made a step forward, for in science the primary principle is to modify and change one's ideas as science advances. Our ideas are only intellectual instruments which help us in penetrating into phenomena; they must be changed when they have played their part."[1]

If the implications of a theoretical system are able to withstand the stringent empirical tests, then the theory itself may rationally be regarded as tenable until contrary evidence appears. Tenability is the utmost that can be affirmed. One is not entitled to assert *simpliciter* that the theory is correct merely because all the implications of the theory that have been tested in experience have been found to be correct; that would be to assume that $((b \supset d).d) \supset b$ [*CKCbddb*] is a valid logical principle, which it is not; it is not tautologous, to use that criterion. There may be other implications of the theory which are incorrect. For

[1] Bernard: *Introduction à l'étude de la médecine expérimentale, loc. cit.* See also the first quoted passage from Peirce in **10·10**.

instance, the Newtonian Theory of Mechanics[1] seemed, for nearly two hundred years, to have no false implications. Yet in the end it was found to be incompatible with some empirical facts, and was replaced by Relativity, and Quantum and Wave Mechanics.

5·09 The Continuance of Observational and Theoretical Research

If the theory put forward to explain the regularities involved in the phenomena seems to be a sound one in the light of an empirically probing examination, further research into the phenomena and into allied phenomena is undertaken both at the observational and at the theoretical levels. This is done in order to increase the knowledge of the facts and of the understanding of them over as wide a range as possible. There is always room for more empirical data, and the continual improvements in observational instruments and in experimental techniques bring a wider and more precise acquaintance with relevant features of Nature. This acquaintance may have to bring about a modification of previously accepted scientific laws. Their modification may lead to the amendment of the theories built upon them.

Continuance of research in the theoretical direction is pursued primarily with a view to solving, in terms of the accepted theories, interesting problems concerning the phenomena. The problems frequently consist of special cases that require the introduction into the theory of additional notions and basic formulae for their solution. For example, Newtonian Mechanics has four main starting-points: the three Laws of Motion and the Law of Gravitation. But by these alone the distinctive mechanical properties of deformable bodies cannot be adequately

---

[1] Newton, I. (1642-1727): *Philosophiae Naturalis Principia Mathematica* (London, 1687).

separated from those of rigid bodies. Nor are all rigid bodies, or all deformable bodies, mechanically uniform; the mechanical properties of the gyroscope present special problems of their own that are different from those of the pendulum, and the mechanical properties of an association of waves of the same invariable frequency are different from those of an association of waves of various frequencies superimposed upon each other (this latter kind of association being called in Classical mechanics a *group of waves* and in Wave Mechanics a *wave packet*).

Empirical advances affect theoretical developments and these reciprocally stimulate the advancement of empirical knowledge by their suggestion of hitherto unconceived or untested possibilities. For example, observational and experimental data in the fields of genetics and cytology together, motivated Sutton's Chromosome Theory of Heredity[1] according to which the hereditary factors are carried in the (observable) chromosomes, the existence and properties of these latter having been discovered by cytologists, in the course of the nineteenth century, working quite independently of geneticists. But Sutton's theory itself helped towards the learning of many new cytological and genetic facts. Thus, on his theory, there should be linkage between certain hereditary factors, that is to say, in contradiction to Mendel's Law of Independent Assortment, there are organisms in which, whenever one character due to a hereditary factor is possessed, then always a particular other character due to a hereditary factor is also possessed; there should be such linkage because there are far more genetic factors than there are chromosomes, so that if an organism possesses a character ψ, which is due to a hereditary factor, then it must also possess all the characters ψ_1, ψ_2, ..., ψ_n which are due to hereditary

[1] Sutton, W. S. (1876-1916): "On the morphology of the chromosome group in Brachystola magna", *Biol. Bull.*, 1902, **4**, 24-39.

factors and which are carried in the same chromosome as ψ. Many instances of such linkage were indeed subsequently found; for instance, in the fruit-fly *Drosophila melanogaster*, which has only four chromosome pairs, black body-colour and curved wings—characters due to hereditary factors—are always found together.

Sutton's Chromosome Theory illustrates an important aspect of theories: they often serve to bring together what before appeared to be separate. They serve to interrelate phenomena. What Herschel says about the observer and experimenter having to be ready to perceive interconnections of phenomena applies too to the theorist: "To make a perfect observer, however, either in astronomy or in any other department of science, an extensive acquaintance is requisite, not only with the particular science to which his observations relate, but with every branch of knowledge which may enable him to appreciate and neutralise the effect of extraneous disturbing causes. Thus furnished, he will be prepared to seize on any of those minute indications, which (such is the subtlety of nature) often connect phenomena which seem quite remote from each other. He will have his eyes as it were opened, that they may be struck at once with any occurrence which, according to received theories, ought not to happen; for these are the facts which serve as clues to new discoveries. The deviation of the magnetic needle, by the influence of an electrified wire, must have happened a thousand times to a perceptible amount, under the eyes of persons engaged in galvanic [= electrical] experiments, with philosophical [= scientific] apparatus of all kinds standing around them; but it required the eye of a philosopher [= scientist] such as Oërsted to seize the indication, refer it to its origin, and thereby connect two great branches of science."[1]   Hence,

[1] Herschel: *Preliminary Discourse on the Study of Natural Philosophy*, p. 132.

although the scientific study of a group of phenomena or type of phenomenon begins with simple, isolated cases, yet, in due course, through extensive and intensive empirical and theoretical investigation, it grows until not only are more complex cases dealt with, but the properties belonging to phenomena of other, and apparently unaffiliated, sorts are discovered, thoroughgoing mutual connections being shown and explained. The wheel of discovery and explanation then turns full circle, but progressively, not statically, for more and more ground is continually covered.

5·10 The General Features of Scientific Observation

It is clear from the account we have been giving of the operational pattern of science that observation and experimentation, on the one hand, and the construction of scientific laws and theories, on the other, form the basis of scientific work. In this section we shall consider further the general nature of observation. Experimentation will be the subject of Chapter Eight, and the construction of laws and theories will be the subject of Chapter Ten.

Ordinary observation is fragmentary. One does not plan one's course of perception, but takes things as they come; in this sense, ordinary observation is passive. In scientific observation, on the contrary, there is active organisation of experience, and the observation of phenomena is actively planned and pursued. This permits the scientist to obtain a systematic knowledge of phenomena.

Astronomy affords a simple example illustrating the difference between the systematic and active observation of the scientist and the fragmentary and passive observation of the layman. The attention the layman pays to the positions and relations of the stars is sporadic and incurious. Usually the only reason he looks at the stars at all is for the practical purpose of forecasting the immediate weather; the notice given the stars is merely incidental to an examination of the sky briefly conducted for that purpose. But the astronomer makes a lengthy, careful and minute study of the stars and their groupings; he commits himself to the laborious task of plotting the stars in their courses, through the months and the years.

The observations of science are sequential: they are followed up. The astronomer keeps track of the stars and of their positions relative to other stars, over long periods of time. The geneticist follows, for generation after generation, the character of the organisms he breeds. There are two main reasons for scientific observation being sequential. The first is that some regularities of nature are periodic; they can be discovered and the rational affirmation of them can be supported only by continual or regular observation. The second reason for sequential observation is that the scientist needs to be reasonably sure that the sample he has used from the whole population of phenomena into which he is inquiring is a fair or typical one; he needs to test the hypothesis that the properties he has found in his sample are also properties of the unexamined members of the same population, and, if there is variation, to discover the nature and extent of it.

Scientific observations must be adequate. The anatomist's description of the human backbone must take into account all its parts and structure, and the relevant anatomical connections; the whole length of the backbone, both dorsal and ventral, must be included.

Observations must also be precise; this requires painstaking attention to detail. The precision of an observation is distinct from its adequacy, for adequacy as such demands no more than that there be a complete survey of the material. The accuracy of that survey is another aspect. The botanist might observe the structure and parts of a plant, but the value of what he does is much enhanced if his series of observations is accurate and not vague.

Because so much observation in science employs artificial aids to perception or uses measuring instruments, precision and adequacy are relative to the power and sensitivity of the tools made use of. Optical telescopes are unable to help the eye beyond certain distances, and thermometers can measure temperatures accurately only to within certain limits, depending on the calibration. The great importance of instrumental aids to scientific knowledge is illustrated by the fact that when, during the Middle Ages, the Ptolemaic, Geocentric Theory of Planetary Motion was accepted, the heliocentric theory was not unknown but was rejected as refutable by observational data. On the heliocentric hypothesis there should be a stellar parallax with respect to each of the nearer "fixed" stars: if the Earth moved round the Sun, each of the nearer fixed stars should appear during the year to move in the opposite direction to that of the Earth's track round the Sun. But in the Middle Ages the naked eye could not discern the apparent motion of the nearer fixed stars which was to be expected on the heliocentric hypothesis. Not until the invention of the telescope (at the beginning of the seventeenth century) did it become possible to obtain positive evidence that the nearer fixed stars do indeed appear as the heliocentric theory implies. Even the nearer fixed stars are at such great distances from the earth that the yearly apparent, elliptical motion is not visible to the naked eye since the apparent, elliptical track is so extremely small. By means of the telescope, astronomers have been able to plot the annual, apparent tiny ellipses traced out in the sky by many hundreds of stars.

Observation must be impartial. The scientist, like others, is liable to prejudice, picking out those features of phenomena that fit in with habits of perception and preconceived ideas; thus he may fail to observe the presence of the unexpected unless this is too gross to pass unnoticed. The scientist must remain alert with sharp and open mind ready to perceive novelty. Earnest curiosity and conscientiousness alone can overcome the propensities conditioned by previous thought and experience.

The scientific observer does not merely observe. He also records what he observes. And here again he is obliged to be conscientious and circumspect. He must take every care that his records adequately and accurately express what he has observed together with the relevant circumstances. In addition he should distinguish and separate the data of experience from interpretations and explanations of them.

Recordings of observations are essential in scientific work. Memory cannot retain all the data and is liable to weaken and to err; besides, memory is private but scientific evidence and so the recordings thereof must be open to the public. A notebook account of observations may be useful to contemporaries and to posterity; the observational data of other workers can then be compared. However, it is clear that such comparisons, which are made for the purpose of advancing scientific knowledge, will be of relatively little value unless the work compared was objective.

The reason for avoiding the mixture of fact with interpretation and explanation, in the description of observations, is that the interpretation or explanation may be incorrect. If their expression is interwoven with that of the empirical data, their invalidity will contaminate the reliability of the latter, and will also make it difficult to know exactly what were the observer's empirical data as such, for the latter, could they be extracted, could still be valuable as material for the construction of laws and theories. If the notebook is a pure record of the observations, it can remain a useful source even after current interpretations and explanations have been outmoded.

Psychology does not lie within the field of reference of this book. Nevertheless, the psychological side of observation is in its own way important and deserves a few words here. Observation is not a simple act. There is always selection and elimination from what is "given" in perceptual awareness. Too much is given for all to be properly noticed and recorded. One chooses what is thought to be most relevant and significant. Besides, language is too crude and limited to express the subtleties and varieties of phenomena and their properties.

Finally, a great deal of observation, particularly in astronomy, physics, and chemistry, consists in making measurements. Measurement is fundamental to the physical sciences as they have developed historically, and it requires a lengthy treatment of its own. This will be given in the next chapter. Suffice it at this point to remark that the properties coming under observation are of two kinds, qualitative and quantitative. Usually qualitative properties, such as those of colour, shape, smell, texture, and pattern, are observed directly either by the bare senses or through an instrument that aids perception; the shape of an object, for example, is observed either by the naked eye or by the naked eye looking through a telescope or down a microscope. On the other hand, quantitative properties are observed indirectly. In order to discover empirically the length or weight of an object, one examines not simply or even primarily the object itself but the instrument being used for measuring length or weight. Hence, measurement might be called *indirect observation*. This has complex characteristics of its own[1].

[1] For a sophisticated modern view of the nature of observation and the role of observables in physics, cf. Hanson, N. R.: *Patterns of Discovery* (Cambridge, 1958).

EXERCISES

E5·10·1. According to Herschel (and many other writers on scientific method), scientific laws are classificatory propositions of the form "all s is t" or "every member of s is a member of t". This sort of proposition is called a *general proposition*. There are three other forms of this: "no s is t", "some s is t", and "some s is not t". In terms of BA (in particular, BAH₁), "all s is t" can be expressed as "$s\_çt = ù$" and "some s is not t" can be expressed as "$s\_çt \neq ù$" Express the other two schemata of general propositions similarly in terms of BA.

E5·10·2. "All s is t" can also be expressed in terms of the FC, as "$PxCbxdx$", where "b" ("d") expresses the defining properties of s (t). Similarly, "some s is t" can be expressed as "$SxKbxdx$". Express "no s is t" and "some s is not t" in terms of the FC.

Give the BA transforms of E5·10·3 to E5·10·11 and give suppositional method proofs thereof. The first six of these formulae are *syllogistic schemata*, that is concrete exemplifications of them are *syllogisms*.[1]

E5·10·3. If all s is t and all w is s, then all w is t.

E5·10·4. If no s is t and all w is s, then no w is t.

E5·10·5. If no s is t and some w is t, then some w is not s.

E5·10·6. If some s is t and all s is w, then some w is t.

E5·10·7. If some s is not t and all s is w, then some w is not t.

E5·10·8. If all s is t and no t is w, then no w is s.

E5·10·9. If some s is t, no s-and-e is w, and all s-and-t is e, then some s is not w.

E5·10·10. If all s is t, no w is e, and all t is w, then no s is e.

E5·10·11. If all s is t, no w is e, and all $çe$ is $çt$, then no w is s.

E5·10·12. Give the FC transforms of E5·10·3 to E5·10·11 and give suppositional method proofs, in the FC, of such transforms.

---

[1] For a detailed treatment of Syllogistic Theory, cf. Łukesiewicz: *Aristotle's Syllogistic*, second edition (Oxford, 1957).

CHAPTER SIX

MEASUREMENT

6·01 Introduction

After a brief clarification of the process of counting (which is measurement of "discrete properties"), we consider primarily the measurement of continuous quantity-types such as length. The nature of units and standards of measurement is explained, as is the distinction between fundamental and derived units and the resulting distinction between fundamental and derived quantity-types. Attention is then limited, for simplicity, to quantity-types analysable in terms of the fundamental units of Length, Mass, and Time. The use and calibration of instruments for measuring such quantity-types is described. Next, because the theory of scientific measurement needs to make use of the real number system, axiomatic foundations of this system, based on ideas due to Dedekind, are presented. After this, we proceed to expound the elements of the method of Dimensional Analysis, showing by examples its effectiveness in enabling the structure of physical laws to be, within limits, determined *a priori*. Finally, a treatment of "errors of observation" is offered. Careful measurements of a quantity Q usually yield slightly different results; the nature and sources of such variations are described. The theoretical problem is to estimate the real value of Q from these varying results; this problem is of fundamental importance for the whole range of science that is associated with measurements. In this connection the notions of the arithmetic mean and of the measures of dispersion (variance, standard deviation, etc.) of a body of measurements are introduced. The role of measurement in science and the significance of such aspects as errors of observation and Dimensional Analysis are dealt with in Chapter Eight.

6·02 Counting

A statement of the sort "all s is t" will be called a *universal* statement. The scientist wishes to discover and justify true universal statements. Often, the members of the set s in which he is interested seem to share a discrete quantitative property: they have a property in relation to which it is sensible to ask, "How many?" How many vertebrae has the human backbone? How many pairs of chromosomes have the somatic cells of a dog? How many satellites has the planet Jupiter? The answers to such questions are obtainable by a process of counting, provided of course that what is to be counted comes within the field of observation. Counting as such involves direct observation; in this respect, it is not like other species of measurement.

That counting in science is not always a simple proceding bound to yield accurate results even when what is counted is directly or photographically observed is illustrated by the fact that all the texts on genetics published before 1958 give the normal number of chromosome pairs in man as 24; since 1956, however, it has become established that the normal number is only 23.[1]

There are four conditions to be fulfilled if counting is to be possible. (i) There must be available a sufficient supply of non-negative integers with which to do the counting. (ii) The objects (where, as always, we are using the term "object" in the broadest sense) to be counted must be individuated, must appear or be capable of being made to appear as distinct from one another and from other objects. (iii) The differences between the objects to be counted must be negligible for the purposes of counting; that is, the objects must be homogeneous in some respect or respects. (iv) The objects to be counted must be finite in number. In short, counting as practised in science presupposes that there is a set u the membership of which is determined by the possession of certain definite, observable properties, and that it is possible in observation to establish a one-one correspondence between u and N_m, where m is some member of the set $N^{\geq}$ of non-negative integers.[2] For example, consider the (unit) set s containing the planet

---

[1] See the paper in *The Lancet*, April 4 1959, pp. 709-11, and the references there given.

[2] $N_0 \leftrightarrow \{0\}$

Jupiter as its member. Let the set u contain the satellites of Jupiter as its members; so $x \in u$ if and only if x has the defining properties of being a satellite of Jupiter. It is irrelevant for finding out how many satellites Jupiter has, whether the members of u differ from one another in various ways; in order to find out how many satellites Jupiter has one may neglect the fact that the objects satisfying the defining properties of being a satellite of Jupiter have different mean distances from the planet, have different sidereal periods, have different eccentricities of their orbits and have different diameters, for they are homogeneous in the relevant respects. The defining properties of being a satellite of Jupiter must be such that if an object has them it must be discernible that it has them. In fact, it is possible through observation to establish a one-one correspondence between u and N_{12}. Accordingly, the astronomer asserts the law: Jupiter has 12 satellites. The set t whose members are all the objects having 12 satellites includes the set s that has the planet Jupiter for its sole member: (all) s is t, i.e. $s \subseteq t$. In general, then, for cases where it seems appropriate, the scientist tries to obtain true statements of the sort "all s is t", where s is a set of objects of a kind in which the scientist is interested, t is a set of objects which have m things ($m \in N^{\geq}$) belonging to a set u, the defining conditions for an object to be a member of u forming a discrete quantitative property of each member of s.

In the remaining sections of this chapter we shall be primarily concerned with measurement in the narrower sense that excludes mere counting.[1]

---

[1] For a general discussion of Measurement, cf. Campbell, N. R. (1880-1949): *Measurement and Calculation* (London, 1928). The article by Helmholtz, H. L. F. (1821-94): "Zählen und Messen erkenntnistheoretisch betrachtet", originally published in a Festschrift for Eduard Zeller in 1887 and reprinted in Helmholtz's *Wissenschaftliche Abhandlungen III* (Leipzig, 1892), has been the source and basis of many subsequent treatments of the principles of measurement.

6·03 Units and Measurement

Quantities are measured by reference to standards. The standards are arbitrary; Nature does not impose any particular ones. The length of an iron bar is measured by reference to the centimetre standard or to the foot standard or to some other chosen standard. The standard is chosen after duly considering theoretical or practical conveniences. For measuring a single type of quantity, such as length, several different standards may be used; there are in principle no unique standards. However, the measurement of every quantity requires the use of some standard. The length of an iron bar is not simply x, say 56·4; it is x centimetres (cm) or x feet (ft) or x multiples of some other unit of length. And if it is 56·4 cm, then it is not 56·4 times any other unit of length. Hence the necessity for specifying the unit employed.

What does it mean to say that the length of an iron bar is 56·4 cm? Omitting refinements, it means that if 56 copies of the centimetre standard, together with $\frac{4}{10}$ of a copy of that standard, were linearly juxtaposed, the initial point of the first of these segments coinciding with a point at one end of the iron bar, then the final point of the last of these segments would coincide with a point at the opposite end of the iron bar.

It is thus clear that the result of every process of measuring an instance of a property consists of a pure number as the "factor" of some standard of magnitude for the type of quantity measured. So it consists of a pure number— what is called the *numeric* of the measurement—as the factor of the unit of magnitude employed. Of course, each standard of magnitude is of unit magnitude with respect to itself; just one copy of the centimetre standard is needed to cover the length of another such copy.

It is a readily comprehended consequence of the description of measurement we have given that every numeric is a ratio. In the case of the iron bar, the length is to the length of the centimetre standard as 56·4 is to 1. We can symbolically express the general case as follows. Let Q be any measurable property possessed by any object x; let $Q(x)$ be the magnitude of the property Q as possessed by x; and let U be any standard or (synonymously) any unit of magnitude for measuring Q. Then

(6·031) $Q(U) = U.$

For some number q,

(6·032) $Q(x) : Q(U) = q : 1,$

and therefore

(6·033) $q = Q(x)/Q(U).$

It follows from (6·033) and (6·031) that

(6·034) $Q(x) = qU.$

Thus, the length (Q) of the iron bar (x) is 56·4 (q) times the centimetre (U). Conversely, if it is given that $Q(x) = qU$,

(6·035) $q = Q(x)/Q(U),$

by virtue of (6·031).

Each kind of measurable quantity Q has a special range of standards. Lengths cannot be measured in grams or forces in centimetres. It would be nonsense to claim that the length of an object is 5 grams (gm) or that a hammer strikes a nail with a force of 300 cm. Length and force are different kinds of quantity, and length and mass are different kinds of quantity. If Q_1 and Q_2 are different kinds of quantity, then a standard or unit of magnitude U that belongs to the range of standards appropriate for measuring Q_1 (or Q_2) cannot be used for measuring Q_2 (or Q_1).

At first sight there is a vast number of different kinds of quantity. If science is to be able to measure all the kinds of quantity that occur in Nature—and it would have to be able to accomplish this if it was to be adequate—a correspondingly large number of ranges of standards would need

to be established. Length, mass, time, velocity, acceleration, momentum, energy, force, frequency, volume,
density, and pressure are only some of the better known
types of quantity dealt with in physics. Is a separate
range of standards necessary for each of them? Fortunately
the answer is in the negative. All these types of quantity
are analysable into a few of them. Volume can be analysed
in terms of length, so that a standard for length serves also
as one from which a standard for volume can be derived;
e.g. the volume of a body x is *q cubic centimetre* or *r cubic
feet*, that is q cm^3 or r ft^3. Similarly, velocity can be
analysed in terms of length together with time; a body's
velocity (which, for simplicity, we are not distinguishing
from its speed, although that distinction can be made by
the sort of analysis—what is known as *dimensional analysis*
—we have here in mind) is the distance it traverses in a
given time. Hence the unit of velocity is the ratio of the
unit of length to the unit of time. If the unit of time is
the second (sec), then, the centimetre being the chosen
unit of length, the velocity of x can be described as being
q cm sec^{-1} (where "sec^{-1}" can be read as "per second").
Again, momentum is analysable into mass and velocity,
and so into mass, length, and time.

All the kinds of quantity hitherto conceived or encoun-
tered in mechanics can be analysed in terms of one or more
of length, mass, and time. There is no universal agreement
in contemporary physics whether thermal and electromagnetic quantitative properties are also analysable into
length, mass, and time. It is usual to treat both temperature, and either permittivity (the dielectric constant)
or magnetic permeability or both, as unanalysable into
length, mass, and time, leaving their ultimate reducibility
to these mechanical kinds of quantity an open question.
Because of their special difficulties we shall henceforth

disregard thermal and electromagnetic kinds of quantity, and restrict ourselves to the mechanical ones.

6·04 Quantity-Types and Systems of Units

Length, mass, and time are taken as fundamental in mechanics; they are often called *absolute units* or *fundamental units*, and the kinds of quantity analysable into them are often called *derived units*. The term "unit" in this context signifies merely kind of quantity. It is perhaps unfortunate to use the same term "unit" both for a kind of quantity and for a standard by reference to which the magnitude of any instance of the kind of quantity can be measured. Therefore we shall prefer to describe length, mass, and time as *fundamental quantity-types*, and the kinds of quantity analysable into them as *derived quantity-types*.

Although length, mass, and time are taken as fundamental and although they seem indeed to be of pervasive importance in Nature, nevertheless, other kinds of quantity could have been taken as fundamental instead; to do that, however, would not in general be advantageous but would, on the contrary, produce unnecessary difficulties and unnecessary complications in physical formulae. It must, none the less, be emphasised that the quantity-types of length, mass, and time are not intrinsically fundamental; they are, for the purposes of physical analysis, postulated to be fundamental, much as (2·161) to (2·1610) are not intrinsically axiom schemata but are postulated to be axiom schemata for certain logical purposes.

A set having for its sole members one standard of length, one standard of mass, and one standard of time is called a *system of units*. Three systems of units are currently employed in pure and applied science. The first is the C.G.S. system, in which the centimetre, gram, and second are the units. The second system is the M.K.S. system, in which the metre, gram, and second are the units; this system has several advantages over other systems; it is particularly convenient in electro-magnetic theory and practice, where it is becoming increasingly used. The third system is the F.P.S. system, in which the foot, pound (mass), and second are the units; this system is used only among applied physicists, especially by British trained or influenced engineers.

The metre (m) is at present defined as the length of a line between two points engraved on a platinum-iridium bar at 0° Centigrade, the bar being kept at the International Bureau of Weights and Measures at Sèvres, near Paris; the centimetre is defined as $\frac{1}{100}$ of the metre. According to Michelson,[1] this metre standard, of which of course there are numerous more or less exact copies, all over the world, can be taken out and examined only once in ten years. Michelson himself had advocated over a long period that the red wave-length of cadmium should be adopted as the standard of length; this standard would be more widely available and less liable to fluctuations and disturbances. His proposal has increasingly obtained the favour of physicists as experimental techniques to determine the red wave-length of cadmium have improved, and it will almost certainly obtain final sanction within the next few years.

For science, it is supposed that it is in principle possible to construct a scale whereby any length whatever can be measured in terms of decimal multiples and sub-multiples of the metre, and, more generally, of U_L, where U_L is the standard of length in any system of units. A scale is formed by marking on a rod of negligible cross-section a zero point, called the *origin* of the scale, and another point, conventionally to the right of the zero point, so that the length of the segment from the zero point to this second

[1] Michelson, A. A. (1852-1931): *Studies in Optics*, p. 52 (Chicago, 1927).

point (called the *unit point* of the scale) is identical with U_L. We call this length from the origin to the unit point the *unit length*. From the unit point towards the right, unit lengths are marked off on the rod until the right-hand point of the next unit length would not lie on the rod. Then the length of the segment from the origin to the nth point on its right is nU_L. Suppose that the rod has m unit lengths marked off on it. If a length to be measured is greater than mU_L, one slides the rod to the right until the origin occupies the point of the distance that had been occupied by the right-hand point of the mth unit distance, the length of the distance from the newly-placed origin being added to the length of that part of the distance already covered; and so on. In this way the rod can be used to measure all non-negative integral multiples of the unit length U_L. With the rod as so far calibrated a distance whose real length is qU_L can be measured to within an accuracy of U_L: for some non-negative integer k,

$$(6.041) \quad kU_L \leq qU_L \leq (k+1) U_L.$$

Next, let each unit length marked off on the rod be divided into 10 equal parts. We call the length between any two points of calibration on the rod the 10^{-1} *unit length*. With the rod as so far calibrated a distance whose real length is qU_L can be measured to within an accuracy of $10^{-1}U_L$: for some non-negative integers k_0 and k_1,

$$(6.042) \quad (k_0 + k_1 10^{-1}) U_L \leq qU_L \leq (k_0 + (k_1 + 1) 10^{-1}) U_L.$$

More generally, let each 10^{-n} unit length marked off on the rod ($n = 0, 1, 2, \ldots$) be divided into 10 equal parts. We call the length between any two points of calibration on the rod the 10^{-n+1} *unit length*. With the rod thus calibrated, a distance whose real length is qU_L can be measured to within an accuracy of $10^{-n+1}U_L$: for some non-negative integers $k_0, k_1, k_2, \ldots, k_{n+1}$,

$$(6\cdot043) \quad (k_0 + k_1 10^{-1} + k_2 10^{-2} + \ldots + k_n 10^{-n})\, U_{\mathrm{L}} \leq q U_{\mathrm{L}}$$
$$\leq (k_0 + k_1 10^{-1} + k_2 10^{-2} + \ldots + (k_n + 1)10^{-n})U_{\mathrm{L}}.$$

The gram is at present defined as the mass of a lump of platinum-iridium kept at the International Bureau of Weights and Measures. For science, it is supposed that it is in principle possible to construct a scale of masses whereby any mass whatever can be measured in terms of decimal multiples and sub-multiples of the gram, and, more generally, of U_{M}, where U_{M} is the standard of mass in any system of units. The physicist assumes that the mass of the physical system obtained by juxtaposing or coalescing n replicas of the unit U_{M} of mass is equal to nU_{M}; and he assumes, further, that the standard of mass and its replicas can be divided into 10^n parts having equal mass, namely, a mass of $10^{-n}U_{\mathrm{M}}$,

The most usual way of measuring the mass of a body is to weigh it in a laboratory balance, though, obviously the direct use of this method is restricted to bodies that are neither very large nor extremely small. It should be pointed out that in this procedure of weighing there is no supposition of the identity of mass and weight; what is supposed is that equality of weight is a reliable criterion of equality of mass. The object whose mass is to be measured is placed in one pan A of the balance. In the other pan B are placed as many replicas of the unit U_{M} as possible, subject to the condition that pan B must not sink below the level of pan A. If the real mass of the object in pan A is qU_{M}, then for some non-negative integer k_0,

$$(6\cdot044) \quad k_0 U_{\mathrm{M}} \leq q U_{\mathrm{M}} \leq (k_0 + 1)\, U_{\mathrm{M}}.$$

Next, pan B receives as many replicas of the 10^{-1} unit mass as possible, subject to the condition that pan B must not sink below the level of pan A. Then for some non-negative integers k_0 and k_1,

$$(6\cdot045) \quad (k_0 + k_1 10^{-1})\, U_M \le q U_M \le (k_0 + (k_1 + 1)\, 10^{-1})\, U_M.$$

More generally, pan B receives as many replicas of the 10^{-n} unit mass as possible, subject to the condition that it must not sink lower than the level of pan A. For some non-negative integers $k_0, k_1, k_2, \ldots, k_n$,

$$(6\cdot046) \quad (k_0 + k_1 10^{-1} + k_2 10^{-2} + \ldots + k_n 10^{-n})\, U_M \le q U_M$$
$$\le (k_0 + k_1 10^{-1} + k_2 10^{-2} + \ldots + (k_n + 1)\, 10^{-n})\, U_M.$$

The second is at present defined as $1/86,164\cdot09$ of a sidereal day, a sidereal day being the interval between successive transits of the first of Aries across a selected meridian. Now consider a successively occurring event which takes a second to occur, and which then immediately starts to occur again, repeatedly. This repeated event forms a "clock". A time-piece can be constructed in which the event referred to is the oscillation of the balance wheel. By providing suitable connections and calibrations, such as we are familiar with in our wrist-watches, any time interval can be measured to within an accuracy of 1 sec. The scientist supposes that it is in principle possible to construct a scale of times whereby any time ($-$ interval) whatever can be measured in terms of decimal multiples and sub-multiples of the second, and, more generally, of U_T, where U_T is the standard of time in any system of units. It is further assumed that the unit U_T of time can be divided into 10^n parts having an equal time-interval, namely, a time-interval of $10^{-n} U_T$.

Analogously to the situations in the case of length and mass, if the real time-interval between two instantaneous events is $q U_T$, then for some non-negative integers $k_0, k_1, k_2, \ldots, k_n$,

$$(6\cdot047) \quad (k_0 + k_1 10^{-1} + k_2 10^{-2} + \ldots + k_n 10^{-n}) U_n \le q U_T$$
$$\le (k_0 + k_1 10^{-1} + k_2 10^{-2} + \ldots + (k_n + 1)\, 10^{-n})\, U_T.$$

6·05 The Number System: Integers, Rational Numbers, Real Numbers

We have used phrases such as "suppose the real length of x is qU_L". q is a number. But what sort of number can it be? In view of the inequality (6·043), it cannot be, in general, merely a non-negative integer; *e.g.* if $4·02$ m $\leq q$ m $\leq 4·03$ m, then q cannot be an integer at all. Thus, in general, q must be at least a non-negative rational number, a rational number being a ratio of integers such that the second term of the ratio is not zero.

Suppose that the inch is the chosen unit of length. Consider a circle whose diameter is one inch exactly. What is the length of the circumference of this circle? The answer is: π in. But π is an irrational number, that is, it is a number which is not equal to any rational number. So it seems necessary, at least theoretically, to include non-negative real numbers among the possible values for numerics.

The set $\mathbf{Z}$ of all the integers possesses the following properties except (6·0510):

(6·051) $\mathbf{Z} \neq \emptyset$;

(6·052) $\mathbf{Z}$ is closed under a 2 place single-valued operator $+$;

(6·053)   For all members $x, y,$ and z of $\mathbf{Z}, (x + y) + z = x + (y + z)$;

(6·054)   There is a single member 0 of $\mathbf{Z}$ such that for all members x of $\mathbf{Z}$, $0 + x = x + 0 = x$;

(6·055)   For each member x of $\mathbf{Z}$ there is a single member $-x$ of $\mathbf{Z}$ such that $(-x) + x = x + (-x) = 0$;

(6·056)   For all members x and y of $\mathbf{Z}$, $x + y = y + x$;

(6·057) $\mathbf{Z}$ is closed under a 2 place, single-valued operator $\times$;

(6·058)   For all members $x, y,$ and z of $\mathbf{Z}, (x \times y) \times z = x \times (y \times z)$;

(6·059)   There is a single member 1 of $\mathbf{Z}$ such that for all members x of $\mathbf{Z}$, $1 \times x = x \times 1 = x$;

(6·0510) For each member x of $\mathbf{Z}$ there is a single member x^{-1} of $\mathbf{Z}$ such that $x^{-1} \times x = x \times x^{-1} = 1$;

(6·0511) For all members x and y of $\mathbf{Z}$, $x \times y = y \times x$;

(6·0512) For all members $x, y,$ and z of $\mathbf{Z}$, $x \times (y + z) = (x \times y) + (x \times z)$;

(6·0513) For all members $x, y,$ and z of $\mathbf{Z}$, if $x \neq 0$ and $x \times y = x \times z$, then $y = z$;

(6·0514) $\mathbf{Z}$ has a non-empty proper subset $\mathbf{N}$ which is closed under $+$ and $\times$, and which is such that for every member x of $\mathbf{Z}$, either $x \in \mathbf{N}$ or $x = 0$ or $(-x) \in \mathbf{N}$, these three alternatives being mutually exclusive;

(6·0515) $\mathbf{N}$ is a well-ordered set.

Any set which has the properties (6·051) to (6·055) is called an *additive group*; an additive group which also has the property (6·056) is called an *abelian* or *commutative additive group*. Any set which has the properties (6·051) and (6·057) to (6·0510) is called a *multiplicative group*; a multiplicative group which also has the property (6·0511) is called an *abelian* or *commutative multiplicative group*. A set which has the properties (6·051) to (6·0513) except (6·0510), the member 0 defined in (6·054) being different from the member 1 defined in (6·059), is called an *integral domain*. An integral domain is simply-ordered, cf. E4·7·72, if and only if it has the property (6·0514); this is a theorem that has to be established, not a definition. (By definition, $x > y$ if and only if $y - x \in N$.) A set which has all the properties (6·051) to (6·0513), that is, an integral domain with the property (6·0510), is called a *field*. The difference between a field and an integral domain is that a field is stipulated to be closed under division, whereas no such stipulation is made with respect to an integral domain.[1]

The set Z of all the integers is an integral domain; in fact Z is a simply-ordered integral domain with a proper subset—the well-ordered set N of all the positive integers. The set Q of all the rational numbers is a field. One knows from one's work in arithmetic and algebra that there is a "natural" ordering of the rationals: if x, y, z, and w are integers, then $x/y < z/w$ if and only if $x \times w < y \times z$. Posing the definition of the set Q^+ of all the positive rationals:

(6·0516) For all members x and y of the set Z of all the integers,

$x \times y^{-1} \in Q^+$ if and only if $x \times y \in N$;

it follows that Q is simply-ordered. However, unlike N, Q^+ is not naturally well-ordered.

From a theoretical standpoint it can be said that the reason for extending N to Z is to obtain a set which will be closed under subtraction as well as under what N is closed under, and the reason for extending Z to Q is to obtain a set which will be closed under division as well as under what Z is closed under. Similarly, the reason for extending Q to the set R of all the *real numbers* is to obtain a set which will be closed under root extraction as well as under what Q is closed under. $3-4 \notin N$, so Z is introduced whereby $3-4 \in Z$; $3/4 \notin Z$, so Q is introduced whereby $3/4 \in Q$; $\sqrt[3]{4} \notin Q$, so R is introduced whereby $\sqrt[3]{4} \in R$. That $\sqrt[3]{4} \notin Q$ can be shown as follows. Suppose $\sqrt[3]{4} \in Q$; then there are some integers x and y ($y \neq 0$) such that $\sqrt[3]{4} = x/y$. If x and y have common factors, let m and n be the integers resulting from dividing x and y by all their common factors. Thus, $\sqrt[3]{4} = m/n$ where m and n have 1 as their greatest common divisor. Since

---

[1] The concepts mentioned in the text were gradually introduced and elaborated by many mathematicians in the nineteenth century. The decisive modern step, which initiated Modern Abstract Algebra, was taken by Steinitz, E. (1871-1928): "Algebraische Theorie der Körper", *Journal f.d. reine u. angew. Math.*, 1910, **137**, 167-308.

$\sqrt[3]{4} = m/n$, it follows that $m^3 = 4n^3$, and so $2 \mid m$. But if $2 \mid m$, then for some integer m_1, $m = 2m_1$. Hence $8m_1{}^3 = 4n^3$, and so $2 \mid n$. Consequently $2 \mid m$ and $2 \mid n$, contrary to the hypothesis that 1 is the greatest common divisor of m and n. Therefore the original supposition that $\sqrt[3]{4} \in \mathbf{Q}$ must be rejected.

An ordered set s that is a subset of an ordered set t is said to have an *upper (lower) bound* if and only if there is some member y of t such that, for every member x of s, $x \le y$ $(y \le x)$. And s is said to have a *least upper (greatest lower) bound* if and only if it has an upper (lower) bound y such that, if z is any upper (lower) bound, then $y \le z$ $(z \le y)$.

An ordered pair (u, w) of non-empty subsets u and w of the ordered field $\mathbf{Q}$ of rational numbers is called a *(Dedekind) cut* in $\mathbf{Q}$ if and only if (a) $u\_w = \emptyset$, (b) $u\_w = \mathbf{Q}$, and (c) for all members x of u and for all members y of w, $x < y$, *i.e.* $x \le y$ but not $y \le x$.[1] For example, x and y being rational number variables, and "$X \ge Y$" being synonymous with "$Y \le X$",

(6·0517) $(\{x : x < 1\}, \{y : y \ge 1\})$,

(6·0518) $(\{x : x < 1/2\}, \{y : y \ge 1/2\})$,

(6·0519) $(\{x : x^3 < 4\}, \{y : y^3 > 4\})$,

are cuts in $\mathbf{Q}$ whereas $(\{x : x < 1\}, \{y : y \ge 2\})$, and $(\{x : x < 1\}, \{y : y \ge 0\})$ are not cuts in $\mathbf{Q}$, for the former does not satisfy (b) and the latter does not satisfy (a) or (c). A cut in $\mathbf{Q}$ whose first and second components are s and t respectively will be denoted by "$/s, t/$". $/s, t/$ is said to be a *rational real number* if and only if either s has a least upper bound (lub) in $\mathbf{Q}$ or t has a greatest lower bound (glb) in $\mathbf{Q}$; by (a), these alternatives are mutually exclusive. $/s, t/$ is said to be an *irrational real number* if and only if it is not a rational real number. $\mathbf{R}$ is the set of all the rational together with all the irrational real numbers.

The cut $/\{x : x < 1\}, \{y : y \ge 1\}/$ is intended to be the "same" as the rational number 1. So is the cut $/\{x : x \le 1\}, \{y : y > 1\}/$. For rational real numbers, we shall assume that the element of equality always occurs in the right-hand component of a cut. This assumption amounts to adding a clause (d) to the above definition of a cut: no member of u can equal the lub of u in $\mathbf{Q}$ if there is one, but some member of w can equal the glb of w in $\mathbf{Q}$ if there is one.

The cut $/\{x : x^3 < 4\}, \{y : y^3 > 4\}/$ is intended to be the "same" as $\sqrt[3]{4}$. The set $\mathbf{R}$ is intended to provide a simply-ordered set sufficiently enlarged from the set of rational numbers or from the set of rational real numbers whereby in every cut $/s, t/$ the right-hand component t has a glb—in $\mathbf{R}$. If it be asked what $\sqrt[3]{4}$ is, the answer

---

[1] Cuts and the associated account of real numbers are due to Dedekind, R. (1831-1916): *Stetigkeit und irrationale Zahlen* (Brunswick, 1872); *Was sind und was sollen die Zahlen*? (Brunswick, 1888).

then is that $\sqrt[3]{4}$ is the glb of the right-hand component in the cut $/\{x : x^3 < 4\}, \{y : y^3 > 4\}/$. It is easy to see that this account of the irrational number $\sqrt[3]{4}$ is impredicative; cf. E4·11·102. The same remark applies, of course, to all other irrational numbers.

Thus it is seen that in every cut the right-hand component has a glb—in **R**. It is not hard to show that this glb is also the lub, in **R**, of the left-hand component. Hence, in every cut the left-hand component has a lub and the right-hand component has a glb, these bounds being in **R**.

We shall use the Greek letters θ, ϕ, and ψ, with or without subscripts, as variables for cuts. If any cut $\theta = /s, t/$, then we use the notations "$p_1\theta$" for s and "$p_2\theta$" for t.

For all cuts θ and ψ, $\theta = \psi$ if and only if they are identical ordered pairs, and $\theta < \psi$ if and only if $p_1\theta \subset p_1\psi$. These are definitions. As a theorem, it now follows that **R** is a chain.

For all cuts θ and ψ, $\theta + \psi$ is by definition equal to the ordered pair (s, t) where s is the set of all the rational numbers x such that $x = x_1 + x_2$, $x_1 \in p_1\theta$, $x_2 \in p_1\psi$, and where t is the set of all the rational numbers y such that $y = y_1 + y_2$, $y_1 \in p_2\theta$, $y_2 \in p_2\psi$. It can be shown that this ordered pair (s, t) is itself a cut. For any cut θ, $-\theta$ is by definition equal to the ordered pair (u, w) where u is the set of all the rational numbers x such that $-x \in p_1\theta$, and where w is the set of all the rational numbers y such that $-y \in p_2\theta$. It can be shown that this ordered pair (u, w) is itself a cut. By definition, for any cut θ, the *absolute value* or *modulus* of θ, denoted by "$|\theta|$", is equal to θ if $/\{x : x < 0\}, \{y : y \geq 0\}/\leq \theta$, and is equal to $-\theta$ if $\theta < /\{x : x < 0\}, \{y : y \geq 0\}/$; in other words, the modulus of a real number θ is θ if θ is non-negative, and is $-\theta$ if θ is negative. By definition, for all cuts θ and ψ, (i) if θ and ψ are non-negative, then $\theta \times \psi$ is equal to the ordered pair (e, u) where e (u) is the set of all the rational numbers x (y) such that $x = x_1 x_2$, $x_1 \in p_1\theta$, $x_2 \in p_1\psi$ ($y = y_1 y_2$, $y_1 \in p_2\theta$, $y_2 \in p_2\psi$); (ii) if θ and ψ are both negative, then $\theta \times \psi$ is equal to $|\theta| \times |\psi|$; (iii) if one of θ and ψ is non-negative, the other being negative, then $\theta \times \psi$ is equal to $-(|\theta| \times |\psi|)$. It can be shown that each of the ordered pairs arising from this definition of multiplication of real numbers is itself a cut, *i.e.* a real number. It can also be shown that for each member θ of **R** there is a member θ^{-1} of **R** such that $\theta \times \theta^{-1} = /\{x : x < 1\}, \{y : y \geq 1\}/$; unless $\theta = /\{x : x < 0\}, \{y : y \geq 0\}/$.

It follows from all this that **R** is an ordered field. It is also what is called a *complete* ordered field: every non-empty subset of **R** that has a lower (upper) bound in **R** has a glb (lub) in **R**.[1]

---

[1] For the general theory of the Number System cf. Birkhoff and MacLane S. (1909-): *A Survey of Modern Algebra*, revised edition (New York, 1953); Ritt, J. F. (1893-1951): *Theory of Functions*, revised edition (New York 1947); and Thurston, H. A. (c. 1920-): *The Number System* (Glasgow, 1956).

EXERCISES

Demonstrate by reference to the postulates (6·051) to (6·059) and (6·0511) to (6·0515), that the set **Z** of all the integers possesses the properties E6·5·1 to E6·5·9.

E6·5·1.   (a) $(x + y) z = xz + yz$;   (b) $x + y = x + z$ implies $y = z$.

E6·5·2.   If $xy = 0$, then $x = 0$ or $y = 0$.

E6·5·3.   For any x and y there is a single z such that $y + z = x$.

*E6·5·4.   (a) $(- x)(- y) = xy$;   (b) $- (- x) = x$;   (c) $- x = (- 1) x$.

E6·5·5.   (a) $x < y$ if and only if for all z, $x + z < y + z$;   (b) if $0 < z$, then $xz < yz$ if and only if $x < y$.

*E6·5·6.   If (i) $s \subseteq \mathbf{N}$, (ii) $1 \in s$, and (iii) for all members n of $\mathbf{N}$, if $n \in s$, then $n + 1 \in s$; then $s = \mathbf{N}$.

E6·5·7.   (A generalisation of E6·5·6.)   If (i) $s \subseteq \mathbf{N}$, (ii) $x + 1 \in s$, but $x \notin s$, and (iii) for all members n of $\mathbf{N}$ such that $x < n$, if $n \in s$, then $n + 1 \in s$; then $s = \mathbf{N} - \mathbf{N}_x$. (Here $x \in \mathbf{N}^{\geq}$.)

E6·5·8.   **General Principle of Mathematical Induction:** For all n of $\mathbf{N}$ such that, for some x of $\mathbf{N}^{\geq}$, $x < n$, let t be the set of formulae $b(n)$ and let u be the set of correct (valid, true) formulae $b(n)$, i.e. $b(n) \in u$ if and only if $b(n)$ is a correct formula.   If (i) $b(x + 1) \in u$ and (ii) for all n of $\mathbf{N}$ such that $x < n$, if $b(n) \in u$, then $b(n + 1) \in u$; then for all n of $\mathbf{N}$ such that $x < n$, $b(n) \in u$.

E6·5·9.   **General Principle of Course-of-Values Induction:** For all n of $\mathbf{N}$ such that, for some x of $\mathbf{N}^{\geq}$, $x < n$, let t be the set of formulae $b(n)$ and let u be the set whose members are those among the formulae $b(n)$ that are correct.   If, for all $n < k$ for some k of $\mathbf{N}$, $b(n) \in u$ implies $b(k) \in u$, then for all n of $\mathbf{N}$ such that $x < n$, $b(n) \in u$.

E6·5·10.   Show that **R** is a chain.

E6·5·11.   Show in detail that **R** is a field.

E6·5·12.   Show that if $\theta < \psi$, then there is some rational real number ϕ such that $\theta < \phi < \psi$.

*E6·5·13.   **Dedekind's Theorem:**[1]   If s and t are sets of real numbers such that (i) $s \neq \emptyset$ and $t \neq \emptyset$, (ii) $s \_ t = \emptyset$, (iii) $s \_ t = \mathbf{R}$, (iv) for every member θ of s and for every member ψ of t, $\theta < \psi$; then there is one and only one real number ϕ such that $\theta \leq \phi$ for every member θ of s and $\phi \leq \psi$ for every member ψ of t.

---

[1] Dedekind: *Was sind und was sollen die Zahlen?*

*E6·5·14. Show that if s is a non-empty subset of R and s has a lower bound, then s has a glb.

E6·5·15. Show that if s is a non-empty subset of R and s has an upper bound, then s has a lub.

E6·5·16. **The Archimedean Continuity Principle:**[1] If θ and ψ are positive real numbers, then for some positive integer n, $n\theta > \psi$.

6·06 Units and Dimensions

In order to show or to state that a quantity-type Q partakes merely of length, one represents it by "[L]". Q is said to have the *dimensions* of L, and the assertion to this effect is written as

(6·061) $[Q] = [L]$.

Similarly,

(6·062) $[Q] = [M]$

and

(6·063) $[Q] = [T]$

signify that a quantity-type Q has the sole dimensions of mass and has the sole dimensions of time respectively. It is evident that the only quantity-types whose dimensions are [L], [M], and [T] are length, mass, and time respectively: the fundamental quantity-types. If it is assumed that (i) there is a set D having [L], [M], and [T] as members, and (ii) D is an abelian multiplicative group, cf. **6·05**, then it becomes possible to represent derived quantity-types by expressions symbolising powers and sub-multiples of [L], [M], and [T] and compounds of them. We now make these assumptions.

Area is analysable into length × length:

(6·064) $[\text{Area}] = [L] \times [L] = [L^2]$.

---

[1] This Principle is generally called the *Axiom of Archimedes*. This name and the first modern recognition of the Principle's importance are due to Stolz, O. (1842-): "Zur Geometrie der Alten, insbesondere über ein Axiom des Archimedes", *Math. Ann.*, 1883, **22**, 504-19.

Area, then, has the dimensions of L^2.   Velocity is analysable into length $\times$ time:

(6·065)   [Velocity] $= [L]/[T] = [LT^{-1}]$.

Velocity has the dimensions of LT^{-1}.   Acceleration is analysable into length $\div$ (time $\times$ time):

(6·066)   [Acceleration] $= [L]/([T] \times [T]) = [LT^{-2}]$.

Acceleration has the dimensions of LT^{-2}.   Momentum is analysable into mass $\times$ velocity, that is, into mass $\times$ (length $\div$ time):

(6·067)   [Momentum] $= [M] \times ([L]/[T]) = [LMT^{-1}]$.

Momentum has the dimensions of LMT^{-1}.

We shall call all expressions of the form "$L^x M^y T^z$, where x, y, and z are members of Z, *dimensional expressions*. (It is to be remembered that, by definition, $U^{\circ} = 1$ and that $1 \in D$.)   The use of the term "dimensional" here is derived from the cases $[L^2]$ and $[L^3]$ for area and volume.   An area is two dimensional with respect to length and a volume is three dimensional with respect to length.   The term "dimension" is extended from these cases so as to apply to all the powers and sub-multiples of L, M, and T, the term referring to the indices themselves.   Thus it may be said that the dimensions of velocity are 1 in length and -1 in time since [velocity] $= [LT^{-1}]$.   The term "dimension" is finally further extended so as to be applicable in the sort of way indicated by our use of it in the preceding paragraphs.

There are two important points to notice about dimensional expressions.   The first is that such expressions contain no symbols for mathematical constant quantities, that is, for real numbers.   For example, kinetic energy is defined to be equal to the product of half of the mass and the square of the velocity: $\frac{1}{2}mv^2$.   But the dimensional expression for kinetic energy is $[L^2MT^{-2}]$; the fraction $\frac{1}{2}$

has dropped out. For any real number x, the dimensions of x are 0 in length, mass, and time:

(6·068) $[x] = [L°M°T°]$.

Hence, a dimensional expression can determine a quantity-type only to within a mathematical constant.

The second point is this. One useful way of interpreting a dimensional expression is as an index to the unit of measurement of the quantity-type that the expression represents. Since the dimensional expression for area is $[L^2]$, the unit of measurement for area is the square of the unit of measurement for length; in the M.K.S. system the unit of measurement for area is, then, the square metre, denoted by "m^2". Since the dimensional expression for force is $[LMT^{-2}]$, the unit of measurement for force is the product of the units of length and mass, divided by the square of the unit of time; in the M.K.S. system the unit of measurement for force is the metre-kilogram per second per second, which is called a *newton*.

6·07 The Method of Obtaining Dimensional Expressions for Quantity-Types

Given a quantity-type, how can its dimensional expression be obtained? The practical procedure to follow is:

(i) Write down a defining equation of the quantity-type;

(ii) Enclose each side of the equation within square brackets;

(iii) Substitute dimensional expressions throughout the equation, putting or leaving the symbol for the quantity-type with which one is concerned on its own within square brackets;

(iv) Employing standard algebraic devices—in fact, technically, those devices that are valid within an abelian multiplicative group—stand this latter dimensional expression on its own on one side of the equation and reduce all the dimensional expressions, which are on the other side, to a single one.

We give three examples to illustrate these steps.

Example I.—Velocity.

(6·071)   velocity = distance/time;

(6·072)   [velocity] = [distance/time];

(6·073)   [velocity] = [L]/[T];

(6·074)   [velocity] = [LT^{-1}].

Example II.—The gravitational constant G.

(6·075) $F = Gm_1m_2/r^2$;

(6·076) $[F] = [Gm_1m_2/r^2]$;

(6·077) $[LMT^{-2}] = [G] [M^2]/[L^2]$;

(6·078) $[G] = [L^3M^{-1}T^{-2}]$.

In the equation (6·075) F is the force of attraction between any two particles, whose masses are m_1 and m_2 and whose distance apart is r.

Example III.—Planck's constant h.

(6·079) $E = h\nu$;

(6·0710) $[E] = [h\nu]$;

(6·0711) $[L^2MT^{-2}] = [h] [T^{-1}]$;

(6·0712) $[h] = [L^2MT^{-1}]$.

In the equation (6·079) E is the energy of a photon (light quantum) and ν is the frequency of the photon.

EXERCISES

E6·7·17. Give the dimensional expression for force if force is analysable into mass × acceleration.

E6·7·18. Give the dimensional expression for pressure if pressure is analysable into force ÷ area.

E6·7·19. Give the dimensional expression for terrestrial gravity g, a defining equation being $g = Gm/r^2$ where G is the gravitational constant, m is the mass and r is the radius of the earth.

E6·7·20. Give the dimensional expression for $2\pi x/g$ where x is a length and g is terrestrial gravity.

E6·7·21. Give the dimensional expression for $gx \cos 3\theta$; angle is dimensionless, *i.e.* has the dimension (exponent) 0 in length, mass, and time.

E6·7·22. If the unit of acceleration is x m/sec^{-2} and the unit of time is y sec., what are the units of length and velocity?

6·08 Dimensional Analysis

The study of quantity-types with respect to their dimensional expressions, and of the methods of arriving at physical laws from the nature and relations between such expressions, is called *Dimensional Analysis*. "It happens not infrequently that results in the form of 'laws' are put forward as novelties on the basis of elaborate experiments which might have been predicted *a priori* after a few minutes' consideration [using the methods of Dimensional Analysis]," wrote Lord Rayleigh[1] the first outstanding advocate and user of the methods of Dimensional Analysis in physics. These methods are primarily useful in their enabling the physicist to determine *a priori* what is the structural relationship—the relationship apart from mathematical constants—between one quantity-type and others, or, to express the utility with greater accuracy and modesty than Rayleigh has done in the passage quoted, in their enabling the physicist to determine *a priori* what is the law governing a quantity-type Q on the supposition that the only relevant quantity-types are Q_1, Q_2, ..., Q_n.

The fundamental method of Dimensional Analysis rests on the requirement that a necessary condition for the validity of a physical law is that this law be unaffected by

[1] Rayleigh, J. W. S., 3rd Baron (1842-1919): "The Principle of Similarity", *Nature*, 1915, **95**, 66-8.

the choice of any particular system of units; the law must be invariant under changes in the units of measurement employed. As Sir Joseph Larmor put it: "Mere change in the magnitudes of the ordered scheme of units of measurement that is employed must not affect sensibly the forms of the equations that are adequate expressions of the underlying relations of the problem."[1] This requirement leads to the adoption of the *Principle of Dimensional Homogeneity*: in a physical equation all the terms must have the same dimensional expression.[2] If a physical equation has $n + 1$ terms $q_i Q_i$ ($i = 0, 1, 2, \ldots, n$; $q_i \in \mathbf{R}$), then by virtue of the Principle of Dimensional Homogeneity if for some i such that $0 \leq i \leq n$

$$(6 \cdot 081) \quad [Q_i] = [\mathrm{L}^{x_i} \mathrm{M}^{y_i} \mathrm{T}^{z_i}],$$

then for all i such that $0 \leq i \leq n$,

$$(6 \cdot 082) \quad [Q_i] = [\mathrm{L}^{x_i} \mathrm{M}^{y_i} \mathrm{T}^{z_i}].$$

The elementary and basic technique in Dimensional Analysis may be described as follows.[3] If Q_o is the quantity-type in which one is interested, (i) choose the quantity-types $Q_1, Q_2, \ldots, Q_n$ which are supposed to be the only quantity-types upon which Q_o depends. (ii) Set

$$(6 \cdot 083) \quad Q_0 = f(Q_1, Q_2, \ldots, Q_n).$$

(iii) Assume that the functional equation (6·083) implies

$$(6 \cdot 084) \quad Q_0 = q\,(Q_1^{x_1},\ Q_2^{x_2},\ \ldots,\ Q_n^{x_n}),$$

where q is a real number. This assumption is in need of and can be given mathematical justification, but this requires the use of more advanced mathematics than we can presume the reader to possess. Suffice it to say here

---

[1] Larmor, J. (1857-1942): "The Principle of Similarity" (letter to Editor), *Nature*, 1915, **95**, 644.

[2] Fourier, J. B. J. (1768-1830): *Théorie Analytique du Chaleur*, §§ 157 *et seq* (Paris, 1822).

[3] For the general theory, cf. Focken, C. M. (1901-): *Dimensional Methods* (London, 1953); Lanchester, F. W. (1868-1946): *The Theory of Dimensions and Its Applications for Engineers* (London, 1936).

that this justification presupposes that Q_0 is a *continuous* function of Q_1, Q_2, ..., Q_n. (iv) Express (6·084) as a dimensional equation:

$$(6·085) \quad [Q_0] = [Q_1^{x_1}] [Q_2^{x_2}] \ldots [Q_n^{x_n}].$$

(v) Substitute dimensional expressions for the "Q_i". (vi) Use the Principle of Dimensional Homogeneity to obtain the numerical values of the exponents x_i. Finally, (vii) substitute these values in (6·084). We illustrate this technique by the following four examples.

Example I.—What is the distance s traversed in time t by an object falling from rest from a position near the earth's surface?

(i) Suppose that the only relevant quantity-types for the determination of s are (terrestrial gravity) g and t.

(ii) Set $s = f(g, t)$.

(iii) Since $s = f(g, t)$,

$$(6·086) \quad s = q(g^x t^y).$$

(iv) The dimensional transform of (6·086) is
$$(6·087) \quad [s] = [g^x] [t^y].$$

(v) Since $[s] = [L]$, $[g] = [LT^{-2}]$, and $[t] = [T]$,

$$(6·088) \quad [L] = [L^x T^{-2x+y}].$$

(vi) By the Principle of Dimensional Homogeneity, $x = 1$ and, since $y - 2x = 0$, $y = 2$.

(vii) Substituting these values in (6·086) gives

$$(6·089) \quad s = qgt^2.$$

The value of the constant q cannot be determined *a priori*. It has to be learned from experience. Experience teaches that the value of q is $1/2$. However, except for this constant, one can determine the law of free fall completely independently of experience provided the initial choice of relevant quantity-types is correct and adequate.

The remaining examples are presented more briefly.

Example II.—In Example I, if the mass m of the falling object, but not the earth's mass, were held to be relevant (as the Aristotelian Jesuits with whom Galileo came in conflict believed), can it still be shown that s is proportional to gt^2 and is independent of m?

(6·0810) $s = f(g, m, t)$.

(6·0811) $s = q (g^x m^y t^z)$.

(6·0812) $[s] = [g^x] [m^y] [t^z]$.

(6·0813) $[L] = [L^x T^{-2x}] [M^y] [T^z] = [L^x M^y T^{-2x+z}]$.

By the Principle of Dimensional Homogeneity, $x = 1$, $y = 0$, and $z = 2$.   Hence again

(6·0814) $s = qgt^2$.

Example III.—What is the period of time t for a planet to make one complete revolution round the Sun?

Suppose that the only relevant quantity-types for the determination of t are the universal constant of gravitation G, the masses m_1 and m_2 of the planet and of the Sun respectively, and the mean distance s of the planet from the Sun.

(6·0815) $t = f (s, m_1, m_2, G)$.

(6·0816) $t = q (s^x m_1^y m_2^z G^w)$.

(6·0817) $[t] = [s^x] [m_1^y] [m_2^z] [G^w]$.

(6·0818) $[T] = [L^x] [M^y] [M^z] [L^{3w} M^{-w} T^{-2w}]$
                  $= [L^{x+3w} M^{y+z-w} T^{-2w}]$.

By the Principle of Dimensional Homogeneity, $x + 3w = 0$, $y + z - w = 0$, and $-2w = 1$, and so, solving these simultaneous equations, we find that $x = 3/2$, $w = -(1/2)$, and $z = -(y + 1/2)$.   Substituting these results in (6·0816), and then squaring each side, we get

(6·0819) $t^2 = q^2 s^3 m_1^{2y} m_2^{-2y+1} G^{-1}$.

Hence the square of the period of time is proportional to the cube of the distance: Kepler's Third Law of Planetary Motion.

Example IV.—What is the period t of a simple pendulum swinging with a smallish amplitude in an evacuated chamber at a constant temperature?

Suppose that the only relevant quantity-types for the determination of t are the length l of the cord supporting the bob, the mass m of the bob, and g.

(6·0820) $t = f(l, m, g)$.

(6·0821) $t = q(l^x m^y g^z)$.

(6·0822) $[t] = [l^x][m^y][g^z]$.

(6·0823) $[T] = [L^x][M^y][L^z T^{-2z}] = [L^{x+z} M^y T^{-2z}]$.

By the Principle of Dimensional Homogeneity, $x + z = 0$, $y = 0$, and $-2z = 1$, and so, solving these simultaneous equations, we find that $x = 1/2$, $y = 0$, and $z = -(1/2)$. Substituting these values in (6·0821) gives

(6·0824) $t = q l^{1/2} g^{-1/2} = q(l/g)^{1/2}$.

EXERCISES

E6·8·23.   What is the centripetal acceleration a of a particle moving with uniform speed u in a circle, supposing that the only relevant quantity-types are u and the radius r of the circle?

E6·8·24.   What is the tension F in a thin circular wire rotating with uniform speed in its own plane about an axis through and perpendicular to its centre, supposing that the only relevant quantity-types for determining F are the radius r of the wire, its linear density d, and the angular momentum ω of the rotation? The dimensional expression for F is $[LMT^{-2}]$, for d is $[L^{-1}M]$, and for ω is $[T^{-1}]$ (since angle is dimensionless).

E6·8·25.   What is the excess gaseous pressure P in a soap bubble, supposing that the only relevant quantity-types for determining P are the radius r of the bubble and its surface tension F? The dimensional expression for P is $[L^{-1}MT^{-2}]$ and for F is $[MT^{-2}]$.

E6·8·26.   What is the velocity of propagation u of a wave in deep water, supposing that the only relevant quantity-types for determining u are the wave-length s, the density d of the liquid, and g?

E6·8·27.   What is the rule for converting a measurement (or calculation) in one system S_1 of units into one of another system S_2 of units?

6·09 Errors of Observation

In the everyday use of the term "measurement" in science no distinction is drawn or maintained between measurement and calculation. In practice, even quantities belonging to fundamental quantity-types are calculated rather than measured; for example, the astronomer calculates, not measures, the masses and distances of heavenly objects. And in practice too, quantities belonging to derived quantity-types are evaluated by means of apparatus other than measuring rods, balances, and clocks; such are speedometers and manometers. In fact, the scientist who wants to know the magnitude of some quantity is prepared to employ any available tools, whether simple or complex apparatus, mathematical and physical formulae, or mathematical tables; provided that they enable him to make an accurate assessment of the value of the quantity. To obtain the materials for the rational making of this assessment often requires the use of several different instruments and of many items from the stock of mathematical and scientific knowledge.

Every magnitude whatever that is arrived at by any route ultimately involving the measurement of fundamental quantity-types is treated in science as a measurement. Henceforth we shall follow this broader sense of the term "measurement", and indeed this broader sense has already, on occasion, been assumed in the use of the term in previous sections.

All scientific measurement of all quantity-types is approximate, if only because of the limitations of the instruments employed. The scientist never knows from making a measurement or series of measurements of a distance what exactly is the magnitude of the distance, for the calibration marks on the measuring rod do not exactly coincide with the extremes of the distance being measured. The calibration marks have properties which prevent them being perfect physical representations of (Euclidean) geometrically ideal points and lines; the vertical strokes on a measuring rod have width; they are not sheer length without breadth. Analogous remarks apply to the other instruments employed for measuring other quantity-types.

Although the scientist cannot know the exact values of the quantities he measures, he nevertheless ordinarily assumes that these quantities do have exact values; he does not usually doubt the existence of *the* length in a given direction and of *the* mass of an observable object, or doubt the existence of *the* time at which an event occurs. Thus the scientist feels himself forced to regard the measurements he obtains as approximations to some real value the nature of which has to be inferentially estimated from the evidence provided by his measurements. Any deviation from the real value is called an error of observation. Errors of observation are usually given a threefold classification: instrumental errors, personal errors, and accidental errors.

Instrumental errors are of several kinds, of which we may mention two. The first is that to which we have already referred, namely, the lack of precision due to the physical properties of the instruments used for making measurements, in particular the calibration and similar marks on the instruments. Calibration marks possess magnitudes that interfere with the attainment of a knowledge of the exact values of the quantities being measured. Suppose, for example, that the calibration marks on a rod for measuring length have a width of $10^{-m}U_l$; then each measurement of length made with this rod must, from the point of view of the observer, be only an approximation to the real length, the measurements obtained being subject to an error of at least $10^{-m}U_L$. But also, measuring instruments have only a finite number of calibration marks, and so each measurement made with the help of such an instrument is liable to have an inaccuracy relative to the "coarseness" of the degree of calibration. If a rod for measuring length is calibrated just so far as $10^{-m}U_L$, then a measurement recorded as "xU_L" expresses a range of possible values of the length measured, the range being from $(x - \frac{1}{2}10^{-m}) U_L$ to $(x + \frac{1}{2}10^{-m}) U_L$. An important consequence is that if a scientist wishes to measure a length to within an accuracy of say 0·01 m, it is futile for him to use a measuring rod calibrated only in units and tenths of a metre. The second kind of instrumental error is due to an inaccurate setting of an instrument, or to some other sort of regular factor. Such errors are said to be *systematic*. An inaccurate setting of an instrument occurs when the calibration marks are wrongly numbered or when the mechanism of the instrument is faulty. A concrete example is afforded by a tube, with an affixed scale, that is not kept vertical when the height of a liquid in the tube is being measured; the inclination will tend to make the readings of the height too large. Another kind of systematic error, and one that lies not in the instrument but in the external conditions, deserves notice; this source of error is typically periodic in character. "Some classes of observations are affected by meteorological conditions which are approximately reproduced in cycles of a year; the errors introduced are thus periodic in character. The observer, then, should always be on the look-out for possible systematic error and, if this is confirmed, he should devise means for its eradication. He may even be led to make a fundamental discovery. The classical example is Bradley's discovery of the phenomenon of aberration. Attempting to derive the parallax of the second-magnitude star γ Draconis, Bradley measured, with a fixed instrument, the star's declination at transit as opportunity permitted; he found that his measures revealed a periodic variation with the period of a year, but 90° out of phase with the anticipated periodic variation associated with parallax displacements and of magnitude far in excess of any possible observational error. He was led to reflect on how such a periodicity could arise and, eventually, to explain the phenomenon in terms of what we now call "annual aberration". A few years later he discovered, by similar methods, the phenomenon of nutation".[1]

Personal errors are also of two kinds. The first kind is that due and common to observers as such. Such personal errors arise from human physiological and psychological features. There are physiological and psychological influences on and limitations to the nature and range of perception. The second kind of personal error is that attributable and peculiar to the individual observer. It is a striking fact about scientific activity that different observers obtain different measurements for the very same instance of a quantity even when they use the same instruments. "The following times were obtained by ten different students using the same pendulum and the same watch: 37·2, 37·0, 36·9, 36·7, 36·8, 36·2, 35·4, 37·2, 36·7, 36·8 seconds for 20 swings and 73·8, 74·3, 74·0, 74·2, 74·4, 74·0, 73·0, 74·1, 73·6, 74·7 seconds for 40 swings."[2] The errors arising from the idiosyncrasies of the individual observer constitute what is called the *personal equation* of the observer. "The history of personal equation goes back to near the

[1] Smart, W. M. (1889-): *Combination of Observations*, pp. 38-9 (Cambridge, 1958). Smart's book provides the general theory of Errors of Observation.

[2] Topping, J. (1904-): *Errors of Observation and their Treatment*, p. 12 (London, 1955).

end of the eighteenth century when the "eye and ear" method / In this method the observer, listening to the beats of the sidereal clock nearby, estimated to a tenth of a second the time of transit of the star across a wire; hence the name of the method. / of observing transits was practised. In 1796 Maskelyne, fifth Astronomer Royal, wrote: / Greenwich Observations 3. / "My assistant, Mr David Kinnebrook, who had observed transits of stars and planets very well in agreement with me all the year 1794 and for a great part of [1795], began from the beginning of August last to set them down half a second later than he should do according to my observations; and, in January [1796] he increased his error to eight-tenths of a second. As he had unfortunately continued a considerable time in this error before I noticed it, and did not seem to me likely ever to get over it and return to the right method / Maskelyne averred that Kinnebrook had fallen "into some irregular and confused method of his own". / of observing, therefore, although with reluctance, as he was a diligent and useful assistant to me in other respects, I parted with him."[1]

Accidental errors are those which are due to random irregularities in observational and instrumental conditions. These errors are often ultimately the effects of atomic and molecular behaviour. In applications of electrical engineering these effects are associated with noise, *e.g.* there is the crackling noise heard from wireless and television sets and heard over the telephone. The meaning of the term "noise" has modernly been generalised so as to apply to other random phenomena which are caused by the basic particles of Nature. Refined measuring devices can be affected by the motions of these particles. Indeed, fluctuations in measuring instruments produced by these motions can in some circumstances be graphically recorded. Being random, these motions will cause the readings made

[1] Smart: *Combination of Observations*, pp. 37-8.

with the instrument to fluctuate randomly; on the other hand, being random, these fluctuations in the pointer indications of the instrument will concentrate about a central value: this is learned from experience. But accidental errors are bound up as much with what is being measured as with the instruments of measurement. For instance, in astronomical observations there are randomly fluctuating atmospheric conditions which prevent or disturb the taking of precise measurements.

6·10 The Limits of Error

Let Q be any measurable quantity whose real value is $x_q U$, U being the unit of measurement. Suppose that n measurements of Q are made ($n \in \mathbf{N}$) yielding $x_1 U$, $x_2 U$, ..., $x_n U$. By definition,

(6·101) $e_i U = (x_i - x_q) U$;

$e_i U$ is called the *error* in $x_i U$. Again, by definition,

(6·102) $f_i = e_i U / x_q U$;

f_i is called the *fractional error* in $x_i U$.

The symbol "Σ" has a function in algebra similar to that of "$\cup$" in the theory of sets. We explain its use by a few examples. "$\underset{n \in \mathbf{N_3}}{\Sigma} n$" is a shorthand expression denoting $1 + 2 + 3$; "$\underset{i \in \mathbf{N_4}}{\Sigma} x_i$" is a shorthand expression denoting $x_1 + x_2 + x_3 + x_4$; "$\underset{i \in \mathbf{N_4}}{\Sigma} e_i U$" is a shorthand expression denoting $e_1 U + e_2 U + e_3 U + e_4 U$.

By (6·091)

(6·103) $x_i U = x_q U + e_i U$,

and this, by (6·092), leads to

(6·104) $x_i U / x_q U = 1 + f_i$

and so to

(6·105) $\quad x_i U = x_q U + (x_q U)(f_i).$

Hence, on adding the n terms $x_i U$ and then dividing each side by n,

(6·106) $\quad \dfrac{1}{n} \underset{i \in \mathbf{N}_n}{\Sigma} x_i U = x_q U + \dfrac{1}{n}(x_q U) \underset{i \in \mathbf{N}_n}{\Sigma} f_i.$

The term on the left-hand side of (6·096) is called the *arithmetic mean* or the *expected value* of the n measurements $x_i U$. We shall denote it by "$E(x_i U)_n$". Looking at the second term on the right-hand side of (6·106), it is clear that if the sum of the f_i's is small, then, as n increases, the magnitude of that term decreases and thus the arithmetic mean of the n measurements approximates very closely to the real value of the quantity measured. This conclusion provides a justification for careful measurement and for repeating the process of careful measurement, because careful measurement reduces the size of f_i and repetition increases the magnitude of n.

We shall now show that the arithmetic mean does not differ from the real value $x_q U$ by more than the largest error in the measurements made. The modulus of a number x is the value of x regardless of sign, cf. **6·05** penultimate paragraph; thus the modulus $|-3|$ of -3 is 3 and $|4·01| = 4·01$. By (6·102)

(6·107) $\quad (x_q U) \underset{i \in \mathbf{N}_n}{\Sigma} f_i = \underset{i \in \mathbf{N}_n}{\Sigma} e_i U.$

Suppose $|e_j U|$ is the lub (cf. **6·05**) of the set having the moduli of the errors for its members. Then

(6·108) $\quad \left| e_j U \right| \geq \dfrac{1}{n} \left| \underset{i \in \mathbf{N}_n}{\Sigma} e_i U \right| = \left| \dfrac{1}{n} \underset{i \in \mathbf{N}_n}{\Sigma} e_i U \right|.$

By (6·106) and (6·097),

(6·109) $\quad \dfrac{1}{n} \underset{i \in \mathbf{N}_n}{\Sigma} x_i U - x_q U = \dfrac{1}{n} \underset{i \in \mathbf{N}_n}{\Sigma} e_i U;$

therefore, using (6·108),

(6·1010) $\left| \dfrac{1}{n} \underset{i \in \mathbf{N}_n}{\Sigma} x_i U - x_q U \right| \leq \left| e_j U \right|.$

Accordingly, the modulus of $E(x_i U)_n - x_q U$ does not exceed the largest modulus of the errors $e_i U$.

By definition,

(6·1011) $r_i U = x_i U - E(x_i U)_n;$

$r_i U$ is called the *residual* of $x_i U$. The modulus of the residual of $x_i U$ will be called the *deviation* of $x_i U$ (from the arithmetic mean). We proceed to demonstrate that the sum of the residuals of n measurements is zero. By (6·091),

(6·1012) $x_i U = x_q U + e_i U;$

by (6·1011),

(6·1013) $x_i U = r_i U + E(x_i U)_n.$

From these two equalities it follows that

(6·1014) $x_q U + e_i U = r_i U + E(x_i U)_n,$

and so, using (6·099),

(6·1015) $\underset{i \in \mathbf{N}_n}{\Sigma} r_i U = \underset{i \in \mathbf{N}_n}{\Sigma} e_i U - n \left(E(x_i U)_n - x_q U \right)$

$= \underset{i \subset \mathbf{N}_n}{\Sigma} e_i U - \underset{i \in \mathbf{N}_n}{\Sigma} e_i U = 0.$

6·11 The Arithmetic Mean and Measures of Dispersion

Suppose n measurements of a quantity Q are made, yielding $x_1 U$, $x_2 U$, ..., $x_n U$. (U might be a compound unit; *e.g.* if Q were a velocity, then U would be equal to $U_L U_T^{-1}$.) In order to be in a position to make a sound judgment about the degree of proximity of the arithmetic mean $E(x_i U)_n$ to the real value $x_q U$ of Q, it is necessary to take into account the scatter or dispersion of the measurements about the arithmetic mean. To give a crude example: if three measurements of the length of an iron bar were made, yielding 45·0 cm, 49·2 cm, and 48·6 cm, the reliance to be placed on their arithmetic mean (47·6 cm) as being a close estimate of the real value is negligible since the three results differ so much, although each purports to be accurate to the nearest tenth of a centimetre. Hence the scientist is obliged, in principle, to accompany the statement of the arithmetical mean of his measurements with indications whereby the accuracy of that value to the real value can be gauged. The basic indication of this kind is the *variance* of the set of measurements. We shall denote the variance of the n measurements $x_i U$ $(i = 1, 2, \ldots, n)$ by "$V^2 (x_i U)_n$". By definition,

$$(6·111) \quad V^2 (x_i U)_n = \left(\frac{1}{n} \underset{i \in \mathbf{N}_n}{\Sigma} r_i^2 \right) U,$$

r_i being the numeric of the residual $r_i U$. The variance is a criterion of scatter in the following sense: the concentration of obtained measurements about the arithmetic mean is inversely proportional to the size of the variance, so that a small variance indicates a heavy concentration about the arithmetic mean whereas a larger variance indicates a slighter concentration about the arithmetic mean. The description of a variance as being small or being large depends on comparisons. For example, the variance of the above-mentioned three measurements of an iron bar is 3·44 cm; this would be regarded as a very large variance, for it is about 7 per cent. of the value of the arithmetic mean. As a general, practical rule, one can say that a variance should not be greater than 1 per cent. of the value of the arithmetic mean; if the value of the variance is greater than that, the measurements have either been taken with insufficient care or some other corrigible factors, especially ones associated with the instruments used, have been crudely affecting the result.

From the variance is derived another important criterion of scatter. This is called the *standard deviation* of the n measurements. The standard deviation is simply the (positive) square root of the variance, and thus it may be aptly denoted by "$V(x_iU)_n$". For instance, in the case of the three measurements of the length of the iron bar, the standard deviation is 1·85 cm.

A third criterion of scatter is called the *coefficient of variation*. The coefficient of variation of n measurements x_iU may be denoted by "$C(x_iU)_n$". By definition,

(6·112) $C(x_iU)_n = (100V(x_iU)_n)(E(x_iU)_n)^{-1}$.

As distinct from the arithmetic mean, variance, and standard deviation, the coefficient of variation is not associated with any unit. The coefficient of variation has the value of 3·88 in the case of the three measurements of the iron bar.

The physicist usually supposes that the measurements of a quantity Q form an unbiased sample from what is called a *normal population*. The nature of a normal population will be explained in more detail in Chapter Eight. At this point it is sufficient to say that the physicist's supposition amounts roughly to the assumption that (i) the set s of all the possible measurements of Q is continuous, *i.e.* it has the same structure as the set **R** of the real numbers; (ii) with each member of s a probability is associated, and the totality of these probabilities is symmetrically distributed; (iii) that possible measurement (called the *mean* of the population) whose probability lies at the centre of the probability distribution coincides with that possible measurement (called the *mode* of the population) with which the maximum of all the probability values is associated. Adopting this assumption of normality we introduce two further criteria of scatter: the *probable* *error* of the arithmetic mean and the *standard error* of the arithmetic mean.

By definition, the probable error (p.e.) of the arithmetic mean of n measurements of a quantity Q is equal to the product of 0·6745 and the standard deviation. It can be shown that the probability of a measurement lying in the range $E(x_iU)_n \pm (0·6745)(V(x_iU)_n)$ is 0·5, so, correlatively (cf. next chapter), the probability that a measurement lies outside that range is also 0·5. Therefore, if a large number of measurements of Q are made, it is to be expected that about half of them will yield results within that range and about half of them will yield results outside that range. If this did not happen, one would be forced to conclude that the measurements obtained did not constitute a fair sample from a normal population.

By definition, the standard error (s.e.) of the arithmetic mean is equal to the quotient of the standard deviation and the (positive) square root of the number n of measurements or, what comes to the same thing,

(6·113) $(\text{s.e.})_n = \sqrt{V^2(x_iU)_n/n}.$

It is customary to find the results of measurements of a quantity Q expressed in scientific reports and literature in the form illustrated by

(6·114) 20·8 cm $\pm$ 0·1 cm.

There are two defects in this method of presentation. The first defect is that no indication is given of the number of measurements made. It might have been 3 or it might have been 1,000. But the reliability of the conclusion is dependent on the number of measurements made. The second defect is that no indication is given of the meaning of "0·1 cm." In fact, judging from scientific practice, an expression of the sort (6·104) may represent any one of three different things. In all three interpretations

"20·8 cm" denotes the arithmetic mean of the measurements made. However, "0·1 cm" can denote, firstly, the probable error, and secondly, the standard error, of the arithmetic mean; and thirdly, the range of the measurements obtained, *i.e.* the difference between the greatest and least of the measurements. It is clearly desirable in enunciating the magnitude of a quantity Q as evidenced by a body of measurements to be so-and-so, to be sufficiently specific as to avoid the two defects mentioned. (It may be remarked, as a practical clue, that in standard Physical Tables the sign $\pm$ is generally followed by the probable error.)

So far we have been considering the arithmetic mean and the criteria of scatter solely in relation to a set of measurements of a particular quantity such as the length of a particular iron bar, or in relation to similar sets such as the set of measurements of the speed of light, all instances of light being assumed to be completely uniform in respect of their speed (otherwise it would not be possible to speak of *the* speed of light). We have not explicitly referred to what might be called *statistical measurements*, that is measurements of different instances of a quantity-type, such as the heights of different human beings or the temperatures of different members of a zoological species. However, the definitions of the arithmetic mean and of the various criteria of scatter can be immediately applied also to statistical measurements, see further, Chapter Eight.

EXERCISES

E6·11·28. Using the data quoted in the penultimate paragraph of **6·08**, find the arithmetic mean, the variance, and the standard deviation of the measurements of the time for (*a*) 20 swings and (*b*) 40 swings of the pendulum.

E6·11·29. (a) Find the most probable value of the speed of light
using the following measurements (*i.e.* find the arithmetic
mean): 299,793·1 km sec^{-1};   299,794·2 km sec^{-1};
            299,792·6 km sec^{-1};   299,776 km sec^{-1};
            299,793 km sec^{-1};   299,789·8 km sec^{-1};
            299,795 km sec^{-1};   299,792 km sec^{-1}.

(b) Find the coefficient of variation, the probable error, and
the standard error of the arithmetic mean.

E6·11·30. **Principle of Least Squares:** If the best estimate (most
probable value) of Q is zU, where zU is defined to be
such that, for all real numbers y,

$$\sum_{i\in\mathbf{N}_n} (x_iU - zU)^2 \leq \sum_{i\in\mathbf{N}_n} (x_iU - yU)^2,$$

the n x_iU being measurements made of Q; then

$$zU = E(x_iU)_n.[1]$$

[1] The beginning student interested in those foundations of Natural
Philosophy concerning measurement and quantity will profit from the
textbook by Feather, N. (1904-): *The Physics of Mass, Length and
Time* (Edinburgh, 1959); the more advanced student, from the
masterly essay by Whitehead: *The Principles of Natural Knowledge*
(Cambridge, 1919).

CHAPTER SEVEN

PROBABILITY

7·01 Introduction

In this chapter we deal with the elements of the mathematical theory of probability. The first few sections, however, are subsidiary. In them the two best-known definitions of probability are presented and discussed. These are, first, the so-called classical definition, according to which the probability of an event is measured by the ratio of the number of favourable cases to the total number of cases, and, second, the frequency definition of von Mises, according to which the probability of a repetitive event is the limit to which the ratios f/n of the relative frequency of the event converges as n tends to infinity.

Next, we point out a distinction between the pure and applied mathematics of probability, calling the former *stochastics* and the latter *statistics*; the mathematical content of this chapter is stochastical, not statistical. A lengthy quotation from Cramér is given to elucidate the relationships between stochastics, statistics and experience.

Apart from concrete applications, the remainder of the chapter consists of formal work—axioms, definitions, theorems, and demonstrations—in stochastics. An axiomatic foundation for elementary probability theory is given, covering just the case of finitely many possible outcomes of a random experiment. The theory is presented and developed in terms of Boolean Algebra and Set Theory. After a number of fundamental theorems have been derived there comes an exposition of Combinatory Analysis—the theory of combinations and permutations—and, lastly, a treatment of conditional probability, that is of the probability of an event on the hypothesis that another event has occurred.

7·02 The Classical Definition of Probability

The best-known definition of probability is that often referred to as the *classical* definition. According to the usual version of this, the probability of an event E is (or is measured by) the fraction whose numerator is the number of cases favourable to the event and whose denominator is the number of all the possible cases, these being equally likely.[1] Sometimes the phrase "equally possible" is used instead of

---

[1] The terminology of "favourable cases" and "unfavourable cases" derives from Bernoulli, Jacques (1654-1705): *Ars Conjectandi* (Basle, 1713); Bernoulli speaks of "casus fertiles seu foecundi" and of "casus steriles".

"equally likely". In the account given by Laplace, to whom the classical definition is often first attributed, "equally possible" and not "equally likely" is used. "The theory of probability," he says,[1] "consists in reducing all the events which can occur in a given circumstance, to a certain number of equally possible cases, that is to say, such that we are equally undecided about their existence, and in determining among these cases the number of those which are favourable to the event whose probability is sought. The ratio of this number to that of all the possible cases is the measure of this probability which is, then, nothing but a fraction whose numerator is the number of favourable cases, and whose denominator is that of all the possible cases." For example, if a die is perfectly symmetrical, then the probability of scoring a six with a single throw is 1/6, because the event of a side of the die falling uppermost can occur (it is supposed from the symmetry) in just six equally likely and mutually exclusive ways of which just one—the side with six dots falling uppermost—is favourable. Similarly, the probability of scoring an even number with one throw of the die is 1/2, because there are six equally likely and mutually exclusive possibilities altogether of which just three— scoring two, scoring four, scoring six—are favourable, so that the required probability is 3/6, = 1/2. And again, the probability of picking at random an ace, king, queen or knave from a properly shuffled pack of ordinary playing cards is 16/52, = 4/13; for there are 52 equally likely and mutually exclusive possibilities, one for each card in the pack, and precisely sixteen of these are favourable.

The classical definition of probability was at least tacitly employed by all the early writers on the subject of mathematical probability, doubtless because their theoretical discussions were immediately connected with concrete problems in games of chance or analogous problems and the definition does assuredly represent a useful postulate for such applications of the theory of mathematical probability. But it has frequently been regarded as the basic principle of the whole theory itself. All elementary textbooks have adopted it, and it is only in recent years that even the advanced treatises have ceased to admit it.

Five objections have been brought against the classical definition of probability:

(i) It is accused of being circular; for it defines probability in terms of equally likely (or equally possible) cases, and is not to describe

---

[1] Laplace, P. S. de (1749-1827): *Théorié Analytique des Probabilitités*, third edition (Paris, 1820); in *Oeuvres Completes de Laplace VII* (Paris, 1886), p. viii. For a general discussion of definitions and philosophical foundations of probability, cf. Carnap: *Logical Foundations of Probability* (Chicago, 1950); Hogben, L. T. (1895-): *Statistical Theory* (London, 1957); and Keynes, J. M. (1883-1946): *Treatise on Probability* (London, 1921).

cases as equally likely (or equally possible) merely another way of describing them as equally probable? Thus the classical definition of probability uses the concept of probability to define that concept, which is a logically vicious procedure. Consequently, also, the definition is essentially uninformative, since it explains what probability is on the assumption that what it is is already known; for seemingly synonymous terms such as "likelihood" and "possibility" are used to define "probability", and if they were not already known, the definition could not be understood.

(ii) It is accused of being superfluous; for although it is useful and perhaps even necessary for certain applications of the theory to concrete situations such as exist in games of chance, it is utterly useless within the theory itself. No more theorems can be obtained by means of it than can be obtained without it. Certainly it enables one to calculate specific probabilities in games of chance and in similar fields. But no part of any purely mathematical theory is concerned with specific calculations relating to real particulars. It is relations that such mathematical theories aim at discovering and establishing. Euclidean geometry, for instance, has not the slightest interest in calculations of the magnitudes of angles of "triangles" in the real world. Its interest is in discovering and establishing relational theorems such as that the sum of the interior angles of a triangle is equal to two right angles. Geometry does not at all enable us to learn *a priori* what magnitude the individual angles of "triangles" possess; that is entirely an empirical matter. All that the geometrical formula, suitably interpreted, commits itself to asserting is: *if* a particular figure in the real world has the properties of a triangle, then the sum of its interior angles is equal to two right angles. And only experience can decide, in any actual case, whether the antecedent condition is fulfilled. Even if the antecedent condition were never satisfied by an actual figure, the geometrical theorem would still be mathematically valid. Analogously, probability theory does not say with respect to a particular die, that the various possible outcomes on throwing it are equally likely. *If* the various possibilities are equally likely, then the suitably interpreted formulae of the theory can be applied to give such and such numerical results, *e.g.* that the probability of scoring two successive sixes is $1/36$. Yet whether this particular die is in fact so constituted as to make the various possible outcomes equally likely is entirely an empirical question. Hitherto, experience has supported the view that when the empirical data conflict with the predictions of the mathematical theory as augmented by the hypothesis of equal likelihood, there is an assignable reason of a physical character. If in a long series of throws of a die the number of times that a six is scored is significantly different from a sixth of the whole number of throws, this deviation is due to the die's centre of gravity not being at its geometrical centre, or due to the fact that six indentations in the side with six dots have removed more matter than has been removed from sides with fewer dots, making that side relatively lighter; or due to some such factor.

(iii) It has been objected against the classical definition of probability that it limits the theory to events where there is only a finite number of possible outcomes, and so also limits the range of applicability of the theory. But such a limitation of the theory to the finite is unnecessary and undesirable. We may mention two simple probability problems involving the infinite. (a) If an ordinary, properly balanced coin is tossed until heads is first scored, what is the probability that heads is first scored on the nth throw? It is not hard to see that n here can be any positive integer whatever. The probability of needing as many as n throws for first scoring heads is $(1/2)^n$. There is no positive integer m of which one is entitled to say: heads must be scored before the $(m + 1)$st throw. Indeed, it is a simple matter to calculate the probability of not scoring heads even with m throws, however large m may be. This probability is $1 - (1/2)^m$, which will never be zero, although it becomes rapidly smaller and smaller as m increases. (b) Suppose a dart is equally likely to hit any point of a dart-board of radius 4 in., and it is given that a dart has hit the dart-board. What is the probability of the point hit being within an inch of an imagined vertical line through the centre of the dart-board? For dealing with this problem mathematically, one regards the physical set-up as analogous to a mathematical one. Thus the dart-board is treated as a circle, the tip of the dart as a geometrical point, and so on. It is apparent that there are infinitely many points of the dart-board that the dart might have hit. Therefore this problem of probabilities cannot be dealt with by a theory based on the classical definition. (In fact such problems as this were investigated by writers like Laplace who nominally accepted the classical definition; these mathematicians sensibly disregarded their definitions when they proved unduly restrictive.) It is intuitively plausible to argue that the probability required is the ratio of the *area* of that strip of the dart-board that is the set of all the points within an inch of the vertical line through the centre, to the *area* of the whole dart-board. In this way a different finite measure of the favourable cases and of the total cases is supplied than the only one envisaged by the classical definition. Using the calculus,

$$(7 \cdot 021) \quad \text{Area of strip} \ = 4 \int_0^1 \sqrt{16 - x^2} \, dx \ \text{in}^2$$

$$(7 \cdot 022) \qquad\qquad = 4 \left[\frac{x \sqrt{16 - x^2}}{2} + \frac{16}{2} \sin^{-1} \frac{x}{4} \right]_0^1 \text{in}^2$$

$$(7 \cdot 023) \qquad\qquad = (2 \sqrt{15} + 32 \sin^{-1} 0 \cdot 25) \ \text{in}^2$$

$$(7 \cdot 024) \qquad\qquad \doteqdot 15 \cdot 829 \ \text{in}^2.$$

The area of the whole dart-board is given by the formula

(7·025)   Area of circle $= \pi r^2$

to be 36π in². Hence the probability value sought is (approximately) $15\cdot829/(36)$ ($3\cdot1416$), which is minutely less than $0\cdot14$.

(iv) It is also objected against the classical definition of probability that it restricts applications of the theory to situations where the possibilities are equally likely, whereas so many situations to which the scientist wishes to apply probability methods do not contain equally likely possibilities. For example, the number of male births in some deme of an animal species may be significantly higher than the corresponding number of female births, and consequently there could be evidence that the two possible outcomes for a birth are not equally likely. Accordingly, a theory based on the classical definition could not be applied to births within that deme. But the mathematical theory can in practice be made to work perfectly well for this and other such situations where one is dealing with unequally likely possibilities. The latter merely affect the probabilities to be assigned to the individual possibilities. These probabilities can be reckoned using the ratios found by experience. If, for instance, the ratio of male to female births is 51/49, then one will assign the probability of a male birth to be $0\cdot51$.

(v) Finally, it is said that the classical definition of probability fails to show why the calculus of probability erected upon it should have any applicability to phenomena; or, putting the matter rather differently, it fails to explain how probability theory is connected with statistical inferences. Since the classical definition does not connect the symmetry of possible outcomes with observable frequency ratios, it is unsatisfactory from the everyday and scientific standpoints, for, from these standpoints, the fundamental feature of probability is its association with such ratios.

7·03 Von Mises' Frequency Conception of Probability

Another kind of explication of probability than that offered by the classical definition has been put forward within the past century and has found considerable and increasingly widespread favour. The basic idea of *frequency* definitions of probability is to relate this concept to observable frequency ratios.[1] If a coin is tossed repeatedly, one can record the observed outcomes of heads and tails as a finite sequence

---

[1] The first clear formulations of this kind of account of probability are due to: Ellis, R. L. (1817-59): "On the foundations of the theory of probabilities", *Trans. Camb. Phil. Soc*, 1849, **8**, 1-6; "Remarks on the fundamental proposition of the theory of probabilities", *Trans. Camb. Phil. Soc.*, 1856, **9**, 605-7; and to Venn, J (1834-1923): *The Logic of Chance* (London, 1866, third edition rewritten, 1888).

One such finite sequence might be, using "H" for a score of heads and "T" for a score of tails:

(7·031) H T T H H T H T H T T H T H H H H T T H T.

Allied to this finite sequence is the finite sequence (7·032) whose nth term indicates the number of heads scored in the first n tosses:

(7·032) $\frac{1}{1} \frac{1}{2} \frac{1}{3} \frac{2}{4} \frac{3}{5} \frac{3}{6} \frac{4}{7} \frac{4}{8} \frac{5}{9} \frac{5}{10} \frac{5}{11} \frac{6}{12} \frac{6}{13} \frac{7}{14} \frac{8}{15} \frac{9}{16} \frac{9}{17} \frac{9}{18} \frac{10}{19} \frac{10}{20}$.

The probability of scoring heads with this coin is the ratio about which the ratios, such as those in (7·032), obtained by conducting extended trials of tossing the coin concentrate. For example, a few of the empirical ratios of the number of heads to the number of trials might be 24/50, 51/100, 246/500, 485/1,000, and 4,895/10,000. These ratios fluctuate between 0·48 and 0·51; but one learns from experience that in the general case as here the relative amount of fluctuation decreases as the number of trials increases.

In more precise mathematical terms, the probability of an event E, *e.g.* a given coin's falling heads uppermost, is, according to the frequency definition, that real number which would be the limit, if an infinite sequence of trials were made, of the allied infinite sequence $\{m/n\}$ where n is the number of trials of which E is a possible outcome and m is the number of occurrences of E in the first n trials. (For present purposes an infinite sequence may be described simply as a sequence like (7·031) and (7·032) but going on forever: it has a nth term for each positive integer n. And an infinite sequence of real numbers $x_1, x_2, x_3, \ldots$ is said to have the real number L as its limit if and only if for every positive real number ϵ there is some positive integer i such that for every positive integer j, $| x_{i+j} - L | < \epsilon$.)

In von Mises' version[1] of the frequency definition of probability, which is the most developed one of the frequency type, there are two principal ingredients. (*a*) Suppose there is a set of objects each of which possess one or another exclusively of a number of characteristics and, by some method or another, members of this set are obtained in succession, one at a time, and their characteristics noted, at each step the set being preserved as it was originally. For simplicity, let us suppose that there are just the two characteristics H and T. Then if this process of obtaining members of the set were continued indefinitely, an infinite sequence such as

H T H T T H H T T H T H T H T T H H T T T H ...

[1] Mises, R. von (1883-1953): "Fundamentalsätze der Wahrscheinlichkeitsrechnung", *Math. Z.*, 1919, **4**, 1-97; "Grundlagen der Wahrscheinlichkeitsrechnung", *Math. Z.*, 1919, **5**, 52-99; *Wahrscheinlichkeit, Statistik und Wahrheit*, (Berlin, 1928, and later editions); *Wahrscheinlichkeitsrechnung* (Vienna, 1931); "On the foundations of probability and statistics", *Ann. Math. Stat.*, 1941, **12**, 191-205.

would be generated. (*b*) An infinite sequence of this sort is said to be an *Irregular Collective* if and only if it fulfils the following two conditions: (i) the relative frequencies of the H's (T's) in the first *n* terms have a limit as *n* tends to infinity; (ii) if infinitely many terms of the infinite sequence are picked out in accordance with any procedure (other than that which generates the infinite sequence), thus giving rise to an infinite subsequence, *e.g.* by picking out every fifth member or every *p*th member, *p* a prime number; then the relative frequencies of the H's (T's) in the first *n* terms of the infinite subsequence have a limit as *n* tends to infinity and this limit is the very same as the limit in the original infinite sequence. (Condition (*b*) (ii) was called by von Mises *the principle of the impossibility of gambling systems*, because if the condition were not fulfilled at say roulette, it would be possible for the gambler to make correct predictions by rule, since the absence of randomness would imply regularity in the occurrence of say black.) The limit of the relative frequencies of the H's in the first *n* terms of an Irregular Collective, as *n* tends to infinity, is, by definition, the probability of H in the set of objects which have either the characteristic H or the characteristic T. Similarly, for the more general case.

Some mathematicians have been severely critical of von Mises' account of probability. Their criticisms are typically those expressed as follows by Goodstein, who uses the terms "sequence" and "frequency" where we have used the terms "infinite sequence" and "relative frequency":

"Unless the sequence is given by a mathematical law (and often even when it is so given) it is impossible to prove that the frequency of an attribute really does tend to a definite limit. In particular, if we are concerned with a sequence of observations (of some phenomenon in nature, say) it is, from the nature of the sequence, *impossible* to prove or disprove the existence of limiting values. For, however many observations we have made, and however regular the frequency of the attribute may have been shown to be, there remains always an *unlimited* number of future observations to be made which may completely change the value of the frequency; *e.g.* if the observations are made on the throws of a coin we may find that after 10^3 throws the frequency of heads is 0·499; and after 10^6 throws it is 0·499999; but there is nothing to prevent 10^{20} throws giving a frequency 0·7. In fact, no matter how great a number of observations we have made this number is utterly insignificant in relation to the unlimited number of possible subsequent throws. . . .

"A similar situation arises when we consider the second condition . . . viz., that the limiting value of the frequency (supposing it exists) must be independent of a random place selection. The number of place selections is unlimited, and so, however many we have tested, there would remain an unlimited number untested. We could never, therefore, prove that the limiting value was unaltered by place selections."[1]

This criticism amounts to maintaining that (a) one can never conclusively establish that an infinite sequence of relative frequencies has a limit, and so one can never determine finally the probability value of an event; and that (b) one can never conclusively establish that any infinite sequence such as say

(7·033)   T H T H H T T T H T H T H T H H T T T T H H T H T H T H H T...

is completely random in the sense demanded by the principle of the impossibility of gambling systems.   In reply to (a) von Mises would maintain that there is adequate empirical support for the view that as the number of trials of tossing a coin, etc., increases, there is a clustering of the frequency ratios; accordingly, there are good grounds for supposing the existence of probability values as limits of infinite sequences of frequency ratios.   Although, therefore, *of course* empirical data cannot be shown decisively to yield such and such a probability value for the occurrence of an attribute, they do provide evidence for what this value is, and more cannot rationally be asked. In reply to (b) von Mises would say that certainly it cannot be conclusively shown that in an infinite sequence such as (7·033) the relative frequencies in all the infinite subsequences have the same limit as in (7·033) itself; but, again, there can be empirical grounds to support the hypothesis that this is so, namely, the fact of making certain successful tests for randomness in the infinite sequence.

The virtues of von Mises' approach have been recognised by those constructively concerned with the mathematical foundations of modern probability and statistical theory; for his approach, unlike the classical, serves to explain the applicability of that theory.   The conceptions of frequency ratios as converging to a limit and of the principle of the impossibility of gambling systems have been recognised as being of fundamental importance and (with some modifications) validity.   The question then arises as to what is mathematically the most appropriate form of theory to embody these conceptions.   And nearly all mathematicians have not adopted the form of theory built directly upon von Mises' ideas because such a formulation brings with it certain purely mathematical complications and difficulties that are avoidable in another form of theory which embodies his ideas rather more indirectly.   This preferred formulation is more general and abstract.[2]

The relationship between probability theory and empirical frequency ratios will be considered further in the next section.

---

[1] Goodstein: "Remarks on von Mises' definition of probability", *Mind*, 1940, **49**, 58-62.

[2] Cf. Doob, J. L. (1910-): "Probability as measure", *Ann. Math. Stat.*, 1941, **12**, 206-14; and von Mises and Doob: "Discussion of papers on probability theory", *Ann. Math. Stat.*, 1941, **12**, 215-17.

7·04 Probability, Statistics and Experience

The development of probability theory has been towards axiomatisation, as a means of bringing economy and, more important, deductive rigour and unity into this field of mathematical inquiry. But probability itself is not explicitly defined, any more than the logical concepts of say conjunction and negation are explicitly defined by the postulates of PCT. The axioms of probability theory implicitly define the concept of probability—enunciate its essential properties; just as the postulates (2·166), (2·167), and (2·168) implicitly define conjunction, and the postulates (2·169) and (2·1610) implicitly define negation. Again, although the propositional calculus interpretation of the system PCT is the intended one, other interpretations are theoretically possible; similarly, although a formal, axiomatised system of probability theory is primarily intended to be about probability, other interpretations are theoretically possible. Finally, the "ordinary meaning" of *probability* is irrelevant except in so far as this is represented by the axioms of the theory, just as the "ordinary meaning" of *implication* is irrelevant in PCT except in so far as this is represented by the postulates of the system.

The term "probability theory" is twofold in its meaning. On the one hand the term signifies the pure mathematics of probability, and on the other hand signifies the applied mathematics of probability—statistics. Three points may be made in this connection. Firstly, it may be useful to introduce the term "stochastics" for the pure mathematics of probability, in parallelism to "statistics". The word "stochastics" is derived from a Greek word which corresponds in meaning to the Latin word "conjectare" signifying to guess or estimate. The title of the first great treatise on the pure mathematics of probability was *Ars Conjectandi*.[2] Secondly, stochastics forms the basis of statistics, for the

[2] Bernoulli: *Ars Conjectandi*.

principal theorems about probabilities in general can be established in stochastics. But thirdly, these theorems are taken by statistics in such a way as to give the stochastical concept of probability an empirical sense and relevance, thus enabling the theorems to be applied in the real world and not studied merely as a segment of conceptual truth. The statistician supposes that the probability of an event is indicated by the observable relative frequency of its occurrence. It follows, incidentally, that the statistician is not concerned with the probability of those events for which no appropriate relative frequencies are obtainable, events such as that Bacon wrote *Hamlet*, that Fermat's Last Theorem is true, that space is Euclidean or that God exists. The statistician limits his considerations to random events, that is to say to events of some well-defined empirical kind, which occur or can be made to occur frequently, whose outcomes are various and such that the occurrence of the individual outcomes cannot be predicted with certainty. Cramér elucidates the nature of statistics and its relations to stochastics on the one hand and to experience on the other as follows:—

"In the most varied fields of practical and scientific activity, cases occur where certain experiments or observations may be repeated a large number of times under similar circumstances. On each occasion, our attention is then directed to a *result of the observation*, which is expressed by a certain number of characteristic features.

"In many cases, these characteristics directly take a quantitative form: at each observation something is counted or measured. In other cases, the characteristics are qualitative: we observe, *e.g.* the colour of a certain object, the occurrence or non-occurrence of some specified event in connection with each experiment, etc. In the latter case, it is always possible to express the characteristics in some numerical form, *e.g.* using "0", "1", "2", etc., according to some conventional system of notation. Whenever it is found convenient, we may thus always suppose that the result of each observation is expressed by a certain number of quantities. . . .

"In some cases we know the phenomenon under investigation sufficiently well to feel justified in making exact predictions with respect to the result of each individual observation. Thus if our experiments consist in observing, for every year, the number of eclipses of the sun visible from a certain observatory, we do not hesitate to predict, on the strength of astronomical calculations, the exact value of this number. . . .

"In the majority of cases, however, our knowledge is not precise enough to allow of exact predictions of the results of individual observations. . . . Even if the utmost care is taken to keep all relevant circumstances under control, the result may in such cases vary from one observation to another in an irregular way that eludes all our attempts at prediction. In such a case, we shall say that we are concerned with a sequence of *random experiments*.

"Any systematic record of the results of sequences of this kind will be said to constitute a *set of statistical data* relative to the phenomenon concerned. The chief object of statistical theory is to investigate the possibility of *drawing valid inferences from statistical data*, and to work out methods by which such inferences may be obtained. . . .

"We have seen that, in a sequence of random experiments, it is not possible to predict individual results. These are subject to irregular random fluctuations which cannot be submitted to exact calculation. However, as soon as we turn our attention from the individual experiments to the whole *sequence of experiments*, the situation changes completely, and an extremely important phenomenon appears: *In spite of the irregular behaviour of individual results, the average results of long sequences of random experiments show a striking regularity. . . .*

"Let us now repeat our experiment $\mathfrak{E}$ a large number of times, and observe each time whether the event E . . . takes place or not. If we find that, among the n first experiments, the event E has occurred exactly ν times, the ratio ν/n will be called the *frequency ratio* or simply the *frequency* of the event E in the sequence formed by the n first experiments.

"Now, if we observe the frequency ν/n of a fixed event E for *increasing values of n, we shall generally find that it shows a marked tendency to become more or less constant or large values of n.* . . .

"The experiments . . . strongly support the . . . conjecture that, *to any event E connected with a random experiment $\mathfrak{E}$, we should be able to ascribe a number P such that, in a long series of repetitions of $\mathfrak{E}$, the frequency of E would be approximately equal to P.*

"This is the typical form of *statistical regularity* which constitutes the empirical basis of statistical theory. . . .

"*In our mathematical theory, we shall accordingly introduce a definite number P, which will be called the probability of the event E with respect to the random experiment.*

"*Whenever we say that the probability of an event E with respect to an experiment $\mathfrak{E}$ is equal to P, the concrete meaning of this assertion will thus simply be the following:* In a long series of repetitions of $\mathfrak{E}$, it is practically certain that the frequency of E will be approximately equal to P. . . .

"The probability number P introduced in this way provides a conceptual counterpart of the empirical frequency ratios. It will be observed that, in order to define the probability P, both the type of random experiment $\mathfrak{E}$ and the event E must be specified. Usually we shall, however, regard the experiment as fixed, and we may then without ambiguity simply talk of the *probability of the event E.*"[1]

Two particular consequences of this clarification may be mentioned. The first is that, in order to ensure the applicability of the theory, the fundamental properties ascribed to P (we shall in fact use the non-italicised "P") must reflect properties of frequency ratios. For example, we must not postulate that the probability of the compound event E_1-or-E_2, where E_1 and E_2 are mutually exclusive possible outcomes of the random experiment $\mathfrak{E}$, is equal to the probability value of E_1 plus the probability value of E_2 unless, as is indeed the case, it corresponds to the empirical situation, namely, that in a long series of repetitions of $\mathfrak{E}$ the relative frequency of E_1-or-E_2 is equal to the sum of the relative frequencies of E_1 and E_2. The second consequence is that the statements within probability theory itself are not probability statements but probability statement schemata.

7·05 Axioms and Fundamental Theorems of Probability Theory

Consider the random experiment that consists in throwing a die once. This experiment can yield six and only six *atomic outcomes* (events): scoring 1, scoring 2, ..., scoring 6; it is assumed that the die will in fact fall to earth and will, when it does so fall, not balance on one of its edges or corners. But these atomic outcomes are not, in a sense, the only possible outcomes of the experiment, for a distinct possible outcome is, for example, that an even number is scored, and another possible outcome distinct from the atomic outcomes is that six is not scored. Such further outcomes as these are called *molecular outcomes*. They are, in the final analysis, built up out of atomic

[1] Cramér, H. (1893-): *Mathematical Methods of Statistics*, pp. 137-8, 141-8, 148-9 (Princeton, 1946).

outcomes. Thus, scoring an even number consists in scoring 2-or-scoring 4-or-scoring 6. It turns out to be practicable to treat events, outcomes, as sets; the various ways of building up molecular out of atomic outcomes have their analogues in Boolean Algebra and Set Theory. Alternations of events correspond to unions of sets; conjunctions, *i.e.* simultaneous or successive occurrences, of events correspond to intersections of sets; and the negation of an event, *i.e.* its failure to occur, corresponds to the complement of a set. In order to avoid higher mathematics, we shall restrict ourselves in what follows to the theory of probabilities associated with those random experiments which give rise to merely finitely many distinct atomic outcomes, and so to merely finitely many distinct outcomes altogether, atomic or molecular. And the treatment will be in terms of Boolean Algebra and Set Theory; hence the reader should revise Chapter Four before going further.

We shall use "S" as a metalinguistic variable to denote *s, t, w, e*, etc., and "X" as a metalinguistic variable to denote *x, y, z*, etc.

Let *1*, called the *sample space*, be a non-empty space (set) of "points" X, and let a be a non-empty family of sets S such that $S \subseteq 1$. The members of a will be called *random events* or simply *events*; the event $\emptyset$ that contains no point X will be called the *impossible event*. Let P or *probability* be a function whose domain is a and whose range is a subset of the set of all the real numbers. If the ordered pair (S, X) is a member of the function P, so that $P(S) = X$, then and only then we shall say that the *probability* (*value*) *of* S *is* X.

(7·051) *Axiom I:* a is a Boolean Algebra of sets.

(7·052) *Axiom II:* $P(1) = 1$.

(7·053) *Axiom III:* For each event *s*, $P(s) \geq 0$.

(7·054)   *Axiom IV:*   For all events s and t such that $s\_t = \emptyset$, $\mathrm{P}(s\_t) = \mathrm{P}(s) + \mathrm{P}(t)$.[1]

If s and t are disjoint, cf. end of **4·10**, then $s\_t = s + t$. Accordingly, (7·054) can be stated in the form:

(7·055) $\mathrm{P}(s + t) = \mathrm{P}(s) + \mathrm{P}(t)$, for all disjoint events s and t.

(7·056)   **The Probability Ordering Theorem:**   For all events s and t, if $s \subseteq t$, then $\mathrm{P}(s) \leq \mathrm{P}(t)$.

Demonstration: If $s = t$, then $\mathrm{P}(s) = \mathrm{P}(t)$ by the definition of a function. If $s \subset t$, then for some non-empty set w such that $s\_w = \emptyset$, it follows that $t = s + w$. Therefore, $\mathrm{P}(t) = \mathrm{P}(s + w)$. But, by (7·055),

(7·057) $\mathrm{P}(s + w) = \mathrm{P}(s) + \mathrm{P}(w)$,

and so

(7·058) $\mathrm{P}(t) = \mathrm{P}(s) + \mathrm{P}(w)$.

By (7·053), $\mathrm{P}(w) \geq 0$. Hence $\mathrm{P}(s) \leq \mathrm{P}(t)$.

(7·059)   **The Probability Bounds Theorem:**   For each event s, $0 \leq \mathrm{P}(s) \leq 1$.

Demonstration: The left-hand member of the inequalities $0 \leq \mathrm{P}(s) \leq 1$ is given directly by (7·053). For each event s, $s \subseteq 1$. By (7·056), $\mathrm{P}(s) \leq \mathrm{P}(1)$. But, by (7·052), $\mathrm{P}(1) = 1$. Hence, $\mathrm{P}(s) \leq 1$.

(7·0510)   **The Impossibility Event Theorem:** $\mathrm{P}(\emptyset) = 0$.

Demonstration: For each event s, $s\_\emptyset = \emptyset$. Therefore, by (7·055),

(7·0511) $\mathrm{P}(s + \emptyset) = \mathrm{P}(s) + \mathrm{P}(\emptyset)$.

But $s + \emptyset = s$; so $\mathrm{P}(s + \emptyset) = \mathrm{P}(s)$.   Hence

(7·0512) $\mathrm{P}(s) + \mathrm{P}(\emptyset) = \mathrm{P}(s)$,

[1] The current axiomatic approach, using Boolean Algebra and Set Theory, is due to Kolmogorov, A. N. (1903-): "Grundbegriffe der Wahrscheinlichkeitsrechnung", *Erg. Math.*, 1933, **2**, No. 3.

and accordingly $P(\emptyset) = 0$, since (7·0512) is transformable into

(7·0513) $P(\emptyset) = P(s) - P(s) = 0$.

(7·0514) **The Complementary Event Theorem:** For each event s, $P(\varsigma s) = 1 - P(s)$.

Demonstration: $s_\smallsmile \varsigma s = \emptyset$ and $s + \varsigma s = 1$. By (7·052), $P(1) = 1$; therefore

(7·0515) $P(s + \varsigma s) = 1$.

By (7·055),

(7·0516) $P(s + \varsigma s) = P(s) + P(\varsigma s)$.

Hence, by (7·0515) and (7·0516),

(7·0517) $P(s) + P(\varsigma s) = 1$,

and so

(7·0518) $P(\varsigma s) = 1 - P(s)$.

It is convenient to introduce the symbol "$\cup$" for the symmetric difference of an indexed family of sets; $\cup$ is to $+$ precisely as $\cup$ is to $\smallsmile$. *E.g.*,

(7·0519) $\underset{i \in \mathbf{N}_4}{\cup} \, N_i = ((N_1 + N_2) + N_3) + N_4$

(7·0520) $= (\{2\} + \{1, 2, 3\}) + \{1, 2, 3, 4\}$

(7·0521) $= \{1, 3\} + \{1, 2, 3, 4\}$

(7·0522) $= \{2, 4\}$.

It is also convenient to use "Π" to symbolise the general product operator, just as "Σ" symbolises the general summation operator. Thus,

(7·0523) $\underset{i \in \mathbf{N}_5}{\Pi} \, i = 1.2.3.4.5$

and

(7·0524) $\underset{i \in \mathbf{N}_3}{\Pi} \, 3^i = 3.3^2.3^3$.

(7·0525) **The Addition of Probabilities Theorem:** If the n events s_i are pairwise disjoint, $(n \in \mathbf{N})$, then

$$\mathbf{P}\left(\bigcup_{i \in \mathbf{N}_n} s_i\right) = \sum_{i \in \mathbf{N}_n} \mathbf{P}(s_i).$$

Demonstration: We proceed by mathematical induction (cf. E6·5·8). (i) If $n = 1$ (7·0525) is trivial. If the 2 events s_i are pairwise disjoint, then, by (7·054),

$$(7·0526) \quad \mathbf{P}\left(\bigcup_{i \in \mathbf{N}_2} s_i\right) = \sum_{i \in \mathbf{N}_2} \mathbf{P}(s_i).$$

(ii) Suppose that, the k events s_i being pairwise disjoint $(i = 1, 2, \ldots, k)$,

$$(7·0527) \quad \mathbf{P}\left(\bigcup_{i \in \mathbf{N}_k} s_i\right) = \sum_{i \in \mathbf{N}_k} \mathbf{P}(s_i).$$

Now consider the event s_{k+1} such that all the $k + 1$ events s_i $(i = 1, 2, \ldots, k + 1)$ are pairwise disjoint. By (7·054),

$$(7·0528) \quad \mathbf{P}\left(\left(\bigcup_{i \in \mathbf{N}_k} s_i\right) + s_{k+1}\right) = \mathbf{P}\left(\bigcup_{i \in \mathbf{N}_k} s_i\right) + \mathbf{P}(s_{k+1})$$

$$(7·0529) \qquad\qquad = \sum_{i \in \mathbf{N}_k} \mathbf{P}(s_i) + \mathbf{P}(s_{k+1})$$

$$(7·0530) \qquad\qquad = \sum_{i \in \mathbf{N}_{k+1}} \mathbf{P}(s_i).$$

From (7·0526) and the derivability of (7·0530) from (7·0527), (7·0525) follows by the Principle of Mathematical Induction.

(7·0531) **The Alternative Events Theorem:** For all events s and t, $\mathbf{P}(s\_t) = \mathbf{P}(s) + \mathbf{P}(t) - \mathbf{P}(s\_t)$.

Demonstration: If s and t are mutually exclusive events, *i.e.* if $s\_t = \emptyset$, then $\mathbf{P}(s\_t) = 0$ and certainly, by (7·054),

$$(7·0532) \quad \mathbf{P}(s\_t) = \mathbf{P}(s) + \mathbf{P}(t) - \mathbf{P}(s\_t).$$

If s and t are not mutually exclusive events, then the sum $\mathbf{P}(s) + \mathbf{P}(t)$ has included, twice, the probabilities connected with the points of 1 that are common to s and t, once in connection with $\mathbf{P}(s)$ and once again in connection with $P(t)$. Therefore the proper probability value of s_t is given by the sum $P(s) + P(t)$ minus $P(s\_t)$. (The general form of this theorem is set as an exercise below.)

Examples.—We shall assume in these illustrations and applications of the theory, and in working the exercises the student should make the same assumption, that each possible atomic outcome of a random experiment has the same probability value; so that if there are n atomic outcomes s_i, $P(s_i) = 1/n$.

(I) What is the probability of not scoring 6 with a single throw of a die? There are 6 possible atomic outcomes $\{\bar{\imath}\}$, $(i = 1, 2, 3, \ldots, 6)$, where "$\{\bar{\imath}\}$" denotes the event that the side of the die marked with i dots turns out to be face uppermost. Each atomic possibility is assigned the probability of $1/6$; in particular, then, $P(\{\bar{6}\}) = 1/6$. By virtue of Theorem (7·0514), the probability of not scoring 6, *i.e.* $P(\varsigma\{\bar{6}\})$, is equal to $1 - P(\{\bar{6}\})$, $= 5/6$. The same result can be obtained by using Theorem (7·0525), since the event of not scoring 6 is the same as the event of scoring 1-or-scoring 2-or ... -or-scoring 5, these alternatives being mutually exclusive; therefore

$$(7\cdot0533) \quad P(\underset{i \in N_5}{\cup} \{\bar{\imath}\}) = \underset{i \in N_5}{\Sigma} P(\{\bar{\imath}\}) = 5/6,$$

because, for each i, $P(\{\bar{\imath}\}) = 1/6$.

(II) What is the probability of scoring more than 4 with a single throw of a die? We want to know the probability of the molecular event $\{\bar{5}\}\_\{\bar{6}\}$. Since $\{\bar{5}\}$ and $\{\bar{6}\}$ are mutually exclusive, Axiom (7·054) applies:

$(7\cdot0534)$
$$P(\{\bar{5}\}\_\{\bar{6}\}) = P(\{\bar{5}\}) + P(\{\bar{6}\}) = 1/6 + 1/6 = 2/6 = 1/3.$$

(III) What is the probability of drawing a heart or a royal card (knave, queen or king) from an ordinary, duly shuffled pack of cards? There are 52 possible atomic events, to each of which is assigned the probability of $1/52$. There are 13 hearts and 12 royal cards, 3 of the latter being also among the former. Applying Theorem $(7 \cdot 0531)$, the probability required is equal to $13/52 + 12/52 - 3/52$, $= 22/52$, $= 11/26$.

EXERCISES

Demonstrate E7·5·1 to E7·5·7.

E7·5·1. $\underset{i \in \mathbf{N}_4}{\cup} s_i = s_1 + (s_2 \smallfrown \varsigma s_1) + (s_3 \smallfrown \varsigma (s_1 \smallfrown s_2)) + (s_4 \smallfrown \varsigma (s_1 \smallfrown s_2 \smallfrown s_3))$.

E7·5·2. More generally, $\underset{i \in \mathbf{N}_n}{\cup} s_i = \underset{i \in \mathbf{N}_n}{\cup} (s_i \smallfrown \varsigma \underset{j \in \mathbf{N}_{i-1}}{\cup} s_j)$.

E7·5·3. $\mathbf{P} (\underset{i \in \mathbf{N}_n}{\cup} s_i) = \underset{i \in \mathbf{N}_n}{\Sigma} \mathbf{P} (s_i \smallfrown \varsigma \underset{j \in \mathbf{N}_{i-1}}{\cup} s_j)$.

E7·5·4. $\mathbf{P} (\underset{i \in \mathbf{N}_n}{\cup} s_i) \leq \underset{i \in \mathbf{N}_n}{\Sigma} \mathbf{P} (s_i)$.

E7·5·5. $\mathbf{P} (\underset{i \in \mathbf{N}_3}{\cup} s_i) = \underset{i \in \mathbf{N}_3}{\Sigma} \mathbf{P} (s_i) - \Sigma \mathbf{P} (s_i \smallfrown s_j) + \mathbf{P} (s_1 \smallfrown s_2 \smallfrown s_3)$, the second summation being taken over all the possible distinct subscripts.

E7·5·6. More generally, $\mathbf{P} (\underset{i \in \mathbf{N}_n}{\cup} s_i) = \underset{i \in \mathbf{N}_n}{\Sigma} \mathbf{P} (s_i) - \Sigma \mathbf{P} (s_{i1} \smallfrown s_{i2}) +$
$\Sigma \mathbf{P} (s_{i1} \smallfrown s_{i2} \smallfrown s_{i3}) - + \ldots \mp \mathbf{P} (s_1 \smallfrown s_2 \smallfrown \ldots \smallfrown s_n)$,
the second and later summations being taken over all the possible distinct subscripts; and the final sign being— if n is an even number and being $+$ if n is an odd number.

E7·5·7. The axioms $(7 \cdot 051)$ to $(7 \cdot 054)$ are mutually consistent.

7·06 Combinatory Analysis

We shall next present the simplest elements of that branch of arithmetic-cum-algebra known as Combinatory Analysis[1] or, more popularly, as the theory of combinations and permutations. In the past the importance of Combinatory Analysis to probability theory has been very much overrated; for it has few important applications outside finite sample spaces, whereas the main emphasis in

[1] Founded by Pascal: Letters to Fermat, P. (1601-65) dated July 29th, 1654 and 24th August, 1654; *Traité du Triangle Arithmétique* (Paris, 1665).

the general theory of probability is on infinite sample spaces. In spite of this cautionary remark, it must be affirmed that Combinatory Analysis is definitely useful in dealing with the elements of probability theory, both stochastical and statistical.

(7·061) **The Size 2 Cartesian Product Set Theorem:** If a finite set s has m members x_i ($i = 1, 2, 3, \ldots, m$) and a finite set t has n members y_j ($j = 1, 2, 3, \ldots, n$), then the set e consisting of all the possible ordered pairs (x_i, y_j) has mn members.

Demonstration: A *Cartesian product set of size* 2, the "factors" being s and t, is the set, denoted by "$s \times t$", which consists of all the possible ordered pairs (x, y) where $x \in s$ and $y \in t$; for instance, $\{1, 3, 5\} \times \{2, 3\}$ $= \{\{1, 2\}, \{1, 3\}, \{3, 2\}, \{3, 3\}, \{5, 2\}, \{5, 3\}\}$; cf. **4·08**. Similarly, and more generally, the product set $s_1 \times s_2 \times \ldots \times s_n$ of size n, which we shall denote by "$\bigwedge_{i \in \mathbf{N}_n} s_i$", is the set which consists of all the possible ordered n-tuples ($x_1, x_2, \ldots, x_n$) where $x_i \in s_i$.) Construct a table, listing vertically the m members of s and listing horizontally, beginning north-east of the vertical list, the n members of t. Now fill in the body of the table as though it were a multiplication table in the following way: construct all the ordered pairs (x_1, y_1), (x_2, y_1), $\ldots$, (x_m, y_1) for the first column; construct all the ordered pairs (x_1, y_2), (x_2, y_2), $\ldots$, (x_m, y_2) for the second column; $\ldots$; construct all the ordered pairs (x_1, y_n), (x_2, y_n), $\ldots$, (x_m, y_n) for the nth column. Each column contains m ordered pairs and there are n columns; hence there are $n \times m$, $= mn$, ordered pairs altogether. Thus e has mn members.

(7·062) **The Size n Product Set Theorem:** If each finite set s_i has m_i members ($i = 1, 2, \ldots, n$), then the set $\bigwedge_{i \in \mathbf{N}_n} s_i$ has $\Pi_{i \in \mathbf{N}_n} m_i$ members.

Demonstration: We proceed by mathematical induction. (i) If $n = 1$, (7·062) is trivially valid; and if $n = 2$, (7·062) reduces to the already established (7·061). (ii) Suppose that the assertion of (7·062) holds for the jth case so that the set $\bigwedge_{i \in \mathbf{N}_j} s_i$ has $\prod_{i \in \mathbf{N}_j} m_i$ members. Now the set $\bigwedge_{i \in \mathbf{N}_{j+1}} s_i$ has $\prod_{i \in \mathbf{N}_{j+1}} m_i$ members, for, as in the demonstration of Theorem (7·061), $(j + 1)$-tuples can be formed by listing vertically the members of $\bigwedge_{i \in \mathbf{N}_j} s_i$, listing horizontally the members of s_{j+1}, and filling in the body of the table. Thus there will be $\prod_{i \in \mathbf{N}_j} m_i$ ordered pairs in each column and there will be m_{j+1} columns. Therefore the total number of ordered pairs in the table, and so the total number of members of $\bigwedge_{i \in \mathbf{N}_{j+1}} s_i$, is $\prod_{i \in \mathbf{N}_{j+1}} m_i$. (iii) From (i) and (ii), Theorem (7·062) follows by the Principle of Mathematical Induction.

There are two ways of making ordered selections of members from a set or "population". In the first way, which is called *ordered sampling with replacement*, each item of the selection is made from the whole population; the population from which the selections are made remains constant throughout the process of sampling. In the second way, which is called *ordered sampling without replacement*, once a member of the population has been selected, it is not allowed to be reselected; the population does not remain constant, for if a member x_i of the population is selected at the ith step in drawing an ordered sample, it is not available to be drawn at any of the $(i + j)$th steps. For example, suppose the population is the set of integers $\{1, 2, 3, 4\}$; then possible ordered samples of size 3 if (and only if) the sampling is with replacement are $\{3, 2, 3\}$ and $\{1, 1, 1\}$, and possible ordered samples of size 3 if the sampling is without replacement are $\{4, 2, 3\}$ and

{3, 1, 4}, these two ordered samples being possible also, of course, if the sampling is with replacement. Clearly, if and only if sampling is with replacement can the size of an ordered sample be greater than that of the population.

(7·063) **The Number of Ordered Samples Theorem:** The number of different ordered samples of size m from a population of size n is n^m if the sampling is with replacement and is $\prod_{i \in \mathbf{N}_{m-1}^{\geq}} (n - i)$ if the sampling is without replacement.

Demonstration: The first part of this theorem follows directly from Theorem (7·062); this is seen by setting all the s_i to be equal to one another, so that all the m_i become equal to one another, and by substituting "m" for "n". Considering next the case of sampling without replacement, there are n ways of filling the first place of the ordered m-tuple and n-1 ways of filling the second place; hence, by Theorem (7·061), there are $n (n - 1)$ ways of filling the first two places. There are then $n - 2$ ways of filling the third place, so by applying Theorem (7·061) again, there are $n (n - 1) (n - 2)$ ways of filling the first three places. And so on, until Theorem (7·061) has been applied $m - 1$ times altogether.

We next introduce two abbreviative notations. First, for all n of $\mathbf{N}$,

(7·064) $(n)_m \leftrightarrow n (n - 1) (n - 2) \ldots (n - m + 1)$.

For instance, "$(10)_3$" denotes $10 (10 - 1) (10 - 2)$, $= 720$. Second, for all n of $\mathbf{N}$,

(7·065) $n! \leftrightarrow n (n - 1) (n - 2) \ldots 2.1 = \prod_{i \in \mathbf{N}_n} i$; $0! \leftrightarrow 1$.

For instance, "10!" denotes 10.9.8.7.6.5.4.3.2.1, $= 3,628,800$. ("!" is often read as "factorial".)

Example I.—Four of the decimal digits 0, 1, 2, ..., 9 are chosen at random, the selection being with replacement;

what is the probability that they are all different? By the second part of Theorem (7·063), there are $(10)_4$ different ordered 4-tuples in which no terms are repeated, and by the first part of that theorem there are altogether 10^4 different ordered 4-tuples, the selection being with replacement. Therefore the probability required is $(10)_4/10^4$, $= 0·5040$.

Example II.—A house is divided into 10 flats and in the hall on the ground floor is a single telephone for all the tenants; if one evening the telephone rings 8 times, what is the probability that at least one of the tenants receives an incoming call more than once? The easiest way to deal with this problem is to find the probability that no tenant receives more than one call and then, in accordance with the Complementary Event Theorem, to find the difference between 1 and this probability. The probability that no tenant receives more than one call is the same as the probability that all the calls are for different tenants. Applying Theorem (7·063), we have that this probability is $(10)_8/10^8$, $= 0·01814000$. Hence the probability that at least one tenant would receive more than one call is 0·98186000.

We shall say that two ordered samples without replacement of size k are *essentially different* if and only if there is at least one member of the population which occurs as a term in one of the ordered samples but not in the other. For example, if the population is $\{1, 2, 3, 4\}$, then the ordered samples without replacement $(1, 3)$ and $(3, 1)$ are not essentially different, whereas $(1, 3)$ and $(1, 4)$ are essentially different, as are $(1, 3)$ and $(2, 4)$ also.

(7·066) **The Non-Essentially Different Samples Theorem:** In sampling from a population of n members, each subpopulation of m members can give rise to $m!$ ordered samples of size m that are not essentially different.

Demonstration: By Theorem (7·063), there are $(m)_m$ ordered samples of size m from the sub-population $\{x_1, x_2, \ldots, x_m\}$; but none of these can be essentially different. Since $(m)_m = m!$, (7·066) is established.

(7·067) **The Essentially Different Samples Theorem:** If the sampling is without replacement, then the number of essentially different ordered samples of size m from a population of size n is $(n)_m/m!$.

Demonstration: By Theorem (7·063), if the sampling is without replacement, then there are $(n)_m$ different ordered samples of size m from a population of n members. But, by Theorem (7·066), each of these possible samples is a member of a set of m possible samples that are not essentially different. Therefore, the number of ordered samples of size m that are essentially different is $(n)_m/m!$.

In the usual terminology, essentially different ordered samples of m from n objects are called *combinations*, and non-essentially different ones are called *permutations*. *E.g.* (1, 3, 2) and (3, 2, 1) are different permutations of size 3 from the set $\{1, 2, 3, 4\}$ of size 4, and (1, 3, 4) and (3, 2, 1) are different combinations of size 3 from the set $\{1, 2, 3, 4\}$ of size 4. The number of different combinations of size m from a set of size n is usually denoted by "$\binom{n}{m}$"; less frequently by "$_nC_m$". By Theorem (7·065), $\binom{n}{m} = (n)_m/m!$.[1] $\binom{n}{m}$ is the number of ways of choosing, regardless of order, m members from a set of n members. Thus, the number of combinations of size 3 from the set $\{1, 2, 3, 4, 5\}$ of size 5 is $(5)_3/3!$, $= 60/6$, $= 10$; these combinations are (1, 2, 3), (1, 2, 4), (1, 2, 5), (1, 3, 4),

---

[1] For historical details on combinational symbolism, see Cajori, F. (1859-1930): *History of Mathematical Notations*, I, II (Chicago, 1929); especially II, § 439 *et seq.*

(1, 3, 5), (1, 4, 5), (2, 3, 4), (2, 3, 5), (2, 4, 5), (3, 4, 5); but there are 60 permutations of size 3 from that set of size 5: (1, 2, 3), (1, 3, 2), (2, 1, 3), (2, 3, 1), (3, 1, 2), (3, 2, 1), etc., 3!, = 6, permutations for each of the 10 combinations.

(7·068) **The Hypergeometric Distribution Theorem:** If a population contains n members of which i have the property c and j have the property d, c and d being mutually exclusive (like red and black) and $i + j$ equalling n, then if m members of the population are chosen without replacement and without regarding order, the probability that exactly k of the m chosen members $(0 \leq k \leq m$ and $0 \leq k \leq i)$ have the property c is $\binom{i}{k}\binom{j}{m-k}\bigg/\binom{n}{m}$.

Demonstration: The total number of ways of choosing m objects out of n, regardless of order and without replacement, is $\binom{n}{m}$. There are $\binom{i}{k}$ ways of choosing k objects having the property c, and there are $\binom{j}{m-k}$ ways of choosing the remaining $m - k$ objects (having the property d); so, by Theorem (7·061), there are $\binom{i}{k}\binom{j}{m-k}$ ways of choosing exactly k members of the population with the property c. Therefore the probability required is $\binom{i}{k}\binom{j}{m-k}\bigg/\binom{n}{m}$; this latter is called the *hypergeometric distribution*.

EXERCISES

Demonstrate E7·6·8 to E7·6·13.

E7·6·8. $\binom{n}{m} = n!/m!\,(n - m)!$.

E7·6·9. $\binom{n}{m} = \binom{n}{m - n}$.

E7·6·10. $\dbinom{n}{m-1} + \dbinom{n}{m} = \dbinom{n+1}{m}$.

E7·6·11. **Binomial Theorem:** $(x+y)^n = \sum\limits_{m\in\mathbf{N}_n^{\geq}} \dbinom{n}{m} x^{n-m}y^m$, for positive integers x, y, and $n \in \mathbf{N}_n^{\geq}$.[1]

E7·6·12. $\dbinom{n}{m}$ is the number of ways in which a set of n objects can be divided into 2 disjoint sets containing m and $n-m$ objects.

E7·6·13. The number of ways of dividing a set of n objects into m pairwise disjoint sets containing $n_1, n_2, \ldots, n_m$ objects respectively, $\sum\limits_{i\in\mathbf{N}_m} n_i = n$, is $n! / \prod\limits_{i\in\mathbf{N}_m} (n_i!)$.

E7·6·14. What is the number of distinct Boolean polynomials in n variables?

E7·6·15. How many functions can have $\{p, q\}$ as domain and $\{0, 1\}$ as range? List them.

E7·6·16. How many functions can have $\{x_1, x_2, \ldots, x_m\}$ as domain and $\{y_1, y_2, \ldots, y_n\}$ as range, $m \geq n$?

E7·6·17. What is the number of possible ordered samples of size n from a population of size 2 if the sampling is with replacement? What is the bearing of this on the construction of truth tables?

E7·6·18. What is the probability of scoring n sixes in n successive throws of a die?

E7·6·19. If 5 cards are picked at random from an ordinary pack, what is the probability that there are exactly 2 aces among the 5 chosen?

E7·6·20. If 13 cards are picked at random from an ordinary pack what is the probability that they contain 7 hearts, 5 diamonds, 1 club, and no spades?

E7·6·21. If 13 cards are picked at random from an ordinary pack, what is the probability that they contain 2 aces, 2 queens, 2 kings, and no other picture cards or aces?

---

[1] First published demonstration by Bernoulli: *Ars Conjectandi*, p. 89. The theorem was first enunciated by Briggs, H., (1561-1630): *Arithmetica Logarithmica* (London, 1620); and by Newton: letters to Oldenburg of 13th June and 24th October, 1676. The numbers $\dbinom{n}{m}$ are often called the *binomial coefficients*.

E7·6·22. What is the probability of choosing at random a particular one of the possible ordered samples of size m from a population of size n when the sampling is (i) with replacement and (ii) without replacement? Show that, when n is large, these two probabilities are practically the same.

7·07 Conditional Probability

By way of definition,

(7·071) $P(s/t) \leftrightarrow P(s\_t)/P(t)$, $P(t) \neq 0$.[1]

"s/t" may be read: "s given t" or "s occurs on condition that t occurs". (7·071) is intended as the definition of what is called *conditional probability*. The following problem illustrates this idea. What is the probability, if a family contains two children and we know that one child is a boy, that the other child is also a boy? Let t be the event of whose occurrence we know and let s be the event, of whose occurrence we do not know, that the other child is also a boy. Since there are two children in the family, we can say that there are 4 possible child-pairs: by Theorem (7·063), there are 2^2 possible ordered samples of size 2 with replacements from the population {boy, girl}, these being (boy, boy), (boy, girl), (girl, boy) (girl, girl). Since three out of these four possible samples include a boy, it follows, by Theorem (7·0525) and our standard assumption that all the atomic outcomes are equiprobable, that $P(t) = 3/4$; and, since just one out of the four possible samples includes two boys, it follows that $P(s\_t) = 1/4$. Therefore

$$P(s/t) = (1/4)/(3/4) = 1/3.$$

(7·072)   **The Joint Events Theorem:**

$$P\left(\bigcap_{i \in \mathbf{N}_n} s_i\right) = \prod_{i \in \mathbf{N}_n} P\left(s_i / \bigcap_{j \in \mathbf{N}_{i-1}} s_j\right), P(s_j) \neq 0.$$

[1] Laplace: *Théorié Analytique*; *Oeuvres Completes VII*, p. xiii. Laplace expresses the principle of conditional probability in the form: $P(s\_t) = P(s) P(t/s)$; he uses ordinary, non-mathematical language. A novel and interesting approach to mathematical probability, taking conditional probability as fundamental, is given by Koopman, B. O. (1900-): "The axioms and algebra of intuitive probability", *Ann. of Math.*, 1940 (2), **41**, 269-92; and "Intuitive probabilities and sequences", *Ann. of Math.* 1941 (2), **42**, 169-87.

Demonstration: We proceed by mathematical induction. (i) If $n = 1$, (7·072) is trivially valid; and if $n = 2$, (7·072) reduces to the definition (7·071). (ii) Suppose that

$$(7·073) \quad P\left(\bigcap_{i \in \mathbf{N}_m} s_i\right) = \prod_{i \in \mathbf{N}_m} P\left(s_i / \bigcap_{j \in \mathbf{N}_{i-1}} s_j\right).$$

Now

$$(7·074) \quad P\left(\bigcap_{i \in \mathbf{N}_{m+1}} s_i\right) = P\left(\bigcap_{i \in \mathbf{N}_m} s_i \_ s_{m+1}\right).$$

From this and by (i) for $n = 2$, it follows that

$$(7·075) \quad P\left(\bigcap_{i \in \mathbf{N}_{m+1}} s_i\right) = P\left(\bigcap_{i \in \mathbf{N}_m} s_i\right) P\left(s_{m+1} / \bigcap_{i \in \mathbf{N}_m} s_i\right).$$

Hence, by (7·073),

$$(7·076) \quad P\left(\bigcap_{i \in \mathbf{N}_{m+1}} s_i\right) = \left[\prod_{i \in \mathbf{N}_m} P\left(s_i / \bigcap_{j \in \mathbf{N}_{i-1}} s_j\right)\right]\left[P\left(s_{m+1} / \bigcap_{i \in \mathbf{N}_m} s_i\right)\right]$$
$$= \prod_{i \in \mathbf{N}_{m+1}} P\left(s_i / \bigcap_{j \in \mathbf{N}_m} s_j\right).$$

Hence the supposition that (7·072) holds for the mth case implies that it holds also for the $(m + 1)$st case. (iii) By the Principle of Mathematical Induction applied to (i) and (ii), (7·072) may be asserted.

By definition, s and t are said to be *independent* if and only if $P(s\_t) = P(s) P(t)$. Using "ind" as short for "is independent of", the definition is: for all s and t,

$$(7·077) \quad (s \text{ ind } t) \leftrightarrow (P(s\_t) = P(s) P(t)), \quad P(s) \neq 0,$$
$$P(t) \neq 0.$$

(7·078) **The Mutual Independence Theorems:** If s ind t, then t ind s.

Demonstration: If s ind t, then, by definition, $P(s\_t) = P(s) P(t)$. But $t\_s = s\_t$, and so $P(t\_s) = P(s\_t)$. Hence $P(t\_s) = P(s) P(t) = P(t) P(s)$. Therefore t ind s.

(7·079) **Conditional Probability for Independent Events Theorem:** If s ind t, then $P(s/t) = P(s)$.

Demonstration: If s ind t, then, by definition, $P(s\_t)$ $= P(s) P(t)$. Now by (7·071), $P(s/t) = P(s\_t)/P(t)$. Therefore, $P(s/t) = P(s) P(t)/P(t)$, $= P(s)$.

(7·0710) **The Atomic Outcome Conditional Probability Theorem:** If all the s_i are pairwise disjoint ($i = 1, 2, \ldots, n$), $P(s_i) \neq 0$ and $\underset{i \in \mathbf{N}_n}{\cup} s_i = 1$, then $P(t) = \underset{i \in \mathbf{N}_n}{\Sigma} P(s_i) P(t/s_i)$.

Demonstration: Suppose that all the s_i are pairwise disjoint and that $\underset{i \in \mathbf{N}_n}{\cup} s_i = 1$. Since $t = 1\_t$,

(7·0711) $\quad P(t) = P(1\_t)$.

Therefore,

(7·0712) $\quad P(t) = P(\underset{i \in \mathbf{N}_n}{\cup} s_i\_t)$

(7·0713) $\qquad\qquad = P(\underset{i \in \mathbf{N}_n}{\cup} (s_i\_t))$

(7·0714) $\qquad\qquad = \underset{i \in \mathbf{N}_n}{\Sigma} P(s_i\_t)$

(7·0715) $\qquad\qquad = \underset{i \in \mathbf{N}_n}{\Sigma} P(s_i) P(t/s_i)$,

(7·0713) following from (7·0712) by the distributive law of intersection over symmetric difference; (7·0714) following from (7·0713) by the Addition of Probabilities Theorem (7·0525); and (7·0715) following from (7·0714) by the Joint Events Theorem (7·072).

(7·0716) **The Probability of Causes Theorem:**[1] If all the s_i are pairwise disjoint ($i \in \mathbf{N}_n$), $P(t) \neq 0$, $P(s_i) \neq 0$ and

---

[1] This theorem is often called *Bayes' Theorem*. It is in fact the analogue for finite sample spaces of a theorem due to Bayes which is applicable in continuous sample spaces (*i.e.* $1 \infty \mathbf{R}$). Bayes, T., (1702-61): "An essay towards solving a problem in the doctrine of chances", *Phil. Trans. Roy Soc.*, 1763, **53**, 370-418.

$$\bigcup_{i \in \mathbf{N}_n} s_i = 1, \text{ then } P(s_j/t) = \frac{P(s_j) P(t/s_j)}{\sum\limits_{i \in \mathbf{N}_n} P(s_i) P(t/s_i)}.$$

Demonstration: By Theorem (7·072),

(7·0717) $P(s_{j\_}t) = P(s_j) P(t/s_j).$

Since $t\_s_j = s_{j\_}t$,

(7·0718) $P(t\_s_j) = P(s_{j\_}t),$

and, again by (7·072),

(7·0719) $P(t\_s_j) = P(t) P(s_j/t).$

From these three equalities (7·0717) to (7·0719), it follows that

(7·0720) $P(s_j) P(t/s_j) = P(t) P(s_j/t).$

Hence,

(7·0721) $P(s_j/t) = \dfrac{P(s_j) P(t/s_j)}{P(t)}.$

But, by Theorem (7·0710),

(7·0722) $P(t) = \sum\limits_{i \in \mathbf{N}_n} P(s_i) P(t/s_i).$

Substituting this equality in (7·0721) gives finally

(7·0723) $P(s_j/t) = \dfrac{P(s_j) P(t/s_j)}{\sum\limits_{i \in \mathbf{N}_n} P(s_i) P(t/s_i)}.$

In Theorem (7·0716), t can be interpreted as an *effect* of one or another of the *causes* s_i; the theorem permits one to calculate the probability that any particular one, s_j, of the possible causes is the cause of t. However, in order to be able to apply the theorem in an actual situation, one has to know (i) that the event t whose cause is being investigated has only a finite number of possible causes, (ii) what these possible causes are, and (iii) how to determine the probability value of each of them. It does not often happen that these three epistemic conditions are fulfilled.

In order to illustrate Theorem (7·0716), we consider the following, somewhat artificial, problem. Suppose one is conducting a clinical trial in which three drugs a, b, and c are being tested for their value as therapeutic agents in the treatment of some disease X; and let it be supposed further that each of these drugs has certain side-effects, in particular that each can lead to a skin rash whose nature is the same in all three cases; and finally let it be supposed that if any subject taking part in the experiment is affected by this skin rash, it is attributable to the drug treatment. Now if a is used in 15 groups of patients such that 5 per cent. in each group are affected by the rash, b is used in 20 groups such that 4 per cent. in each group are affected by the rash, and c is used in 17 groups such that 6 per cent. are affected by the rash, then assuming that all the groups are otherwise uniform, if it is given that a particular subject Y in the trial has the rash, what is the probability that Y belongs to a group in which drug c is being used? Let t be the event that Y has the rash, and let s_1, s_2 and s_3 be the events that drug a, drug b and drug c respectively are used in the group to which Y belongs. On making suitable substitutions in the Probability of Causes Theorem we have that

$$(7·0724) \quad P(s_3/t) = \frac{P(s_3) P(t/s_3)}{P(s_1) P(t/s_1) + P(s_2) P(t/s_2) + P(s_3) \times P(t/s_3)}.$$

Now $P(s_3)$, that is the probability that a person taking part in the trial belongs to a group in which c is used, is 17/52, for there are 52 groups altogether of which 17 contain the subjects being treated with c. $P(t/s_3)$, that is the probability that Y has the rash if he is in a group whose members are being treated with c, is given to be 6 per cent. Obtaining similarly the numerical values for the other terms in (7·072), we have that

$$(7·0725) \quad P(s_3/t) = \frac{\frac{1}{5}\frac{7}{2} \times \frac{6}{100}}{\frac{1}{5}\frac{5}{2} \times \frac{5}{100} + \frac{2}{5}\frac{0}{2} \times \frac{4}{100} + \frac{1}{5}\frac{7}{2} \times \frac{6}{100}}$$

$$(7·0726) \qquad\qquad = \frac{1}{2}\frac{0}{5}\frac{2}{7} \doteq 0·4.^{[1]}$$

EXERCISES

E7·7·23. For the illustration of the Probability of Causes Theorem given in the text, evaluate $P(s_1/t)$ and $P(s_2/t)$.

E7·7·24. Show that the number of the members of the set of the different ordered samples that are not essentially different from (0, 0, 1, 1, 1) is 5!/2! 3!; show that the number of members of the set of the different ordered samples that are not essentially different from (0, 0, 1, 1, 2, 3, 3, 4, 4, 4) is 10!/2!2!1!2!3!.

E7·7·25. Show that the number of members of the set of the different ordered samples that are not essentially different from an ordered sample of size n in which there are n_1 occurrences of x_1, n_2 occurrences of x_2, ..., n_m occurrences of x_m, $\underset{i\in\mathbf{N}_m}{\Sigma} n_i = n$, is $n! / (\underset{i\in\mathbf{N}_m}{\Pi} n_i!)$. Cf. E7·6·13.

E7·7·26. What is the probability that a poker hand, *i.e.* a group of 5 cards that are successively drawn without replacement from an ordinary pack of cards, contains exactly 2 eights?

E7·7·27. What is the probability that a poker hand contains exactly 1 king and exactly 2 nines?

---

[1] Introductory treatments of the general theory of Mathematical Probability that presuppose little more mathematics than the Calculus, are given by: Cramér: *Elements of Probability Theory and some of its Applications* (New York, 1955); Feller, W. (1906-): *An Introduction to Probability Theory and its Applications*, second edition (New York, 1957); and Neyman, J. (1894-): *First Course in Probability and Statistics* (New York, 1950). The standard treatise on stochastics, in English, is Loève, M. (1907-): *Probability Theory: Foundations, Random Sequences* (New York, 1955).

There is no modern work on the history of probability theory; the most recent is Czuber, E. (1851-1925): *Die Entwicklung der Wahrscheinlichkeitstheorie und ihre Anwendungen* in *Jber. D.M.V.* (Leipzig), 1899, **7**, An older book, still useful for its detailed analyses of the writings considered, is Todhunter, I. (1820-84): *History of the Mathematical Theory of Probabilities, from the time of Pascal to that of Laplace* (Cambridge, 1865).

E7·7·28.   What is the probability that a poker hand is a flush, *i.e.* all the cards therein are of the same suit?

E7·7·29.   What is the probability that a poker hand is a royal straight, *i.e.* consists of a ten, knave, queen, king, and ace?

E7·7·30.   What is the probability that a poker hand is a royal straight flush, *i.e.* is both a royal straight and a flush?

E7·7·31.   Show that if the n events s_i are pairwise independent, then
$$\text{P}\left(\bigcap_{i\in\mathbf{N}_n} s_i\right) = \prod_{i\in\mathbf{N}_n} \text{P}\,(s_i).[1]$$

E7·7·32.   **De Méré's Problem:**[2] If in throwing a pair of dice there is a run without double-six being scored, how long would the run have to be before the probability of scoring a double-six is greater than $\frac{1}{2}$?

*E7·7·33.   In sampling with replacement from an ordinary pack of cards, drawing one card at a time, what is the probability that 8 drawings will be required until at least one card of each suit has appeared?

E7·7·34.   Suppose P is any function satisfying the axioms (7·051) to (7·054); such a function is often called a *finite probability distribution function*. Let $s_1, s_2, \ldots, s_n$ be all the possible atomic outcomes of an appropriate random experiment $\mathfrak{E}$. By definition, the *m*th *moment* of P is $\sum_{i\in\mathbf{N}_n} i^m\,\text{P}\,(s_i)$. The *m*th moment is usually denoted by "μ'_m". μ_1 is called the *expectation*, *expected value* or *mean* of P. (i) What is the connection between this sort of mean and that defined by (6·106)? (ii) What is the mean of the finite probability distribution function associated with the random experiment of (*a*) throwing a die once, (*b*) throwing a pair of dice once?

E7·7·35.   By definition, the *m*th *moment about the mean* of a finite probability distribution function P is $\sum_{i\in\mathbf{N}_n} (i - \mu'_1)^m\text{P}\,(s_i)$, the s_i being the possible atomic outcomes of the random experiment with which P is associated. The *m*th moment about the mean is usually denoted by "μ_m". μ_2 is called the *variance* of P, and $\sqrt{\mu_2}$ is called the *standard deviation* of P. (i) What is the connection between this sort of variance and standard deviation and that defined

---

[1] Laplace: *Théorié Analytique*; *Oeuvres Complétes VII*, p. xii.

[2] Méré, A. G. de (1610-85). Pascal, in his correspondence with Fermat (cf. *Oeuvres de Blaise Pascal*, III, edited by Brunschnicg and Gazier (Paris, 1908)), hints that this question was posed to him by de Méré.

in **6·11**?   (ii) What is the variance of the finite probability distribution function associated with the random experiment of (*a*) throwing a die once, (*b*) throwing three dice once?

E7·7·36. Demonstrate: $\sum\limits_{i \in \mathbf{N}_n} c x_i = c \sum\limits_{i \in \mathbf{N}_n} x_i$, where c is a constant.

E7·7·37. Demonstrate: $\sum\limits_{i \in \mathbf{N}_n} (f(i) \pm g(i)) = \sum\limits_{i \in \mathbf{N}_n} f(i) \pm \sum\limits_{i \in \mathbf{N}_n} g(i)$.

E7·7·38. Demonstrate: $\Pi\limits_{i \in \mathbf{N}_n} c x_i = c^n \Pi\limits_{i \in \mathbf{N}_n} x_i$, where c is a constant.

E7·7·39. Demonstrate: For the first moment μ_1 about the mean of any finite probability distribution function P, $\mu_1 = 0$.

E7·7·40. $\mu_2 = \mu_2' - (\mu_1')^2$.

E7·7·41. Suppose that $t\_w = \emptyset$ and that $t\_w = 1$, and, further, that if a sample of size n with replacement is drawn, all the members of the sample are pairwise independent.   Let t_i be the event that a subset of t is chosen for the ith place in the ordered sample ($i = 1, 2, \ldots, n$) and let $\mathrm{P}(t_i) = p$ for each i.   (i) Show that all the ςt_i are pairwise independent, and that $\mathrm{P}(\varsigma t_i) = 1 - p$ for each i. (ii) Show that the probability that j members of the sample are subsets of t is $\binom{n}{j} p^j (1 - p)^{n-j}$, $j = 0, 1, 2, \ldots, n$.

Thus if we denote the event that j members of the sample are subsets of t by "s_j", we can assert:

$$\mathrm{P}(s_j) = \binom{n}{j} p^j (1 - p)^{n-j}.$$

This kind of probability function P is called the *binomial probability distribution function*, for the terms of the expansion of the binomial $((1 - p) + p)^n$ are the values of this function.[1]   "s_j" is regarded as denoting the number of "successes", an event being a success if and only if it is a subset of t.   *E.g.* the probability of scoring 2 heads with a throw of 3 coins, scoring a head counting as a success, is: $\mathrm{P}(s_2) = \binom{3}{2} (1/2)^2 (1/2) = 3/8$; (iii) what is the mean of this P?   (Evaluate $\sum\limits_{j \in \mathbf{N}_3^{\geq}} j\mathrm{P}(s_j)$.

Notice that the s_j are pairwise disjoint, that $\cup\, s_j = 1$ but that they do not all have the same probability value).

---

[1] Introduced and investigated in detail by Bernoulli: *Ars Conjectandi*, p. 227 *et seq.*

*E7·7·42. Show that the mean of the binomial probability distribution function is np, and that the variance is $np(1-p)$.

E7·7·43. What is the probability of scoring 3 heads with a throw of 5 coins? What is the expected number of heads?

E7·7·44. What is the probability of scoring 5 sixes in 25 throws of a die? What is the probability of scoring just one double-six in 25 throws of a pair of dice?

E7·7·45. 40 per cent. of people suffering from disease X die within 6 months from the onset of its symptoms under the standard treatment T_1. 200 people who have just begun to suffer from X are chosen at random from among those suffering from X and are given a new treatment T_2. What is an upper bound to the probability that T_2 is no more effective than T_1 if, after 6 months, 160 out of the 200 subjects are still alive? (One wants to know the probability that a result as good as this *or even one that is better* might be due to chance; therefore to the probability of exactly 160 successes has to be added the sum of the probabilities of $160 + i$ successes, $i = 1, 2, \ldots, 40$.)

*E7·7·46. **Tchebyshev's Inequality:**[1] If the events s_i are mutually exclusive, then, for every real number $\epsilon > 0$,

$$P\left(\bigcup_{i \ge \epsilon}^{\max i} s_i \right) \le \frac{1}{\epsilon^2} \sum_{\min i}^{\max i} i^2 P(s_i),$$

where "min i" and "max i" denote the least, and the largest value of i.

*E7·7·47. **Bernoulli's Law of Large Numbers:**[2] Using E7·7·46, show that, in the case of the binomial distribution of E7·7·41, for every real number $\epsilon > 0$,

$$\mathop{\mathrm{L}}_{n \to \infty} P\left(\left| \frac{S_n}{n} - \frac{1}{n} \sum_{\min j}^{\max j} j\, P(s_j) \right| \ge \epsilon \right) = 0,$$

where "S_n" is the number of successes in the number n of trials.

[1] Tchebyshev, P. L. (1821-94): "Des valeurs moyennes", *Journal de Mathématiques Pures et Appliquées* (2), 1867, **12**, 177-84.
[2] Bernoulli: *Ars Conjectandi*, IV, § 5.

CHAPTER EIGHT

EXPERIMENTATION AND HYPOTHESIS

8·01 Introduction

We begin this chapter by giving some examples of what might be termed "laboratory experiments". These are the sort of experiments that are to be found almost everywhere in physics and chemistry and, though to a somewhat lesser extent, in the biological sciences too. They are experiments which issue in the kind of scientific laws which enable predictions to be made of individual cases. Such laws are unlike statistical hypotheses, for these allow only predictions relating to aggregates to be made. The role and sources of laboratory experimentation are then elucidated a little further; in this connection, dimensional analysis and measurement are briefly referred to once more.

Because statistical methods are playing an increasingly important part in the sciences, especially in the biological ones, some elementary explanation of statistics is given. After explaining the several ways in which the term "statistics" is employed, we proceed to describe the various main topics with which statistical theory is concerned, and which are reflected in the practical techniques employed by scientific research workers who use statistical methods. The general nature of sampling is next considered, this being fundamental to any research involving statistical hypotheses: hypotheses connected with random experiments. Having explained the nature of a frequency distribution, that (continuous) frequency distribution which plays a fundamental role in statistical theory and practice—the so-called normal distribution —is informally introduced. In the final section the notion of test of significance is described and examples are given in which it is applied.

8·02 Examples of Laboratory Experiments

One motive of an experiment is to test a hypothesis. A hypothesis is a proposal that something is the case; whose truth seems worth entertaining in the light of previous knowledge and experience; but which also needs specific empirical investigation to provide definite evidence for its rational acceptance or rejection. For an experiment, the scientist devises and brings about a set of circumstances in which the truth or falsity of the hypothesis to be tested can be decided by observation.

From the time of Aristotle to the first half of the seventeenth century it was a standard principle that "Nature abhors a vacuum", abhors to the extent of never allowing it. In the early 1640s Torricelli showed by experiment that if a tube, more than about two and a half feet long, is filled with mercury and the open end is placed in a vessel full, or partly full, of mercury, then the height of the mercury in the tube does not reach above about two and a half feet; in the topmost portion of the tube "an empty space was formed and nothing happened in the vessel where this space was formed".[1] Thus it appeared that a vacuum could be created. A few years later Torricelli's experiments and their results were reported to Pascal and he, with great care and ingenuity, devised and carried out a series of experiments of his own to test the hypothesis: a vacuum can be created. Having obtained empirical confirmation of the truth of this hypothesis, he wanted to explain it. He proposed, as in fact Torricelli had done before him, that the height of a liquid in a tube depends on the atmospheric pressure. "Everyone has taken as a maxim that nature abhors a vacuum; and almost everyone, especially in earlier times, has maintained that nature cannot allow one and that it would itself be destroyed rather than suffer one. Thus opinions have been divided; some have been content to say only that nature abhors a vacuum, while others have maintained that it cannot suffer one at all. I have laboured, in my *Abrégé du traité du vide*, at destroying this latter opinion and I think that the experiments I have related in that work are sufficient to show conclusively that nature can and does in fact suffer a space, as large as one likes, that is empty of all the sorts of matter that are within our

[1] Torricelli, E. (1608-47): Letter to Michelangelo Ricci of 11th June, 1644.

knowledge and which come within our senses.   My present
work is to examine the truth of the first opinion, and to
seek out experiments which might show whether the effects
that are attributed to the abhorrence of a vacuum ought
really to be attributed to that abhorrence, or whether they
should be attributed to the weight and pressure of the air ".[1]
Pascal remarks that if these effects are indeed to be attributed
to the weight and pressure of the air, then, since, as Torricelli
expresses it in his cited letter, "we live immersed at the
bottom of a sea of elemental air", the effects at ground-
level should be noticeably different from what they are at a
point well above ground-level, say at the top of a mountain.
Himself an invalid, Pascal therefore suggested to his brother-
in-law Florin Périer, who was living in Pascal's home town
of Clermont, in Auvergne, which is at the foot of the Puy-de-
Dôme mountain (about 4,800 ft high), that the height of
mercury in a tube should be measured at the foot of the
mountain and then again at the top of the mountain, the
immediate hypothesis to be tested being that the second
height of the mercury is less than the first height, as the
weight and pressure of the air at the top of the mountain
will be distinctly less than at the bottom.   Périer performed
this experiment, his account of it being as follows:

"The day of Saturday last, the 19th of this month, was very
unsettled; nevertheless since, at five o'clock in the morning, the
weather seemed fine enough and the summit of the Puy-de-Dôme was
visible, I decided to proceed there to make the experiment.   To this
end, I notified several persons of rank in this town of Clermont who
had asked to be advised of the day I was going; some of these are
priests and the rest laymen. . . . We were then, that day, all assembled
at eight in the morning in the garden of the Pères Minimes, which is
almost the lowest point of the town, where the experiment was begun
in the following way.
"Firstly, I poured into a vessel sixteen pounds of mercury which
I had purified during the previous three days; taking two glass tubes
of equal size, each four feet long, hermetically sealed at one end and

---

[1] Letter of Pascal to Florin Périer of the 15th November, 1647.

open at the other, I made with each of them the ordinary experiment of the vacuum in the same vessel. When I brought the two tubes together without lifting them out of the vessel, it was found that the mercury remaining in each of them was at the same level: in each of them it was twenty-six inches three lines and a half above the surface of the mercury in the vessel. I repeated this procedure twice, in the same place, with the same two tubes, with the same mercury and with the same vessel; it was always found that the mercury in the two tubes was at the same level and at the same height as on the first occasion.

"When this had been done, I left one of the two tubes in the vessel for continual observation. I marked on the glass the height of the mercury and, leaving the tube in its place, I requested Father Chastin, one of the monks of the house, a man as pious as he is capable, and who thinks very clearly on these matters, to take the trouble of observing it from time to time during the day so as to see whether there would be any alteration. With the other tube and a part of the same mercury I went, with all these gentlemen, to carry out the same observations at the top of the Puy-de-Dôme, at a height of about 500 toises above the Minimes. There it was found that there did not remain in the tube a height of more than twenty-three inches two lines of mercury, whereas a height of twenty-six inches three lines and a half had been found with the same tube at the Minimes. Consequently there was a difference of three inches one line and a half in the heights of the mercury in the two observed cases. This result so filled us all with admiration and astonishment and so surprised us that we wanted, for our own satisfaction, to repeat the process of observation. I therefore did it five [six] times more, with great accuracy, in various parts of the summit; once under cover in the little chapel that is there, once out in the open, once under shelter, once in the wind, once in good weather and once during the rain and mists which sometimes came over us, having taken care each time to get rid of the air in the tube. And in all these cases there was found the same height of the mercury, twenty-three inches two lines, which makes a difference of three inches one and half lines from the twenty-six inches three and a half lines that were found at the Minimes. With this result we were fully satisfied.

"Afterwards, while descending the mountain, I repeated the observational procedure in the course of the journey, always with the same tube, the same mercury and the same vessel, at a place called *Lafon de l'Arbre*, which is a place much higher than the Minimes but much lower than the summit of the mountain; and there I found that the height of mercury remaining in the tube was twenty-five inches. I went through the procedure a second time in this same place and M. Mosnier, one of those named before, was curious to do it himself:

so he also did it in that same place, and always the same height of twenty-five inches was obtained. . . .

"When we had returned to the Minimes I found there the vessel that I had left for continual observation to be at the same height at which I had left it—twenty-six inches three lines and a half; in which height Father Chastin, who had remained to act as observer, told us that there had been no alteration at any time during the day, although the weather had been very unsettled, being sometimes calm, sometimes rainy, sometimes misty and sometimes windy.

"I performed again the procedure with the tube that I had carried to the Puy-de-Dôme, and with the vessel containing the tube for continual observation. I found that the mercury was at the same level in both these tubes, and at the same height of twenty-six inches three lines and a half, as had been found in the morning with this very tube and as had remained all day with the tube left for continual observation.

"I performed the procedure yet again and for the last time, not only with the same tube which I had used on the Puy-de-Dôme, but also with the same mercury and the same vessel that I had carried there, and I found always the mercury to be at the same height of twenty-six inches three and a half lines, which had been found in the morning. This completed the certainty of our experiments."[1]

The reader should note the extreme care taken by Périer to ensure that the results obtained did not arise from peculiarities in the materials employed; in particular, that the lower readings of the height of the mercury that had been found on the Puy-de-Dôme were not due to alterations in, or to special features of, the tube, portion of mercury or the vessel used there. He wanted to check decisively whether the observed differences between the readings on the ground and those on the summit were due to differences between the materials employed. Hence the importance of his final repetition of the observational procedure described in the last quoted paragraph: if the differences between the ground readings and the summit readings were due to differences between the two sets of materials, it would be impossible to explain satisfactorily why, the vessel and the portion of mercury taken to the Puy-de-Dôme

[1] Périer, F. (1605-72): Letter to Pascal of 22nd September, 1648.

being used, the heights of the mercury in the two tubes should again be equal. Périer wished to put beyond all doubt that the materials employed in the experiment were throughout thoroughly uniform in all relevant respects: there was no instrumental or personal error.

To turn to another example of laboratory experiments, with an entirely different subject-matter, a United States Commission was sent to Havana in 1900 to determine the aetiology of yellow fever. One early experiment proposed by members of the Commission was designed to test the hypothesis that was, then, viewed as worth consideration: yellow fever can be conveyed by mere contact with articles that have been continually touched or breathed upon by yellow fever patients. So volunteers wore the clothes, and slept under the blankets, that had been used by yellow fever patients. Yellow fever did not ensue. In 1898 it had been suggested by Sanarelli that the Bacillus icteroides was responsible for the outbreaks of yellow fever; under the Commission, experiments to test this hypothesis were tried, but none of the volunteers suffered yellow fever as a consequence of being attacked by that bacillus. It was then decided to test experimentally the hypothesis put forward in 1883 by the Cuban doctor Carlos Finlay, that the agent responsible for the infection and transmission of the disease was Aëdes aegypti (the stegomyia mosquito). Twenty-two cases of yellow fever were produced experimentally, fourteen by infected mosquito bites, six by the injection of blood, and two by the injection of filtered blood-serum; this last result showed the existence of a filterable virus (1901). One of the members of the Commission was Jesse Lazear; he was in charge of the collection of mosquitoes used in the experiments and was also responsible for applying the mosquitoes to the volunteers.

In September, 1900, "while Lazear was engaged in placing mosquitoes upon patients in a fever ward, a free mosquito alighted upon his hand and, though seen, was allowed to take its feed of blood.   Five days later he was taken ill and was removed to the yellow fever hospital at Quemados, where he died September 25th, after seven day's illness".[1] Lazear's own personal experiment consisted in testing the hypothesis that a stegomyia mosquito could infect him with yellow fever; the answer was mortally affirmative.   From the hypotheses entertained and the experiments thereupon conducted, the Commission established that yellow fever infection is transmissible by the stegomyia mosquito, that the human incubation period is from two to six days, that the period from a mosquito's biting an infected person to its being able to transmit the infection is usually ten to twelve days and that a person is not capable of infecting a mosquito for more than two or three days after the onset of fever.

A third example of an experiment was the testing of chloroform as an anaesthetic, in 1847.   Chloroform was discovered by Guthrie, a New York chemist, in 1831, and independently and almost simultaneously by Soubeiran in France and von Liebig in Germany; it was first given the name "chloroform" and fully described and prepared by Dumas in France in 1935.

A Scot, David Waldie, suggested, in 1847, in a letter to James Simpson of Edinburgh, that chloroform should be tested for its anaesthetic properties.   With his colleagues Duncan and Keith, Simpson had been trying a large variety of chemical substances in the hope of finding a satisfactory substitute for ether, which had come into medical use in the previous few years but which tended to have deleterious side-effects.   So Simpson, Duncan and Keith carried out an experiment to test the hypothesis that chloroform has anaesthetic properties.   They inhaled the

[1] Article on Lazear, J. W. (1866-1900), in *Dictionary of American Biography*, XI p. 66 (London and New York, 1933).

vapour arising from the liquid; the immediate effect was to make them exhilarated, but then the three of them suddenly fell unconscious.[1]

A fourth example of a laboratory experiment is that due to Foucault to show the rotation of the Earth.[2] It can be established experimentally that the plane of oscillation of a pendulum remains constant even if the plane from which the suspension is made is moved.   Using this fact, Foucault proposed to demonstrate the Earth's motion by suspending a pendulum of large mass from a ceiling and giving it a large oscillatory period, the (apparent) plane of oscillation being indicated by a line, through a heap of sand on the floor under the point of suspension, marked out by the tip of the swinging pendulum; the Earth's motion would soon be shown, by the non-coincidence of the lines marked out on the sand: the pendulum's plane of oscillation would continually be apparently changing.   Foucault conducted this experiment, first in 1849, and again, in more elaborate circumstances, in 1850 and in 1851; his hypothesis was on each occasion strikingly confirmed.

8·03 The Role and Sources of Laboratory Experimentation

The purpose of an experiment is to discover a law of nature.   There are, doubtless, many different sorts of such laws.   We shall refer to a few of them in the following discussion.   But let us preface that discussion by making the remark that frequently the methodologist, as often the scientist, is in fact more concerned with scientific laws than with laws of nature as such; more concerned, that is, with scientific conceptions and their empirical basis or support

[1] Simpson, J. Y. (1811-70), was Professor of Midwifery at Edinburgh.   For biographical details, see Duns, J. (1820-1909): *Memoirs of Sir James Y. Simpson, Bart.* (Edinburgh, 1873); Simpson, Eve, B. (1856-1920): *Life of Sir James Y. Simpson* (Edinburgh, 1896).
[2] Foucault, L. (1819-68): "Démonstration physique du mouvement de la Terre au moyen du pendule", *C.R. Acad. Sci. Paris*, 1851, **32**, 135 *et seq.*

(if any) than with that law of nature (if there is one) that corresponds objectively to the scientific conception. Of course, in so far as scientific laws are substantiated by natural phenomena, they can be regarded as expressing natural laws; but it is important not to confuse a designation with what is designated by it. Of a scientific law one can say that it is true, or false; that it is reasonable or unreasonable in view of all the available evidence: yet such epithets cannot be ascribed to laws of nature themselves. A law of nature is neither true nor false, but just is.

From the human side, then, the purpose of an experiment is to become in a position to formulate a true scientific law about a subject-matter; more precisely, to become in a position to formulate a connected series of scientific laws about a subject-matter, the information necessary for the construction of these scientific laws not being obtainable under ordinary (non-experimental) circumstances. In order to obtain scientifically useful information from an experiment, it is usually necessary to pose beforehand fairly definite questions which the experiment is being designed to answer. As Kant says in a famous passage, speaking of the early founders of modern, experimental science: "They comprehended that reason has insight into that alone which she herself produces on her own plan, and that she must move forward with the principles of her judgments, according to fixed law; compelling nature to answer her questions, without letting herself be led by nature, as it were in leading strings. For otherwise accidental observations, made on no previously determined plan, will never converge towards a necessary law, which is just what reason seeks and desires. Reason, holding in one hand its principles, according to which concordant phenomena alone can be admitted as laws of nature, and holding in the other hand the experiment, which it has devised in accordance with those principles, must approach nature, in order to be taught by it. But the approach must not be as a pupil who agrees to everything the teacher likes, but as an appointed judge, who compels the witnesses to answer the questions which he himself proposes".[1] It will frequently happen, admittedly, that an experimenter will be able, from the experiment, to extract answers to questions which he had not at all previously thought of. However, this will only rarely occur unless he framed the experiment with *some* specific questions in mind.

An important kind of experiment is that undertaken to determine the magnitudes of certain properties of a kind of entity, as *e.g.* the density and boiling point of mercury. From such experiments are obtained the simplest kind of numerical laws; *e.g.* "the specific gravity of mercury is 13·6", "the speed of light is 186,000 miles per second", Three points should be appreciated here. Firstly, only a very few specimens are examined in order to make the required determinations; it is assumed that the specimens dealt with are, at least so far as the properties being measured are concerned, completely typical of the whole class. This assumption is not idly made, for one has usually, at the beginning of the experiment, taken trouble to ensure as far as possible that the particular instance or instances in hand are representative of the whole class of possible instances; in the case of mercury, for example, the chemist will first satisfy himself that the sample of mercury with which he is experimenting is free from impurities, and so, until contrary evidence is shown, can reasonably be considered as a fair sample of the whole "population" (class) of mercury. Secondly, since, as indicated in Chapter Six, all measurement that is not merely counting is to some extent imprecise and gives varied results, numerical laws that are proposed on the

[1] Kant, I. (1724-1804): *Kritik der reinen Vernunft* (Zweite Ausgabe, Riga, 1787); Preface, p. xiv.

basis of the data furnished by the use of measuring instruments are only approximately true, though of course the degree of variation and approximation may be so extremely small and close as to allow one to treat the law as exact for all practical purposes. Thirdly, most, if not all, numerical laws are conditional ones. Boiling points and velocities, for example, are dependent upon the surrounding air pressure or other such factors; *e.g.* at a height, mercury boils at a lower temperature than at ground-level, and the speed of light through water is less than the speed of light through air.

The aim of most experiments in physics is to learn whether there is a numerical relationship between one group of quantitative properties and another such group, and to discover what this relationship is. Boyle had the idea, suggested to him by the experimental researches of Torricelli and Pascal, that there was a numerical relationship between the pressure and volume of a gas at a constant temperature and that the relationship in question was one of inverse proportion. He designed apparatus and an experimental set-up to test this hypothesis that pressure × volume is constant when the temperature is constant and the pressure or volume are varied. His experiments showed that his hypothesis was not altogether confirmed by the observed facts, but that, nevertheless, his hypothesis did fit the data very closely.[1]

It is in this sphere that Dimensional Analysis has its role. In the first place, the methods of Dimensional Analysis can be used to suggest a definite hypothesis, and this will be of a relational kind; if that hypothesis turns out to be justified, one can then perform the necessary experiments to determine the value of the constant q that occurs in dimensional equations; cf. **6·08**. Dimensional

---

[1] Boyle, R. (1627-91): *A Defense of the Doctrine Touching the Spring and Weight of the Air* (London, 1662, second edition).

Analysis is valuable because it promotes efficient experimentation: it enables the physicist to propose beforehand a specific hypothesis or series of connected hypothesis (taking more and more factors into account if the simpler hypothesis proves unacceptable), and so it eliminates a great deal of trial-and-error and of guesswork in the formulation of hypotheses and in the planning of appropriate experiments.

Experiments can also be performed for testing a causal hypothesis: a hypothesis to the effect that, usually under certain restrictive conditions, one event or state "brings about" another event or state. Examples of such causal hypotheses are: Pascal's hypothesis that the magnitude of the air pressure brings about the magnitude of the height of a column of mercury (or any other liquid); Simpson's hypothesis that the inhalation of chloroform vapours brings about unconsciousness and anaesthesia.

Let us remark that closely connected with many causal hypotheses are hypotheses of what might be called *inverse causality*. These are hypotheses to the effect that if an event or state occurs, then another event or state of some kind will be prevented from occurring. Examples of such hypotheses are: Jenner's hypothesis that vaccination prevents smallpox; Lister's hypothesis that spraying the surgical theatre with carbolic acid prevents surgical sepsis; Carnot's hypothesis that friction prevents the construction of a perpetual motion machine.

What is the role of laboratory experimentation? It is to permit the discovery of facts and the checking of hypotheses in a more systematic and careful way than is often possible if the objects of observation are limited to naturally occurring phenomena. The purpose of an experimental set-up is to make certain observations; the experimental set-up is required either because the observations would not otherwise be possible or because at least many of the observations would not be so conveniently available and the conditions under which the observed objects occur would not be so well known. It is important to know the conditions under which a phenomenon occurs (or does not occur) since these may affect its occurrence or non-occurrence. A considerable part of the work of science consists in the attempt to specify more and more adequately and accurately the relevant conditions for the occurrence or non-occurrence of phenomena.

A simple illustration of the necessity for experiment is given by any chemical compound that does not occur in nature, *e.g.* acetylsalicylic acid (aspirin), and is given by any elementary law of physics, such as Galileo's law of free-falling bodies. If we put ourselves back to Galileo's time, it is easy to realise the overwhelmingly great difficulty in devising, from the vast variety and the seemingly profound complexity of the motions to be seen around us in the physical world, any accurate and substantial laws of motion. Only by being able to simplify and abstract from what naturally occurs, in a word only by artificialising phenomena, is it in practice possible to establish sure foundations and to make steady progress in comprehending the laws of nature at work in the real world. Again, recurring to the example of Boyle's law that pressure $\times$ volume is constant, it is readily comprehensible that this hypothesis could hardly be checked outside of an experimental set-up, for in the ordinary course of events a change in the pressure or volume of a gas is accompanied by a change in the temperature also; only in laboratory conditions can the temperature be kept fixed while the pressure or volume are varied. Besides, in the laboratory one can, of course within limits, make as many alterations in the magnitudes of the properties as one wants and obtain as many data as are needed, at one's own convenience. Through the laboratory Nature comes to man, instead of man having to go to Nature and even then not always obtaining what he seeks.

To close this section, we illustrate how scientific hypotheses and laws can be expressed in logical terms.

Example I.—"(All) human beings are vertebrates." In terms of the FC, this amounts to saying: for all individuals x, if x has the property of being human, then it also has the property of being vertebrate. Thus, abstractly,

$$(8\cdot031) \quad (x) [b (x) \supset d (x)] \qquad\qquad PxCbxdx.$$

In terms of BA it amounts to saying: the intersection-class of the class s of human beings, on the one hand, and of the complementary class of the class t of vertebrates (the universe u of discourse being say the class of animals), on the other hand, is (equal to) the null class $\dot{u}$:

$$(8\cdot032) \quad s_{\lrcorner}çt = \dot{u} \qquad\qquad {}_{\lrcorner}sçt = \dot{u}.$$

Example II.—"No inert gas is a good conductor of electricity". In terms of the FC this becomes, abstractly,

$$(8\cdot033) \quad (x) [b (x) \supset \sim d (x)] \qquad PxCbxNdx;$$

that is, if anything is an inert gas, then it has not got the property of being a good conductor of electricity. In terms of BA:

$$(8\cdot034) \quad s_{\lrcorner}t = \dot{u} \qquad\qquad {}_{\lrcorner}st = \dot{u}:$$

the class of inert gases and the class of good conductors of electricity have no overlap.

Example III.—"Vaccination gives protection against (or prevents) smallpox." In terms of the FC this becomes, abstractly,

$$(8\cdot035) \quad (x) [b (x) \supset (d (x) \supset \sim h (x))] \quad PxCbxCdxNhx:$$

"for all x, if x is human, then if x is vaccinated, x is immune from smallpox." In terms of BA,

$(8 \cdot 036)$ $\quad (s_-t)$ $\quad _-w = \dot{u}$ $\qquad\qquad _{--}stw = \dot{u}$:

there is no overlap between the class s_-t of vaccinated persons and the class w of smallpox sufferers.

8·04 The General Nature of Statistics

The term "statistics" is used in four different senses.[1] (i) Systematic collections of numerical and comparable data are said to be statistics. Thus one speaks of the statistics of crime, of smallpox, of a nation's shipping or imports and exports. Also under this heading fall the collections of data formed in the course of particular statistical experiments. (ii) Informal exposition of the methods of collecting, organising and interpreting statistical data is said to be statistics. This sort of statistics may be called *descriptive statistics*. Descriptive statistics is concerned with the methods of sampling, of designing experiments involving random phenomena (cf. 7·04), of extracting the relevant information from statistical data and of evaluating the reliability or acceptability of hypotheses associated with random experiments; but in these concerns of descriptive statistics, mathematical techniques are not employed unless they belong to arithmetic or elementary algebra; in particular, within descriptive statistics itself there is no detailed, mathematical derivation and justification of the methods described and advocated. (iii) Such detailed, mathematical derivation and justification belongs to "statistics" in the sense of the mathematical theory of statistics. As in any branch of mathematics, however, mathematical statistics gives rise to many theoretical problems of its own, that have no immediate and possibly even no mediate connection with descriptive statistics. (iv) The term "statistics", as a plural, is also used as a

[1] For the history of the word *statistics*, see Yule, G. U. (1871-1951): *An Introduction to the Theory of Statistics* (London, 1912, and many later editions [the latest ones with Kendall, M. G. (1907-)], introductory chapter and references given.

name for such measures as the arithmetic mean, the variance and the standard deviation of a collection of statistical data, measures which summarily indicate what can be taken as important indications of the nature of the observed samples and, through the observed samples, of the nature of the population from which the samples have been drawn. In the literature it is usual to name "parameters" the summary measures of the population. For example, a random sample of size 10, with replacement, from the population of the 10 digits 0, 1, 2, ..., 9 might be: 1, 9, 0, 2, 7, 7, 6, 8, 1, 1. The statistic that is the arithmetic mean of this sample has the value of 4·2; the parameter that is the mean of the population has the value of 4·5.

For our elementary purpose we can regard mathematical statistics as simply the mathematical theory underlying the methods of descriptive statistics. This approach, in turn, enables us to concentrate on descriptive statistics, the subject-matters of this being also the subject-matters of mathematical statistics, mathematical statistics, unlike descriptive statistics, dealing with these subject-matters in a rigorous, mathematical way.[1]

Our present use of the term "descriptive statistics" is somewhat wider than is usual, because we are including the practical procedures of what is called *statistical inference*, whereas these procedures are commonly excluded from the field of what is labelled "descriptive statistics". The contents of descriptive statistics, in our sense, may be classified under five headings:

[1] The founders of modern mathematical statistics are: Pearson, K. (1857-1936) and Fisher, R. A. (1890-). The most important of Pearson's papers can be found listed in Kendall: *The Advanced Theory of Statistics II*, (London, 1951), third edition; many of them have been collected and republished under the title *Early Statistical Papers* (Cambridge, 1918). The most important of Fisher's papers have been collectively published under the title: *Contributions to Mathematical Statistics* (New York, 1950).

(i) *Design of Experiments*.[1]—Fundamental to most empirical investigations involving random experiments is the planning of the course and the set-up of the inquiry, in order to ensure that useful and reliable information can be obtained, and obtained as efficiently as possible. To illustrate but one aspect of the need for designing experiments, suppose we wish to test a drug's effectiveness in the treatment of some disease, taking the fatality-rate as the criterion of success or failure, and suppose that the past fatality-rate has been 25 per cent. Now it is pointless to test the drug on a sample of size 4 because the probability that none of the 4 dies is, cf. E7·7·41, equal to 81/256, the probability that 1 dies and the other three recover is 27/64, the probability that 2 die and 2 recover is 27/128, the probability that 3 die and 1 recovers is 3/64 and the probability that all 4 die is 1/256, the fatality-rates per cent. being, respectively, 0, 25, 50, and 100. The recovery of all the patients is the only outcome which gives a result better than that afforded by past experience, yet this outcome could quite easily happen by chance alone, for it can be expected to occur nearly 32 times in 100 trials with 4 patients even if the drug were ineffective. (81/256 $\doteqdot$ 0·32.) If we are led to accept the position that the drug is to be counted as effective if and only if the probability of the most favourable outcome, under its use, is 5 per cent. or less, then one must, in the light of that position, plan the experiment in such a way that the size of the sample chosen is capable of providing the basis for a real test of the effectiveness of the drug: the size of the sample to be

[1] The notion and basic theory of the design of experiments is mostly due to Fisher: *Statistical Methods for Research Workers* (Edinburgh, 1925, and many later editions); and his *The Design of Experiments* (Edinburgh, 1935, and later editions). The mathematical theory, which is of an advanced nature, is to be found compactly in Mann, H. B. (1905-): *Analysis and Design of Experiments* (New York, 1949). A good informal introduction is Brownlee, K. A. (1918-): *Industrial Experimentation*, fourth edition (London, 1949).

dealt with must be large enough to enable the effectiveness of the drug, if any, to show itself as such.

(ii) *Sampling.*—The theory of sampling is clearly to some extent a part of the theory of the design of experiments; yet it is sufficiently important and basic to deserve notice by itself. In the sciences one is always, or almost always, dealing with populations which are too large to allow of an examination of each individual member. To go back to the previous example concerning the testing of the effectiveness of a drug, the disease in question may have sufferers all over the world, and it would in practice be impossible to try out on all of them the effectiveness of the drug—quite apart from the fact that such a proceeding might be unethical since the drug might be worse than the standard treatment itself. Again, if one wishes to investigate experimentally the genetics of *Drosophila melanogaster* or of *Paramecium*, it is totally impossible to collect and to keep together under experimental conditions all the members of these populations. The chief purpose of sampling is to be able to obtain information about certain characteristics of the population as a whole from the characteristics of the few observed members. This information will be rationally obtainable and reliable only if the observed members form a representative sample, that is only if the observed group reflects with reasonable accuracy the proportions among the various sub-populations in the original population. Thus, if a property under consideration might be affected by the sex of the members of the population, then it is necessary to ensure that the sex ratio in the sample is a reasonably accurate approximation to the sex ratio in the whole population. This topic will be examined further in **8·05**.

(iii) *Presentation of Data.*—The results of the relevant observations made in connection with random experiments need to be organised and tabulated. They must be set out in a clear and informative manner. A mere mass of data which have not been suitably systematised and classified are of relatively little use since it is hard, from such a mass, to detect what might prove to be significant trends or relationships. It is to facilitate such detection that, in addition to classificatory tabulation of the data, graphical and diagrammatic representations of the data are provided.

(iv) *Evaluation of Sample Statistics.*—Both for the purpose of enabling comparisons to be made between one series of observations and another and for the purpose of statistical inference, it is required to calculate those values that serve to indicate the characteristics of the data. Especially important are the arithmetic mean and the variance or some other measure of the degree of scatter around the arithmetic mean. The definitions of the most important elementary sample statistics were given in **6·10** and **6·11**; the use of them for statistical inference will be explained in **8·07**.

(v) *Statistical Inference.*—A statistical (random) experiment is undertaken to test a hypothesis. In this context, such a hypothesis is called a *null hypothesis*. For instance, if an experiment is undertaken in order to determine whether a new drug is more effective than an old one in the treatment of some disease, the null hypothesis would be to the effect that the new drug is *not* more effective. If the proportion of successes with the new drug is "significantly" greater than the proportion of successes with the old drug, one has then rational grounds for rejecting the null hypothesis. The meaning of "significantly" will be considered in **8·07**.

In any whole piece of research depending upon the use

of statistical methods, the topics (i) to (v), in that order, have to be dealt with.[1]

EXERCISES

E8·4·1.   Each member of a population can have any one of the 10 properties (denoted by the numerals) 0, 1, 2, ..., 9, these properties being equally likely. Five random samples of size 10 are drawn from the population, the properties possessed by the members examined being: 0, 6, 2, 6, 5, 3, 5, 9, 9, 1; 1, 2, 3, 4, 6, 9, 3, 0, 9, 0; 6, 6, 2, 8, 8, 5, 8, 6, 1, 0; 3, 0, 2, 9, 1, 3, 8, 0, 4, 0; 1, 9, 0, 2, 7, 7, 6, 8, 1, 1.[2] Find the arithmetic mean and the variance of each sample, and the arithmetic mean and the variance of all the examined cases. (N.B.—For reasons which we cannot here explain it is more reliable, in calculating the variance of a sample of size less than 30 or so, to make the denominator $n - 1$ instead of n. The standard deviation will be similarly affected.)

E8·4·2.   140 patients are examined with respect to the possession of a particular characteristic; they are said to have this characteristic; if and only if there is a "positive reaction" to a prescribed chemical test. Of the 140, 38 are males, the rest females; 23 of the males have a positive reaction and 72 of the females have. Set out these data in a table, giving totals and, with each total, an appropriate percentage.

---

[1] An excellent introductory textbook on mathematical statistics is Mood, A. M. (1913-): *Introduction to the Theory of Statistics* (New York, 1950). A good textbook of descriptive statistics is Brookes, B. C., and Dick, W. F. L.: *Introduction to Statistical Method* (London, 1951). The standard advanced treatises are: Cramér: *Mathematical Methods of Statistics*; Kendall: *The Advanced Theory of Statistics*, two volumes. [Kendall's work is now in course of revised publication in three volumes, with Stuart, A. (1922-) as co-author.]

[2] These digits, as are those referred to in **8·6**, have been taken from: Lindley, D. V. (*c*. 1921-) and Miller, J. C. P. (1906-): *Cambridge Elementary Statistical Tables* (Cambridge, 1953).

E8·4·3. NEW CASES OF CARCINOMA OF THE BREAST FIRST TREATED IN THE CAMBRIDGE AREA IN 1947-1950.

STAGE	OPERABLE	INOPERABLE	TOTAL	PER CENT. OF ALL CASES	MEAN AGE (YEARS)
I	137	22			56·7
II	132	14			55·5
IIIa	36	40			66·0
IIIb	45	61			59·5
IV	0	108			62·0
Unstaged	107	3			55·9
Mean					

Complete the above table.[1]

8·05 Sampling[2]

Since the usual aim of a sampling procedure is to obtain a group that is representative of the population from which it is drawn, it is obviously necessary to take steps to avoid what is called *bias* or *selection* in the sample. A sample is said to be biased or selected if it is not representative of the population. If one wishes to know the *frequency distribution* of the height of adult Englishmen, that is the function (whose typical member is) (aU_L, n) where a is an interval, say, 4·5 to 4·6, U_L is a unit of length and n is the non-negative whole number of adult Englishmen having a height that lies in the interval aU_L—then a sample consisting entirely of urban inhabitants, or of mineworkers, or of members of athletic clubs, or of old-age pensioners or of passers-by at 11 o'clock in the morning is likely to be a

[1] Adapted from Brinkley, Diana and Haybittle, J. L.: "Results of treatment of carcinoma of the breast", *The Lancet* (10th January, 1959), 86-90.

[2] For a general, technical treatment, see Cochran, W. G. (1909-): *Sampling Techniques* (New York, 1953).

biased one, for height may well be affected by what comes of, or what led to, living in an urban area, being a mineworker, being a member of an athletic club; and the frequency distribution of height among adult Englishmen as a whole may well differ from the frequency distribution of height among those adult Englishmen who are old enough to be old-age pensioners, for, *inter alia*, the way in which height is distributed in the population may well have altered in the course of a generation or two; analogous remarks apply to adult male passers-by at 11 o'clock in the morning, because these (so far as one can generalise, for the exact reasons will depend upon the exact locality chosen) are not likely to include clerks or factory workers or agricultural workers, but are more likely to be, with a relative frequency considerably greater than their real proportion in the population as a whole, people such as salesmen and professional men.

Volunteers as subjects for an experiment tend to make a sample biased, the factors motivating their action commonly rendering the individuals somewhat exceptional members of the population, or preventing the resultant sample from duly reflecting the proportions in the population. For example, a sample consisting of volunteers for experiments of vision is not likely to contain enough people with myopia or other visual defects; and, again, for medical investigations generally, samples consisting of volunteers are not likely to contain enough female members to reflect the proportion of female members in the whole population, for reasons of modesty and other easily assignable reasons.

With the purpose of obtaining a truly representative sample of the population, one endeavours to obtain a *random sample*. No sample is in itself a random one: the epithet applies to the method of extracting the sample, not to the sample itself; it applies to the (procedure of) sampling, not to the sample. A sample is said to be random if and only if any member of the population is as likely to be chosen as any other by the procedure adopted for extracting members from the population. It can be taken as a fact of experience that, if a large sample is randomly extracted, the proportions between the subclasses in the sample will closely reflect the proportions between those subclasses in the population. (The subclasses might be, for example, males and females.) Paradoxical as it may seem at first sight, random sampling requires very careful forethought and execution. This is because, in practice, the members most readily to hand form, so to speak, only local varieties of the species; in order to get a fair picture of the species as a whole, one has also to go to other parts. From what was said in connection with the example of the heights of adult Englishmen, it is plain that considerable previous knowledge of the subject-matter and population is needed in order to overcome bias and to achieve a sample that is truly representative of the population.

A standard device for the attainment of random samples is the use of what are called *random sampling numbers*.[1] A table of random sampling numbers is a list of the digits 0, 1, 2, ..., 9 which has been compiled in such a way as to ensure that the items in the list are randomly distributed. Suppose we wish to compare the effect of some factor X on a population. We might proceed by drawing two random samples and affecting the members of the first sample by X and keeping the members of the second sample unaffected by X, or inversely: the sample to be affected

[1] Tippett, L. H. C. (1902-): *Random Sampling Numbers, Tracts for Computers No. 15* (London, 1927); Kendall and Babington Smith, B. (1905-): *Tables of Random Sampling Numbers, Tracts for Computers No. 24* (London, 1940); "Randomness and random sampling numbers", *J. Roy. Stat. Soc.*, 1938, **101**, 147-, and *J. Roy. Stat. Soc. Supplement*, 1939, **6**, 51-61. For a different and critical approach, cf. Brown, G. Spencer (1925-): *Probability and Scientific Inference* (London, 1957).

can be decided by say tossing a coin or by some other random experiment. Random sampling numbers can be used for this purpose, and in the following way. Beginning arbitrarily in the list of random sampling numbers, assign a random sampling number, in the order of their occurrence, to each consecutive member of the total random sample being dealt with; this random sample could itself have been obtained by methods analogous to those we are now explaining. Then if a member of the sample has been assigned an even digit (0 included), he is to belong to the subsample to be affected by X, and if an odd digit, he is to belong to the other subsample. Since the digits are randomly distributed in the list of random sampling numbers, the numbers of even and of odd digits in any batch of successive digits from the list tend to be equal. To illustrate, the numbers listed in E8·4·1 are random sampling numbers. Let s (t) be the subsample to which a

(1)	(2)	(3)		(1)	(2)	(3)
0	1	s		6	21	s
6	2	s		6	22	s
2	3	s		2	23	s
6	4	s		8	24	s
5	5	t		8	25	s
3	6	t		5	26	t
5	7	t		8	27	s
9	8	t		6	28	s
9	9	t		1	29	t
1	10	t		0	30	s
1	11	t		3	31	t
2	12	s		0	32	s
3	13	t		2	33	s
4	14	s		9	34	t
6	15	s		1	35	t
9	16	t		3	36	t
3	17	t		8	37	s
0	18	s		0	38	s
9	19	t		4	39	s
0	20	s		0	40	s

(1): Random sampling number. (2): Ordinal number of sample member. (3): Subsample.

member of the total sample of size 40 is to belong if and only if it has assigned to it an even (odd) random sampling number. The outcome is presented in the above table.

In the above table there are 23 even digits and 17 odd digits from the list of random sampling numbers. This is an example of what is called *sampling fluctuation*. With small and medium-sized (random) samples there can be considerable differences between the sampling statistics and the corresponding population parameters; but—and this is the additional point of practical significance—as the size of the sample increases, the proportions of these differences tend to decrease, so that with large samples the discovered statistics can be taken, with a high degree of probability, as accurate indications of the corresponding parameters. This point will be elaborated a little further in **8·07**. The tendency for there to be a decrease in the difference between statistics and parameters is illustrated by the following table, where the whole page of 2,000 random sampling numbers from which those in E8·4·1 were taken, has provided the data.

FREQUENCY OF EVEN AND ODD DIGITS IN A PAGE OF 2,000 RANDOM
SAMPLING NUMBERS

Digits	50	100	200	400	1,000	2,000
Even	27	48	102	202	485	984
Odd	23	52	98	198	515	1,016
Per cent. difference from expectations	8	4	2	1	3	1·6

The last line of this table has been calculated as follows: the number of observed even digits out of the first observed 50 digits is 27; even and odd digits being, by hypothesis, equally likely in the population, the expected number of even digits is 25, and so there is a difference of 2. The percentage difference is given by 100 (2/25)/100, which is 8 per cent. The percentage difference with respect to the odd digits is the same, also 8 per cent. The other percentage differences are calculated in the same way as in this case.

EXERCISES

E8·5·4. Let N (s) be the number of members belonging to a random sample s without replacement. Clearly, if s_1 and s_2 are subsets of s, then $N(s_1 \cup s_2) = N(s_1) + N(s_2) - N s_{1 \cup s_2}$. Show that if the n sets s_i are subsets of s, then

$$N(\underset{i \in \mathbb{N}_n}{\cup}) s_i = \underset{i \in \mathbb{N}_n}{\Sigma} N(s_i) - \Sigma N(s_i \ s_j) + \Sigma N(s_i \ s_j \ s_k) - + \dots \mp N(\underset{i \in \mathbb{N}_n}{\cap} s_i),$$

the summations being taken over all the possible distinct values of the subscripts, and the final sign being $-(+)$ if n is even (odd). Cf. E7·5·6.[1]

E8·5·5. A sample of size 100 without replacement is drawn, and it is classified into three subsets s, t, and w, According to the research worker, 58 members of the sample belong to s, 42 to t, 47 to w, 22 to s_t, 19 to s_w, 16 to t_w, and 12 to s_t_w. Show that at least one of the research worker's statements is incorrect. (Hint: use E8·5·4 and show that N (s_t_w) > 100.)

8·06 The Normal Distribution

We have already in this chapter referred to the idea of a frequency distribution. The table on p. 274 provides an example of a frequency distribution.[2]

This frequency distribution can be represented diagrammatically by the diagram Fig. viii-1, which is called a *histogram*. The area of each rectangle in the histogram is proportionate to the frequency of the individuals whose height is in the interval represented by the base of the rectangle. Upon the histogram has been superimposed a continuous curve. This curve is known as the *normal curve* and the frequency distribution which it represents

[1] For statistical uses of this N operator, see Yule [and Kendall]: *Introduction to the Theory of Statistics*, where it is investigated and used extensively in the opening chapters, though the symbolism there employed is different.

[2] Data from Simpson, G. G. (1902-), Pittendrigh, C. S. (1918-), and Tiffany, L. H. (1894-): *Life*, p. 418 (New York, 1957).

FREQUENCY DISTRIBUTION OF TAIL
LENGTH IN A DEME OF DEER MICE

LENGTH IN MILLIMETRES	FREQUENCY
52-53	1
54-55	3
56-57	11
58-59	18
60-61	21
62-63	20
64-65	9
66-67	2
68-69	1
	Total 96

HISTOGRAM OF TAIL LENGTH IN A DEME OF 96 DEER MICE, WITH
NORMAL CURVE SUPERIMPOSED

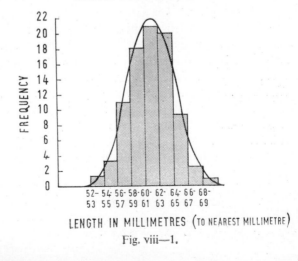

Fig. viii—1.

is known as the *normal distribution*.[1] This distribution is of fundamental importance in statistical theory and practice, for to that distribution a great many, though not all, frequency distributions approximate: as in the present case of the deer mice.

FREQUENCY DISTRIBUTION OF HEIGHT OF BRITISH MEN (1885)

HEIGHT IN INCHES	FREQUENCY PER THOUSAND
58	1
59	1
60	5
61	9
62	20
63	46
64	78
65	115
66	143
67	155
68	143
69	124
70	75
71	46
72	24
73	9
74	3
75	2
76	1

The above table gives the frequency distribution of the height of British adult males, the frequencies being per thousand. They are based on a sample of 8,585.

[1] The importance and basic properties of the normal distribution were first established, primarily in connection with the Calculus of (Astronomical) Observations, by Laplace (cf. his *Théorie Analytique des Probabilités*) and by Gauss, C. F. (1777-1855), (cf. the papers in his collected *Werke*, Volume 4 (Göttingen, 1880)). The thesis that the normal distribution was of universal applicability to natural and social phenomena was first maintained by Quetelet, A. (1796-1874): *Sur l'homme et le développement de ses facultés* (Brussels, 1835), and many other works. For a discussion of Quetelet's ideas and their influence, see Hogben: *Statistical Theory*.

The normal distribution was originally discovered and introduced as the limit of the binomial distribution, by De Moivre, A. (1667-1754): *Miscellanea Analytica de Seriebus et Quadraturis*, Second Supplement (London, 1733, the main work having appeared in 1730).

This frequency distribution can be represented by the following histogram; again, to show the close approximation to the normal distribution, a normal curve has been superimposed.

The *median* of the frequency distribution of a quantitative property is that magnitude of the property which is such that the distribution falls into two halves about it. Thus, in the case of the tail length of deer mice, the median will be that tail length such that half the deer mice have a shorter, and the other half a longer, tail length. The median of a frequency distribution for a sample of size n is calculated as the magnitude of the property that can be regarded as belonging to the $((n + 1)/2)$th member, in the sense illustrated by the following calculation. Starting from the top of the frequency distribution, the first 33 members of

HISTOGRAM OF HEIGHT IN A SAMPLE OF 8,585 BRITISH MEN, FREQUENCIES PER 1,000, WITH NORMAL CURVE SUPERIMPOSED

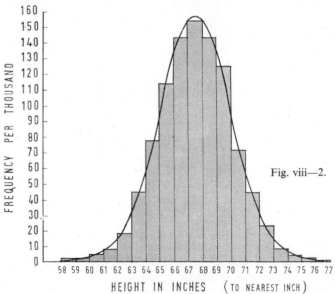

Fig. viii—2.

the sample in the distribution have a tail length of less than 59·5 millimetres, and the next 21 members of the sample in the distribution have a tail length of between 59·5 and 61·5 millimetres. The 48·5th member has a tail length in this latter interval. The tail length of this member is reckoned to be 59·5 + (15·5/21) millimetres, *i.e.* 60·24 millimetres.

The *mode* of a frequency distribution is that magnitude of the property with which the greatest frequency is associated. For instance, in the case of the frequency distribution of the height of British men, given above, the mode is in the interval 67-8 in. It is quite possible for a frequency distribution to have two or more modes; it is then said to be *bimodal* or *multimodal*.

For descriptive statistics, the basic features of the normal frequency distribution are: (i) the mean, median, and (unique) mode coincide; (ii) the distribution is completely symmetrical about the mean; and (iii) it is possible to calculate theoretically the number of the members of a random sample from a normally distributed population that should fall within the interval: mean $\pm n \times$ standard deviation, for each positive integral n; in particular, 68·27 per cent. of the members should fall within the interval : mean ± 1 standard deviation, 95·45 per cent. should fall within the interval : mean ± 2 (standard deviation), and 99·73 per cent. should fall within the interval : mean ± 3 (standard deviation). These results are of great importance in testing the significance of statistical hypotheses, as will be seen in the next section.

EXERCISES

E8·6·6. What are the expected frequencies associated with the binomial distribution $\binom{15}{x}(1/3)^x (2/3)^{15-x}$? Draw a histogram for these frequencies.

E8·6·7. Evaluate the binomial distribution $\binom{10}{x}(1/2)^x (1/2)^{10-x}$, draw a histogram, and superimpose a normal curve. What is the mean, the median and the mode?

8·07 Tests of Significance for Statistical Hypotheses[1]

Suppose that a person A makes a claim to possess genuine telepathic powers, and that an experiment to test his claim is devised in which a pack of 25 cards in 5 "suits", 5 cards per suit, is employed; and suppose, further, that A is informed of the constitution of this pack of cards. Then the probability of a success is 1/5, and the expected number of successes is 5 for each run through the pack. The experimenter adopts as his null hypothesis that there is nothing in A's claim. But he must also, before conducting the experiment, determine a level of significance, that is a probability value such that if the probability of A's score is less than that value, the null hypothesis will be considered as untenable in relation to the known evidence; if A's score has a probability less than the significance level, his score is said to be *significant*. The modal significance level chosen in practice is 5 per cent., *i.e.* 0·05. With this significance level, let us consider the situation that arises if A has a score of 10 successes. Using E7·7·41 and the remark at the end of E7·7 45, the null hypothesis is to be rejected if and only if

$$(8·071) \qquad \sum_{x \in (N_{25} - N_9)} \binom{2,5}{x} (1/5)^x (4/5)^{25-x} < 0·05.$$

With the notation of E7·7·41, $P(s_{10}) = 0·011777$, $P(s_{11}) = 0·004015$, $P(s_{12}) = 0·001171$; even if, contrary to fact, for each i from 13 to 25, $P(s_i) = P(s_{12})$, the sum of the probabilities of the events s_{13}, s_{14}, ..., s_{25} would be equal to no more than 0·015223. Therefore, the total probability is no more than 0·032186, which is less than

[1] The ideas of tests of significance are substantially due to Fisher: they are elaborated in his books *The Design of Experiments* and, more recently, *Statistical Methods and Scientific Inference* (Edinburgh, 1957). The latter work is largely polemical, Fisher criticising relatively recent influential views associated with Neyman, Pearson, E. S. (1895-) and Wald, A. (1902-50). For a lengthy discussion of these views see again Hogben: *Statistical Theory*.

0·05. Accordingly, the null hypothesis must, with the chosen level of significance, be regarded as untenable. Of course, in actual research, a decision of this kind would not be based on a single experiment, but on a series of experiments.

From this last example it is apparent that the use of the binomial distribution function leads to considerable difficulties in computation, unless a computer is available. However, since the binomial distribution is an approximation to the normal distribution (relative frequencies corresponding to probabilities), a more direct and simple method for testing significance is possible. Before explaining the method for the case mentioned above, we shall first deal with some preliminary and related points.

We saw, when considering random sampling numbers, that the arithmetic means and other statistics of samples can differ considerably from the true, *i.e.* population, mean. It can be shown that sample means have a frequency distribution which is approximately normal, the distribution centring round the population mean. Accordingly, from what was said in the last paragraph of **8·06**, one can expect less than 5 per cent. of the sample means to differ from the true mean by more than twice the population's standard deviation. The standard deviation of the sample means can be shown to be equal to the quotient of the population standard deviation and the square root of n, where n is the size of the samples. Hence, the mean of a sample has a probability of no more than 4·45 per cent. of differing from the true mean by more than 2 (standard deviation of population/$\sqrt{n}$). Now, of course, the value of the population standard deviation is not directly known. One then employs the sample standard deviation as an estimate of the population one, this being justifiable if the size n of the sample is not small; it gives good results if n is say 30 or more. Hence, the true mean lies in the interval

$E (x_i U)_n \pm 2$ (s.e.)$_n$ with a probability of rather more than 95 per cent.

So much for the standard error of an arithmetic mean. For our telepathic example, we need to know the *standard error of a proportion*. This standard error is given by the formula:

(8·072) standard error of a percentage $= \sqrt{\dfrac{pq}{n}}$,

where p is the expected number of successes per cent., q is the actual number of successes per cent. and n is the sample size. In the telepathic example, the expected number of successes per cent. is 20 (1 in 5), the actual number of successes per cent. is 40 (10 successes in 25 calls) and the sample size is 25. In this case,

(8·073) standard error of percentage $= \sqrt{\dfrac{20 \times 40}{25}}$,

which has a value of 8.

Therefore, the outcome of 10 successes is to be counted as significant if it involves a percentage of successes which lies outside the interval $[20 \pm 2 (8)]$ per cent., for the probability that an outcome does not lie in that interval is no greater than 4·45 per cent. Since the interval concerned ranges from 4 per cent. to 36 per cent., the outcome of 10 successes (40 per cent. successes) is significant.

Let us give another example in which (8·072) can be employed more conveniently than the binomial distribution function. A die is thrown 200 times. If scoring a six is regarded as being a success, the expected number of successes is 200/6, $= 33\frac{1}{3}$. Suppose that in fact there are 38 successes. Does this show that the die is not a completely fair one? We adopt as the null hypothesis: the die is completely fair—the number of successes is within the number permitted by chance fluctuations. The expected number of successes per cent. is 50/3, the actual number of successes per cent is 19 and the sample size is 200. Using (8·072), we find that the standard error of the percentage of successes is 1·583. Hence, with a significance level of fractionally more than 4·45 per cent., the outcome of 38 successes is to be judged significant if and only if 19 per cent. falls outside the interval [50/3 ± 3·166] per cent., = 13·501 to 19·833 per cent. The outcome is not significant, and we cannot, on the evidence, deny the fairness of the die.

EXERCISES

E8·7·8. A coin is tossed 50 times, and 32 heads are scored. Is the result significant? Use (8·072).

E8·7·9. A coin is tossed 100 times; how many tails would have to be scored to provide adequate evidence of bias?

E8·7·10. In a 600-bed hospital which is always full and in which the patients stay for only a week or so, the fatality-rate is usually about 30 per cent. per annum. Certain new measures are adopted and in the following year the fatality-rate is 27 per cent. Is it likely that this result is due merely to chance if there have been no other relevant changes? (Take the sample size as 30,000.)

E8·7·11. In the table of the frequencies of even and odd digits in a page of allegedly Random Sampling Numbers that was given at the end of **8·05**, we are given the datum that there were only 485 even digits in the first 1,000 digits, and only 984 even digits in the 2,000 digits. Is either of these data good evidence for the view that the sampling giving rise to the numbers was not really random?

CHAPTER NINE

MATHEMATICS AND DEDUCTION

9·01 Introduction

After drawing a distinction between logically complete and logically incomplete derivations of theorems in mathematics ("proofs" versus "demonstrations"), we examine what it means to say of a mathematical theorem that it is true. We explain the reasons that have led the generality of mathematicians and logicians to accept the view that to say of a mathematical proposition p of a system S that it is true is simply to say that p is categorically provable in S; p cannot be regarded as true in the sense of truth that connects p with certain natural facts unless, as relatively rarely happens, the abstractions that p involves in so far as it is a proposition of pure mathematics can be interpreted in terms of objects and relations that occur in nature. But all such interpretations lie outside mathematics itself; they are not a part of the mathematical system S in which p is a theorem. Historically, this approach to mathematical truth has been associated with the rise and extension of modern axiomatics; so we proceed to expound some of the basic ideas of axiomatics, and its advantages and limitations.

9·02 Demonstration and Proof

To say that Mathematics is a deductive science is a platitude. However, it is not in practice a deductive science in so far as being a deductive science requires that all the reasonings offered within the science are of a *strictly* deductive kind. It is clear that so-called proofs in mathematics are not deductive in the way that proofs in Formal Logic, as illustrated in **2·13**, **2·17**, **3·10**, and **3·13**, are deductive. They can, doubtless, be made fully deductive by taking the necessary trouble (which is not small), but, speaking of actualities and not of possibilities, they are not, in general, fully deductive as they stand.[1] What the

---

[1] This thesis has been maintained and discussed by Nidditch: *I.F.L.M.*, Introduction.

mathematician usually offers as a proof is not a complete step-by-step deduction in which each step is explicitly justified as being a postulate, a definition or a consequence, by virtue of explicitly prescribed rules, of preceding steps; it is only a rough outline of such a deduction, many steps and justifications needed for completeness being omitted. Depending on his audience, the mathematician states just those steps and justifications which he judges to suffice to enable the competent members of the audience to realise that the formula which he is putting forward as a theorem is indeed a theorem, *i.e.* a categorically provable formula. Thus, the degree of detail with which the mathematician equips his argument is determined largely by psychological rather than by logical considerations. An argument of this sort, which, at least among those who are aware of logical canons, makes no pretence to being a complete proof with no needed steps whatever missing and no needed justifications whatever missing, is what throughout this text we have been calling a *demonstration*. For us, "demonstration" and "proof" are not synonymous. A proof is a logically complete argument, accompanied by the appropriate justifications; a demonstration is a logically incomplete argument, without full accompaniment of the appropriate justifications, which its author regards as giving the essence of what would be the corresponding proof.

Of course, in English "demonstration" and "proof" are ordinarily synonyms; we are proposing a usage, on the grounds of utility, whereby they would cease, in technical discourse, to be synonyms. Associated with the word "demonstration" will be the verbs "to demonstrate" and "to show"; associated with the word "proof" will be the verbs "to prove" and "to deduce". Which particular words be employed does not in the least matter; what is important is that two sets of words be chosen and consistently employed so that the distinction to which we have drawn attention is marked and preserved.

9·03 Mathematical Truth

For simplicity, in the following discussion (and in **9·04** and **9·05**) we shall suppose that all the theorems of the mathematician are *closed* and not *open* formulae, that is that they do not contain any free occurrences of variables; and we shall also suppose that all the theorems are actual formulae and that none of them is merely a schema of such actual formulae. Accordingly, we shall be supposing that all the theorems of the mathematician are propositions. Finally, we shall disregard Intuitionist mathematics and attend solely to the ordinary mathematics, in which Classical logic is employed.

A proposition is, by definition, a statement that is either-true-or-false. In what way or in what sense can mathematical propositions be described as being true or as being false? There are two simple points which indicate that this question expresses an important problem. The first point is that the truth or falsity of a proposition is normally, without taking notice of the philosophical difficulties, a matter determined by the correspondence or absence of correspondence between the proposition and what the proposition is about (or what it states); and this correspondence or absence of correspondence can usually, *in principle*, be discovered by taking suitable empirical measures of an observational or introspectional kind.[1] But in the case of many mathematical propositions no such correspondence or its absence, were it to exist, could be discovered by empirical methods; for, on the standard or intended interpretation (if there is one) of the mathematical

[1] There are serious philosophical difficulties connected with this Verifiability Principle. See, *e.g.* Ayer, A. J. (1910-): *Language, Truth, and Logic* (London, 1946), revised edition; also O'Connor, D. J. (1914-): "Some consequences of Ayer's verification principle", *Analysis*, 1949-50, **10**, 67-72; and Nidditch: "A note on Church's criticism of Ayer's verifiability principle", *Mind*, 1961, **70**.

proposition, what the proposition is about are abstract, or ideal, not concrete, entities, and therefore there are no natural phenomena to make the proposition true or false; and all the more are there no natural phenomena to make the proposition true or false if it has, as in Boolean Algebra, no standard or intended interpretation. The second point has historically been of greater weight. Since the published construction, first by Lobachevsky in the 1820's and then by others in the later decades of the nineteenth century, of consistent non-Euclidean geometries, that is geometries in which Euclid's Postulate of Parallels is contradicted, it is no longer possible to regard Euclidean geometry in the naïve way that it had been regarded during at least the previous two centuries: as the repository of *the* matter-of-fact truths about physical space. This is not to say that, suitably interpreted, Euclidean geometry is not *the* geometry of physical space. It is to say that any claim to rightful possession of that status has to be established by empirical methods, and cannot be awarded entirely on *a priori* grounds, as it had been earlier when Euclidean geometry had no competitor. Assuming that space is throughout either Euclidean—through each point not on a line AB there is exactly one line parallel to AB—or Lobachevskian—through each point not on a line AB there is more than one line parallel to AB—or Riemannian—through each point not on a line AB there is no line parallel to AB—it is clear that not all three geometries state what is the case about the nature and properties of space.

Let us amplify those two points a little more. Consider a true proposition of everyday life or of science, *e.g.* "The density of gold is greater than the density of mercury". This proposition is about the density of gold and the density of mercury and so, indirectly, about gold and mercury themselves; instances of gold and mercury exist in an ordinary sense and there are in nature certain facts which make it true in an ordinary sense that the density of gold is greater than the density of mercury. The important point is that the physicist would not assert a proposition such as the one mentioned unless he rationally thought that the conceived entities, *e.g.* instances of gold and mercury, that the proposition was directly or indirectly about actually existed. But in the case of many so-called true mathematical propositions, *e.g.* "An infinite subset of a countable set is countable", "There is no rational number q such that $q^2 = 2$", what they are directly or indirectly about cannot be said to exist in an ordinary sense and cannot therefore be said to be true in an ordinary sense. If mathematical notions, such as of irrational numbers and of differentials have existent, objective correlates, the ontological status of these correlates is quite different from the correlates of the notions entertained within the field of the natural sciences and of lay experience.

The second point of difficulty in connection with the idea of mathematical truth is that one mathematical proposition p may be a theorem—and so a truth—in one consistent mathematical system while its negation Np may be a theorem—and so a truth—in another consistent mathematical system. Accordingly, in an ordinary sense of truth, it is not possible for both p and for Np to be true, and yet, from the standpoint of mathematics itself, there is no way of discriminating between these two propositions so far as "real truth" is concerned. To give an illustration of two such propositions p and Np: in a system of Euclidean geometry "The sum of the interior angles of a triangle is equal to two right angles" is a theorem, whereas in a system of Lobachevskian geometry "The sum of the interior angles of a triangle is not equal to two right angles [but to less than two right angles]" is a theorem.

Because of the difficulties involved in the idea of mathematical truth that we have referred to, it has become more and more widely accepted during the past hundred years, with the result that it is now the orthodox doctrine, that to say of a mathematical proposition p that it is true is merely to say that p is true in some mathematical system S, and that this in turn is merely to say that p is a theorem in S. Thus, the *semantic* notion of truth of mathematical propositions is replaced by a *syntactical one*: instead of an ordinary *meaning* of truth, there is offered a criterion of "truth" solely in terms of logic—formal deducibility within a given postulational system. This view of the nature of mathematical truth, to the effect that truth in mathematics is essentially associated with logic rather than ontology—associated with deducibility from postulates adopted as conveniently and fruitfully acceptable for the purposes of developing a certain system—was first put forward with full explicitness and clarity by the Scottish philosopher Dugald Stewart. "Whereas, in all other sciences," he says, "the propositions which we attempt to establish express fact, real or supposed—in mathematics, the propositions which we demonstrate only assert a connection between certain suppositions and certain consequences. Our reasonings, therefore, in mathematics, are directed to an object essentially different from what we have in view, in any other employment of our intellectual faculties—not to ascertain *truths* with respect to actual existence, but to trace the logical filiation of consequences which follow from our assumed hypotheses."[1] By the turn of the present century, Stewart's conception of mathematical truth had become a commonplace. Thus, in about 1896 Peirce wrote:

"The most abstract of all the sciences is mathematics. That this is so, has been made manifest in our day; because all mathematicians now see clearly that mathematics is only busied about *purely*

---

[1] Stewart, D. (1753-1828): *Elements of the Philosophy of the Human Mind II* (Edinburgh, 1818), Chapter II, § 3.1.

hypothetical questions. As for what the truth of existence may be the mathematician does not (*qua* mathematician) care a straw. It is true that early mathematicians could not clearly see that this was so. But for all their not seeing it, it was just as true of the mathematics of early days as of our own. The early mathematician might perhaps be more inclined to assert roundly that two straight lines in a plane cut by a third so as to make the sum of the internal angles on one side less than two right angles would meet at some finite distance on that side if sufficiently produced; although, as a matter of fact, we observe no such tendency in Euclid. But however that may have been, the early mathematician had certainly no more tendency than the modern to *inquire into the truth of that postulate*; but quite the reverse. What he really did, therefore, was merely to deduce consequences of unsupported assumptions, whether he recognised that this was the nature of his business or not. Mathematics, then, really was, for him as for us, the most abstract of the sciences, cut off from all inquiry into existential truth. . . . Mathematics does not undertake to ascertain any matter of fact whatever, but merely posits hypotheses, and traces out their consequences."[1]

And a purely professional mathematician, in the first decade of this century, commenting on the abstract, nominalistic nature of mathematics—abstract in that in mathematical reasoning attention may be paid only to the formal, logical nature of the relevant propositions and not to the meaning of the embodied terms and relations, and nominalistic in that none of these embodied terms and relations (which are, besides, always in principle liable to be open to various satisfactory interpretations and so not to be semantically constant) is entitled to be regarded as designating actually existing entities or relations—said:

"The nominalism of the present day mathematician consists in treating the objects of his investigation and the relations between them as mere symbols. He then states his propositions, in effect,

---

[1] *Collected Papers of Charles Sanders Peirce I*, pp. 23 and 109 (Harvard, 1931). The final quoted sentence was written in 1902. On the historical point, let us remark that in the medieval period geometry was not thought of as the true physics of space, for then, predominantly, space was conceived as the boundaries, not as the container, of bodies. But in the seventeenth and eighteenth centuries, with the rise of modern mechanics with its s's and t's, Euclid's geometry was regarded as absolutely physically true. This is clear from the works of, *e.g.* Spinoza, Newton, and Kant.

in the following form: If there exists any objects in the physical or mental world with relations among themselves which satisfy the conditions which I have laid down for my symbols, then such and such facts will be true concerning them."[1]

In short, there is general agreement that a mathematical theory is, in the now popular phrase, *a hypothetico-deductive system*.[2] It is a system in which there are certain *primitive propositions* (postulates) which are adopted without proof and from which alone all other categorically asserted propositions of the system have to be logically deducible. (We neglect, for simplicity, the presence of definitions.)

9·04 Mathematics and Axiomatics

As already mentioned, mathematicians do not usually give proofs but only demonstrations of their theorems. Hence, in practice, an axiomatic (postulational) piece of mathematics will usually consist of: axioms (or axiom schemata), definitions (or definition schemata), demonstrations and theorems.

Axioms.—An axiom of the system S is a categorically assertible proposition of S, although it is not mediately demonstrated; it is laid down as being assertible without demonstration. The axioms have a content: they are

[1] Bôcher, M. (1867-1918): "The fundamental conceptions and methods of mathematics", *Bull. Amer. Math. Soc.*, 1904-5, **11**, 115-35.

Not all mathematicians take such a nominalistic view of all mathematics. Especially in connection with Set Theory, there have been controversies on the acceptability or truth of proposed axioms. The reader should consult the classical essay by Borel, E. (1871-1956): *Leçons sur la théorie des fonctions* (Paris, 1950, fourth edition; first edition, 1898), studying particularly the discussions between Borel and other eminent mathematicians, which are reprinted on p. 135 *et seq.* and p. 254 *et seq.* And cf. p. 85 above.

[2] This term is due to the Italian logician and mathematician Pieri, who was one of the leading members of Peano's school, that concerned itself with the logical foundations of geometry and arithmetic—and with the purely logical methods associated with or arising from that concern: Pieri, M. (1860-1913): "Della geometria elementare come sistema ipotetico deduttivo", *Memorie della Reale Accademia delle Scienze di Torino* (2), 1899, **49**, 173-222.

composed, formally, of well-formed strings of symbols. The various component symbols are commonly thought of as semantically constant: there is an intended or subjectively inserted interpretation. The component symbols of the mathematical axioms represent, subject to a qualification to be mentioned either logical concepts or what are called the *primitive concepts* of the system. For example, in the axioms (3·051) to (3·056), $+$ and 0 and $-x$ are primitive concepts, whereas "$=$", "$\neq$", "for all", and "member of" denote logical concepts. The primitive concepts are said to be *implicitly defined*[1] by the axioms. Thus, the concept $+$ with respect to an additive group is given implicit definition by (3·051) to (3·056): the primary properties of $+$ within an additive group are determined by those axioms and in that way and to that extent $+$ is defined by them, although, also, none of the axioms specifies what precisely "$+$" is replaceable by, or equal or equivalent to, within the system, and therefore the definition provided is merely an implicit and not an explicit one.

Definitions.—A definition—an *explicit definition*—is a statement in the U-language that a certain symbol is (definition-wise) equal to a certain string of symbols each of which, unless denoting a logical concept, has already been defined implicitly or explicitly, this definition-wise

---

[1] The term "implicit definition" was introduced by Gergonne, J. H. (1771-1859): "Essai sur la théorie des définitions", *Annales des Mathématiquos Pures et Appliques*, 1818, **9**, 1-35.
The sense of the term given by Gergonne is somewhat different from its sense in axiomatics mentioned in the text. "If an expression," he says, "contains a single word whose meaning we do not know, the enunciation of this expression can suffice to reveal its value to us. . . . Sentences of these kinds which bring about the understanding of one of the words composing them, by means of the known significance of the others, might be called *implicit definitions*". Gergonne gives as an example: if the meanings of the words "triangle" and "quadrilateral" are known but the meaning of "diagonal" is not, then "Each of the two diagonals of a quadrilateral divides it into two triangles" is an implicit definition.

equality permitting the substitution of the new symbol for the string and *vice versa*; or it is a statement in the object language that a certain formulary symbol holds if and only if a certain other formulary symbol holds in which all the component symbols, except those denoting logical concepts, have already been defined implicitly or explicitly. Cf. 4·06 and the first footnote therein.

Demonstrations.—A demonstration is a series of statements directed to the establishment of a specific proposition, which is then known to be a *theorem*, this establishment making use of (i) the axioms of the system, (ii) the definitions of the system, (iii) certain principles of deduction regarded as belonging to logic, and (iv) certain results belonging to other portions of mathematics.[1] About (i) and (ii) nothing more need now be said. With respect to (iii), it is usual for the principles of logic employed, whether these be rules of deduction or theorems in some logical calculus, to be employed in a purely unsystematised and implicit manner. The principles of logic to be used in the mathematical axiomatic system are not codified in presenting the foundations of the system; and those employed in any particular piece of reasoning within the system are not explicitly referred to, as justifying the inferences drawn; in practice, the mathematician assumes that all the logical principles needed within an axiomatic system could be codified, and that all the steps in any piece of reasoning within the system could be given full and explicit justification in terms of the axioms, definitions, logical principles, and results incorporated from other branches of mathematics. With respect to (iv), it must be pointed out that almost every axiomatic system of a portion of mathematics

[1] The first conscientious and systematic effort at achieving demonstrations of rigour in mathematics was made by Hérigone, P.: *Cursus Mathematicus I-VI* (Paris, 1644, second edition; first edition, 1634). For some idea of Hérigone's symbolism and approach, see Cajori: *History of Mathematical Notations*, especially I, § 189.

involves certain other portions of mathematics. Let us give three examples. In our axiomatic system for finite probability presented in **7·05** and **7·07** we make use of that portion of mathematics that is concerned with the arithmetic of real numbers and with that portion of mathematics that is concerned with the theory of sets. In an axiomatic system for the real numbers, in which these are dealt with by Dedekind's method, use is made of the arithmetic of the rational numbers. In an axiomatic system for Euclidean three-dimensional space, use is made of the arithmetic of the integers: any *two* points determine a line, a triangle has *three* sides, a quadrilateral has *two* and only two diagonals each of which bisects the quadrilateral into *two* triangles.

When, in the second paragraph of this section, we were speaking of axioms, we said in effect, that these had for their content either logical concepts or primitive concepts of the system—subject to a qualification. The qualification is two-fold and is this: (*a*) it is possible for mathematical concepts belonging to the field in question, say Euclidean geometry, to occur in the axioms without being primitive concepts of the system, for concepts explicitly defined can be introduced into axioms after the definitions have been given; *e.g.* in an axiomatic system for Euclidean geometry the concept of angle might be defined, in terms, ultimately, of concepts used in already introduced axioms, and then this concept can occur in a subsequent axiom. (*b*) Concepts belonging to fields of mathematics other than the one with which the system is directly concerned can also occur in the axioms; *e.g.* in an axiomatic system for Euclidean geometry there might be as axioms "*Two* distinct points determine a straight line" and "For any *three* points belonging to a straight line, there is *one* and only *one* between the other *two* points", in which arithmetical concepts occur; and, again, arithmetical concepts occur in our axioms for probability in **7·05**. (In this paragraph, as elsewhere in the discussion, we have, to avoid circumlocution, not distinguished a concept from its symbolisations.)

As we have remarked, in almost every axiomatic system of a portion of mathematics, use will be made of what belongs to logic and to some other portion of mathematics; any such other theory that is used is said to be an *auxiliary theory*, with respect to the axiomatic system in question.

General axiomatics is the study of the "logical" features of axiomatic systems. These features are mainly connected with the axioms and with the definitions. Related to each specific axiomatic system there will be the study of its logical features, and this particular study will be the *axiomatics* or *metamathematics* of that system.

Concerning the axioms, the axiomatist considers three kinds of questions: are the axioms consistent? are they complete? are they independent? These questions amount to asking: is any of the axioms incompatible with (contradictory to) the remainder? can additional axioms yield further theorems, without making the new system inconsistent? is any of the axioms superfluous, being demonstrable from the remainder? However, these questions are directed not simply at the axioms themselves, but at the whole system including their consequences: it is generally assumed that the logical principles employed in the system are mutually compatible and cannot essentially alter the character of what they are applied to. Thus, the axiomatist's question about consistency is not merely: does any of the axioms contradict any of the other axioms? but also: does any of the *consequences* of the axioms contradict any of the other consequences? Similarly with the other questions.

An axiomatic (postulational) system of mathematics is said to be *simply-consistent* if and only if there is no well-formed formula b such that both b and the negation of b are categorical theorems in the system; cf. **2·19**. A mathematical axiomatic or postulational system S is said to be *simply-complete* if and only if every statement that is "true" in the informal mathematics of which S is an intended formalisation is categorically provable in S. An axiomatic system S of mathematics that is simply-consistent is said to be *absolutely complete* if and only if the addition as an axiom to S of a formula b that is not a categorical theorem in S would result in the system S + b being simply-inconsistent; cf. **2·20**. An axiom d of an axiomatic system S is said to be *independent* if and only if it is not the case that d is a categorical theorem in S − d; hence the axioms are mutually independent if and only if none of the axioms is derivable from the remaining ones. The usual way of showing independence of this kind is to construct a series of models, as illustrated in **4·03**.[1] The definition of independence given in **4·03** is somewhat different from that we have just given, but it is straightforward to show that the two definitions are equivalent; see E9·4·1.

With respect to definitions, the axiomatist deals with the questions associated with the primitive concepts of an axiomatic system.   Such questions are: are all the primitive concepts irreducible to the remainder, that is, can the number of primitive concepts be reduced by our being able to give explicit definitions of some of them? in order to cover a certain mathematical field, which is the most economical set of primitive concepts to employ? Cf. BAH_1 and BAH_2. In the last twenty years of the nineteenth century and the first five years of the twentieth century a great deal of work was done on this aspect of axiomatics, especially in relation to arithmetic and geometry.

---

[1] The procedure, through the construction of models, for testing mutual independence was devised by Peano; cf., *e.g.* his paper: "Sui fondamenti della geometria", *Riv. di Mat.*, 1894, **4**, 51-90.

The leaders and principal workers in this direction were the members of Peano's Italian school, Whitehead in England and Huntington and Veblen in the United States. Since that generation there has been an unfortunate tendency for workers in the foundations of mathematics to be separate from contributors to important advances in everyday, concrete mathematics.[1]

[1] Some of the important works in axiomatics, especially the axiomatics of geometrical systems, published in the period 1880-1905 and one or two published later, are the following. Pasch, M. (1843-1930): *Vorlesungen über neuere Geometrie* (Leipzig, 1882); this book initiated the modern work in axiomatics. Peano: *I Principii di Geometria* (Turin, 1889); *Riv. di Mat.*, **4**, 51-90; his contributions in the various editions of the *Formulaire de Mathématiques* (1895-1910), *e.g.* on definitions in the 1901 edition; and his paper published in *Bibliothèque du Congrès International de Philosophie III* (Paris, 1901), 279 *et seq.* Hilbert: *Die Grundlagen der Geometrie.* Whitehead: *Universal Algebra*; *The Axioms of Projective Geometry* (Cambridge, 1906). Pieri: "I principii della geometria di posizione, composti in sistema logico deduttivo", *Memorie dell' Accademia Reale di Torino* (2), 1898, **48**, 1-62; *ibid*, 1899, **49**, 173-222; and "La geometria elementare", *Memorie di Matematica e di Fisica della Società Italiana delle Scienze*, 1908, **15**, 345 *et seq.* Padoa, A.: "Essai d'une théorie algébrique des nombres entiers, précédé d'une introduction logique à une théorie déductive quelconque", *Bibliothèque du Congrès International de Philosophie III* (Paris, 1901), 309 *et seq*; "La théorie des nombres entiers absolus", *Rev. de Math*, 1902, **8**, 45-54. Huntington: "A complete set of postulates for the theory of absolute continuous magnitude", *Trans. Amer. Math. Soc.*, 1902, **3**, 264-279; *ibid*, 1904, **5**, 288-305; "A set of postulates for abstract geometry, expressed in terms of the simple relation of inclusion", *Math. Ann.*, 1913, **73**, 522-59, reformulated in two papers in *Scripta Mathematica*, 1938, **5**. Moore, E. H.: "On the progress of geometry", *Trans. Amer. Math. Soc.*, 1902, **3**, 142-58. Russell: *Principles of Mathematics.* Veblen: *Trans. Amer. Math. Soc.*, 1904, **5**, 343-84; with Young, J. W. (1879-1932): "A set of assumptions for projective geometry", *Amer. J. Math.*, 1908, **30**, 347-80. Moore, R. L. (1882-): "Sets of metrical hypotheses for geometry", *Trans. Amer. Math. Soc.*, 1908, **9**, 487-512. Schweitzer, A. R. (1877-): "A theory of geometrical relations", *Amer. J. Math.*, 1909, **31**, 365-410.

For later developments, and general discussions of the nature and importance of axiomatics, see: Hilbert and Bernays: *Die Grundlagen der Mathematik I, II*; and Kleene's article on "Mathematics, Foundations of", in the current printing of the *Encyclopedia Britannica.* Also valuable is the lengthy survey given by Bcth, E. W. (1908-): *The Foundations of Mathematics, a study in the philosophy of science* (Amsterdam, 1959).

EXERCISES

E9·4·1. Show that a body of axioms A_1, A_2, ..., A_n for an axiomatic system S are mutually independent in the sense defined in **9·04** if and only if each A_i is an independent axiom in the sense defined in **4·03**.

*E9·4·2. Show by the construction of models that the axioms of PCŁ are mutually independent.[1]

*E9·4·3. Are the axioms of PCF mutually independent? (Try to deduce E2·20·109 (c) from the remainder.)

E9·4·4. Show, by using the set of all the multiples of 2 as a model, that the axioms (6·051) to (6·056) for an additive group are simply-consistent.

E9·4·5. Using the symbol "∘", formulate a set of axioms which can be interpreted both as axioms for an additive and as axioms for a multiplicative group; and hence show that the axioms (6·057) to (6·0512) for a multiplicative group are simply-consistent.

*E9·4·6. Construct, with no more than four axioms, an arithmetic of the *natural numbers* 0, 1, 2, ... having $N^\geq$ and "successor of" as the only primitive concepts; besides, use no more than the concepts of Set Theory, the concept $=$ with respect to objects that are not sets, and the concepts of the Pure Functional Calculus of Order 1 together with the uniqueness quantifier concept "there is a single" (which is definable in the FC with Equality: KSxbxCSybyy$=$x where y is free for x in bx can be given as the *definiens* of S'xbx, "S'" denoting "there is a single"). (Answer:[2] (i) $N^\geq \neq \emptyset$; (ii) for all x, if x is a member of $N^\geq$, then the successor of x is a member of $N^\geq$; (iii) for all m, if $m \neq \emptyset$ and $m \subseteq N^\geq$, then there is some x such that x is a member of m and such that, for no y of m, is x equal to the successor of y; (iv) for all x, y, and z of $N^\geq$, if x is the successor of no y and z is the successor of no y, then $x = z$. Other answers are possible.)

---

[1] For the method of showing independence of postulates of logic, and of rules of inference (first due to Huntington), see Church: *Introduction to Mathematical Logic*, especially § 19.

[2] Pieri: "Sopra gli assiomi aritmetici", *Bolletino dell, Accademia Gioenia in Catania, Serie 2a* (1908). Pieri's axioms are a simplification of the better known set of axioms due to Peano: *Arithmetices Principia*, for instance, the Principle of Mathematical Induction is an axiom in Peano's set, whereas it is obtainable as a theorem in Pieri's system.

E9·4·7. Show that $N^{\geq}$ in the axioms given in E9·4·6 can be interpreted as any well-ordered set of non-negative integers; *e.g.* as the set of all the primes.

E9·4·8. From the axioms in E9·4·6, show that there is a single member of $N^{\geq}$ which is the successor of no other member.

9·05 The Advantages of the Postulational Method

From what was said about axiomatics in the previous section, two points are readily apparent. The first is that the axiomatics of any particular axiomatic system of mathematics is simply the epitheory of that system. The second is that the investigations of axiomatics are applicable also to mathematical systems some or all of whose postulates are axiom schemata and some or all of whose definitional equations are definitional schemata. (An example of a specific definition in Pieri's arithmetic is: 0 is by definition equal to that single member of $N^{\geq}$ which is the successor of no member of $N^{\geq}$, cf. E9·4·6 and E9·4·8; examples of a definition schema, in Pieri's arithmetic, are: (i) x^{+} is by definition equal to the successor of x; (ii) $x + 0 \leftrightarrow x$ and $x + y^{+} \leftrightarrow (x + y)^{+}$, this definition schema being the definition of addition in the arithmetic.) Thus, the methods of axiomatics are relevant to any postulational system of mathematics whether this is a deductive system, in the sense that all the derivations of theorems within it are proofs and not merely demonstrations, or whether it is merely a demonstrative system, its theorems being derived merely by demonstration and not by proof, or whether it is a mixed system, having some proofs and some demonstrations.

It was emphasised by Pasch[1] that theorems in a postulational system of mathematics must not be obtained by making use of the *meaning* of the terms occurring in the postulates, but obtained solely by making use of the logical relationships involved. In the course of establishing

[1] Pasch: *Vorlesungen über neuere Geometrie*, especially p. 98.

a theorem it may be helpful to think of some assigned meaning of the mathematical concepts; however, such thoughts can be no more than psychological, not logical, requirements for the derivation. If meanings of the terms play a part in the derivation itself, the derivation is, by virtue of that fact, logically unsatisfactorily, for logical validity is dependent on the form alone and not in the least on the content of invoked formulae; and if, ultimately, a theorem cannot be derived without semantical considerations—if it cannot be derived by logical syntax alone—then there is an indication of an inadequacy in the postulates or definitions. Accordingly, the mathematician's final derivation of a theorem within a postulational system must be carried through in a purely formal way, in complete abstraction from any particular meaning of the occurring symbols.

The postulational method requires, then, that the symbols of the primitive and other concepts of a system be manipulated as meaningless marks whose role is to serve as pieces in a game that is to be played in accordance with certain prescribed rules: logical rules of inference. Concerning his description of this postulational abstraction from the meanings of the mathematical symbols, Bôcher says: "It may perhaps be said that instead of inviting you to a feast I have merely shown you the empty dishes and explain how the feast would be served if only the dishes were filled. / Notice that just as the empty dishes could be filled by a great variety of viands, so the empty symbols of mathematics can be given meanings of the most varied sorts./"[1]

What are the advantages of the postulational method? (i) At the beginning of **5·02** we quoted Bernard's dictum: "L'art, c'est *moi*; la science, c'est *nous*". General and fundamental features of the sciences, deductive and

[1] Bôcher: *Bull. Amer. Math. Soc.*, 1904-5, **11**, 115-35.

inductive, are their objectivity and their impersonality. The postulational method promotes these features in the realm of mathematics by its emphasis on the logical and syntactical elements and aspects, at the cost of the psychological and semantical ones.

(ii) A postulational, deductive system, with specified rules of deduction, has the advantage of allowing the correctness of any proffered proof to be decisively settled; all that is needed is a quasi-mechanical checking of each step and reference in the proof in comparison with the postulates, definitions, already deduced theorems, and rules of deduction.

(iii) A postulational system, by virtue of its postulates and definitions, provides definite starting points and termini for the derivation of theorems. These postulates and definitions enable one to know exactly what the ultimate grounds for any assertion within the system may be. In reasoning outside of a postulational system, it is difficult to avoid an unterminated regress in attempting to comply with stringent demands for justifications of assertions made; and, not infrequently, such indeterminacy leads to "reasoning" in a circle, the proposition q being offered as the reason for accepting the proposition p when, in fact, q cannot be asserted unless p has already been established.

(iv) The postulational method enables the mathematician to have unity amid variety, to have organisation amid individuality. In any science there is the desire to systematise particular results: to connect them and to show the connection. But it is not merely the results that one wishes to connect; one wishes also to connect together the concepts involved in the results. There is another important and fruitful characteristic of the systematic aspect of mathematical science which is closely bound up with the connection of concepts: in general, the mathematician aims in constructing and developing postulational systems to attain a fundamental economy. He wishes to employ an irreducible paucity of distinct concepts. By having this desire, interesting discoveries have been made in mathematics; *e.g.* it has been discovered that the concept of an ordered pair can be defined by—analysed in terms of—purely set-theoretic concepts, cf. **4·08**, and it has been discovered that the concept of a real number can be defined by—analysed in terms of—concepts of set theory and of the arithmetic of the positive whole numbers.

(v) The postulational method has the outstanding merit of leading to wider generalisations and new mathematical systems. By putting the various systems of numbers on a postulational basis, one can discover that they all share the properties of the system of the whole numbers—which leads to the notion of an integral domain and leads to the realisation of the wider scope of the concepts (terms and relations) involved in the system of whole numbers. This procedure is the comparative anatomy of mathematical systems; and, as in biology the comparative study of structures has enabled classificatory generalisations to be made and has prompted the finding out of the nature and existence of previously unknown morphological features within a given species, so too in mathematics the comparative study of structures brings advances in knowledge. The biological simile can be taken a stage further. Primarily because of the known existence of homologous structures, the Theory of Evolution was put forward; evolution would account for the possibility of making generic and higher classifications. Now, in mathematics one can actually construct high-level systems and then one can make more special systems evolve from these by the additional assignment of more particular features. Leaving this simile with biology and turning to the historically primary way in which the postulational method enables new mathematical systems to be constructed, we may observe that an axiomatic system S_1 based on the mutually independent axioms A_1 to A_n can be changed into a new axiomatic system S_2 simply by negating one or more of the axioms A_1 to A_n and preserving the remainder. (One could also just omit one or more of the axioms, but that procedure would bring us back to the situation dealt with a moment ago in comparison with biology.) Thus, Lobachevsky's Hyperbolic geometry was obtained merely by substituting a contradictory of Euclid's axiom of parallels. Euclid's axiom is to the effect that through a given point not on a straight line there is not more than one line which is parallel to the original line; since the other axioms of Euclidean geometry yield the theorem that through a given point not on a straight line there is at least one line parallel to the original line, it follows that in Euclidean geometry there is, through a given point not on a straight line, one and only one line parallel to the original line. Lobachevsky's contradiction of Euclid's axiom of parallels was to the effect that through a given point not on a straight line there is more than one line parallel to the original line. The new geometrical system of Lobachevsky was sure to be simply-consistent if Euclid's system was simply-consistent and the axioms of the latter were mutually independent. (Inversely, if Lobachevsky's geometry could be shown, irrespective of Euclid's, to be simply-consistent, then by that fact Euclid's axiom of parallels would be shown to be independent of the other Euclidean axioms.)

EXERCISES

E9·5·9. Show that $[s \lor (t \lor t_1)] \supset [t \lor (s \lor t_1)]$ is categorically provable in PCT.

*E9·5·10. Using analogous methods to those used for E9·5·9, establish Bernays' Theorem E2·13·58.[1]

---

[1] Cf. Nidditch: "A note on the redundant axiom of *Principia Mathematica*", *Mind*, 1960, **69**.

E9·5·11.   Give a suppositional method proof of *CCN*bd*A*bd. Cf. (9·0632)

E9·5·12.   Formulate a suppositional method rule whereby, if a schema of logic occurs as a step in a proof structure, then the formula consisting of a mathematical formula of the same form as the schema may be asserted as a subsequent step in the same section.

9·06 Discovery and Proof in Mathematics

Mathematics, it is generally agreed nowadays, is one product of human activity; it has no existence apart from that activity. Yet without doubt many mathematicians feel that their activity as mathematicians is directed towards discovering truths that exist independently of the human mind: that exist eternally. In no way, according to them, is mathematical truth a fabrication of human labour, moulded out of human notions; mathematics is the attempt at finding out a certain objectively existing kind of facts. A mathematician with this approach to his subject will tend to lay little stress on proofs or even on demonstration; for him all that matters is the personal vision, and the communication of that vision, of certain mathematical facts; for him, the derivation of a theorem is mere *gas*.[1]

This Platonic view of mathematics is, or has been, held by many mathematicians, though contemporaneously the proportion of mathematicians with this outlook is very small. Nevertheless, all, or almost all, mathematicians would agree on the fundamental importance of insight or intuition in the obtaining of mathematical truth, however differently the ontological status of this truth may be interpreted. There is also general agreement that in order to arrive at new mathematical knowledge the mind must, in some sense, be active and creative, and there must be

[1] Cf. Hardy, G. H. (1877-1947): "Mathematical Proof", *Mind*, 1929, **38**, 1-25; and *A Mathematician's Apology* (Cambridge, 1940).

processes of mental experiment or of reasoning by analogy.[1] Further, there is general agreement that in practice, even when dealing with a symbolic deductive system, the mathematician is guided, in his endeavours, by a particular interpretation of the formalism which he manipulates. And, finally, there is general agreement that at least for the most part postulational systems of mathematics can fruitfully be constructed only when intuition has already played its part in the creation of new ideas and in the discovery of important or interesting interrelationships between certain concepts; for postulational systems are not built for their own sakes, but built only to organise and generalise those mathematical materials, intuitively and informally obtained, which seem to be worth organising and generalising. The ordinary, discursive operations of the mind in its formative aspect are primary in mathematics.

Yet, if mathematics is to be a deductive science in the full sense, detailed considerations of logic cannot be neglected within it, even if the role of logic is secondary to the role of intuitive formation and interpretation. As we have said elsewhere: "To be sure, we admit the vital importance of creative discovery; we deny, however, that this obviates the obligation to form genuine proofs in order to confirm that the putative discovery *is* a discovery and not a pseudo-discovery. Intuition—whatever that is— may well be the source of new mathematics, and may well be the spirit that gives life to the body of mathematics. But it is recognised that in mathematics the deliverances of intuition are only a beginning, not the end; they have to be checked and controlled by rational regulations. If

[1] Cf. Polyá, G. (1887-): *Mathematics and Plausible Reasoning I, II* (Oxford, 1954). (In his opening pages Polyá says, as so many mathematicians do, that the mathematician is well trained in deductive reasoning; from the logician's standpoint, what he should say is, not "deductive" but "demonstrative" reasoning is what the mathematician learns.)

intuition is the heart of mathematics, logic is the head (and the head is higher than the heart)."[1]

At any rate, from the point of view of the logic of mathematics, the question of proof is fundamental. In this logic one has to be concerned with the deductive ideal of mathematical science, whether or not in their everyday work mathematicians find it useful or practicable to live up to this ideal. Besides this point, there are two others that should be made. The theory of deductive logic of Aristotle and of his successors[2] could not cope with mathematical arguments; very few mathematical arguments indeed can be accurately and adequately formalised by the methods of syllogistic and of the Propositional Calculus. To show concretely that modern logic possesses methods which can cope satisfactorily with any mathematical argument would be valuable if only for making manifest the superiority of this logic over the traditional and the essential unity—by virtue of the deductive method—of Mathematics and Formal Logic. In the second place, it is important to develop deductive techniques and to determine which among them is the most efficient and adaptable for the purposes of Mathematics and Formal Logic.

It seems to the present author that of all the deductive techniques so far elaborated the suppositional method comes nearest to satisfying the requirements of efficiency and adaptability. We shall illustrate one of the ways in which this method can be applied to giving a proof of a mathematical theorem. Other approaches with this method are possible.

---

[1] Nidditch: *I.F.L.M.*, p. 7.

[2] Aristotle (384-322 B.C.): *Prior Analytics*; and other logical writings all of which are usually classified under the title of the *Organon*. See also: Łukasiewicz: *Aristotle's Syllogistic*; Bochenski, I. M. (1902-): *Ancient Formal Logic* (Amsterdam, 1951); *Formale Logik* (Freiburg, Munich, 1956), and the references therein to the logical writings of and on the Stoics and medievals.

The theorem we are going to prove is that in an integral domain: if $xy = 0$, then $x = 0$ or $y = 0$. We shall first demonstrate that in an integral domain

(9·061)   For all x, y, and z, if $x + y = x + z$, then $y = z$.

We shall then be able to demonstrate that in an integral domain

(9·062)   For all x, $x0 = 0$.

In addition to the postulates of an integral domain we may use: the axiom schema of identity

(9·063)   (x) (x = x) $Pxx = x$,

the x denoting any member of the set of objects with which we are dealing; and the usual informal rules pertaining to equalities (identities), which can be regarded as reducing to the single rule to the effect that equals may be substituted for equals, the substitution not necessarily being made in all occurrences.

We proceed to the demonstration of (9·061).   Suppose

(9·064) $x + y = x + z$.

(9·065) $y = 0 + y$ by (6·054)

(9·066) $= (-x + x) + y$ by (6·055)

(9·067) $= -x + (x + y)$ by (6·053)

(9·068) $= -x + (x + z)$ by (9·064)

(9·069) $= (-x + x) + z$ by (6·053)

(9·0610) $= 0 + z$ by (6·055)

(9·0611) $= z$ by (6·054).

Next, we demonstrate (9·062).

(9·0612) $xx = xx$ by (6·057) and (9·063)

(9·0613) $x + 0 = x$ by (6·054)

(9·0614) $x(x + 0) = xx$ by 12, 13, substitution of equals

(9·0615) $xx = xx + 0$ by (6·057) and (6·054)

(9·0616) $x(x + 0) = xx + 0$ by (6·0512), 14, 15, substitution of equals

(9·0617) $x(x + 0) = xx + x0$ by (6·0512)

(9·0618) $xx + x0 = xx + 0$ by 16, 17, substitution of equals

(9·0619) $x0 = 0$ by (9·061) and (9·0618)

We want to amend the body of rules so far given for the suppositional method of proof in the following ways: we want to modify the Rule of Theorem Introduction in such a manner as to allow demonstrated, and not proved, theorems to be introduced into any section of a proof structure; we want to add a Rule of Postulate Introduction whereby any postulate can be inserted as a step in any section of a proof structure; we want to add a Rule of Substitution for Equals, whereby equals may be substituted for equals; and finally, we want to add a Rule of Applicative Substitution whereby if a schema of the PC or FC occurs as a step in some section of a proof structure, then an actual formula instantiating that schema may legitimately be asserted as a subsequent step in the same section. This last rule is a derivable one. The rule of substitution for equals, in the presence of the other rules of the suppositional method, enables one to pass from $x = y$ to $y = x$, and to pass from $x = y$ and $y = z$ to $x = z$.

We shall now prove that in an integral domain

(9·0620) $(x)(y)\{(xy = 0) \supset [(x = 0) \lor (y = 0)]\},$

the x and y here and in the following steps being any members of the integral domain.

$(9 \cdot 0621)$ $|xy|$ $|xy = 0°$

$(9 \cdot 0622)$ $\qquad |\sim x = 0°$

$(9 \cdot 0623)$ $\qquad |(x)(y)(z)[((\sim x = 0).(xy = xz)) \supset (y = z)]$

$(9 \cdot 0624)$ $\qquad |[(\sim x = 0).(xy = x0)] \supset (y = 0)$

$(9 \cdot 0625)$ $\qquad |xy = 0$

$(9 \cdot 0626)$ $\qquad |(x)(x0 = 0)$

$(9 \cdot 0627)$ $\qquad |x0 = 0$

$(9 \cdot 0628)$ $\qquad |xy = x0$

$(9 \cdot 0629)$ $\qquad |(\sim x = 0).(xy = x0)$

$(9 \cdot 0630)$ $\qquad |y = 0$

$(9 \cdot 0631)$ $\qquad (\sim x = 0) \supset (y = 0)$

$(9 \cdot 0632)$ $\qquad (\sim b \supset d) \supset (b \lor d)$

$(9 \cdot 0633)$ $\qquad [(\sim x = 0) \supset (y = 0)] \supset [(x = 0) \lor (y = 0)]$

$(9 \cdot 0634)$ $\qquad (x = 0) \lor (y = 0)$

$(9 \cdot 0635)$ $\qquad (xy = 0) \supset [(x = 0) \lor (y = 0)]$

$(9 \cdot 0636)$ $(x)(y)\{(xy = 0) \supset [(x = 0) \lor (y = 0)]\}$

References.—23: (6·0513), postulate in. 24: 23, uq ex. 25: 21, tf. 26: (9·062), theorem in. 27: 26, uq ex. 28: 25, 27, sub for equals. 29: 22, 28, con in. 30: 29, 24, imp ex. 31: 22, 30, imp in. 32: E9·5·10, theorem in. 33: 32, applic sub. 34: 31, 33, imp ex. 35: 21, 34, imp in. 36: 35, uq in. [(6·057) is used implicitly.]

EXERCISES

E9·6·13. Formulate a rule for the suppositional method whereby from x = y and b (x), where y is free for x, then b (y) may be asserted as a subsequent step; here the x and y denote any members (or names of members) of the explicit or implicit basic set with which one is dealing. This is the Rule of Substitution for Equals. (With no more than the 19 rules of alt in, alt ex, con in, con ex, imp in, imp ex, neg in, neg ex, neg² ex, re, tf, pq in, pq ex, uq in, uq ex, df in, df ex, post(ulate) in, sub for equals, an adequate body of postulates for Set Theory, and the postulates for the integral, rational and real number systems of **6·05**, one can, by the suppositional method, prove all the ordinary theorems, in these systems, that are demonstrated or employed in the usual informal, demonstrative mathematics.)[1]

E9·6·14. Show from the postulates for an integral domain in **6·05** that if $x \in \mathbf{Z}$, then $-x \in \mathbf{Z}$ and $-(-x) \in \mathbf{Z}$.

E9·6·15. Give a suppositional method proof of the theorem:
$$(x) \, [(x \in \mathbf{Z}) \supset (-(-x) = x)].$$

E9·6·16. Prove that if $x \equiv y \pmod{m}$, where $m \in \mathbf{N}$, then x and y leave the same remainder on division by m.

E9·6·17. Formulate the ordinary Principle of Mathematical Induction as a rule of inference for the suppositional method of proof.

---

[1] According to the famous Incompleteness Theorem of Gödel: "Über formal unentscheidbare Sätze der Principia Mathematica und verwandter Systeme I", *Monatsh. Math. Phys.*, 1931, **38**, 173-98,— no simply-consistent system S of arithmetic even of merely the natural numbers can be such that every statement that is true in the informal arithmetic of which S is the intended formalisation is categorically provable in S; that is, if S is simply-consistent, then it is simply-incomplete. For details, see Kleene: *Introduction to Metamathematics*; Ladrière, J.: *Les Limitations Internes des Formalismes* (Louvain, 1957).

CHAPTER TEN

DEDUCTION AND HYPOTHESIS IN THE INDUCTIVE SCIENCES

10·01 Introduction

Considering the inductive sciences, we begin by dealing with the nature and role of scientific explanation. We then explain at length the nature of abduction (hypothesis) with particular reference to the views of Peirce. Again in particular reference to his views, the various kinds of induction are treated, and their relations to abduction elucidated. Also, the relationship of deduction to abduction and induction is clarified. We next refer to the attempts to bring all induction and abduction within the scope of a theory of quantitative probability; two of the theorems most frequently used or mentioned in connection with such attempts—the Rule of Generalisation and the Rule of Succession—are explained, their consequences pointed out, and finally demonstrations of them given. Next, we sketch that view of science, increasingly favoured since the general recognition of the difficulties confronting a quantitatively probabilistic treatment of induction and abduction, according to which science operates essentially through the use of the hypothetico-deductive method. Finally, we refer to the doctrines of Positivism and Operationalism, which are rather extreme expressions of the empirical nature of science, and which have been of considerable influence and importance in modern discussions of the philosophy and logic of science, cf. **5·02**.

10·02 Scientific Explanation and Deduction

Everyone recognises the importance of theories for science. Commonly, indeed, precise and adequate theories are regarded as being the ultimate goal of all scientific activity; observations and experiments are treated as simply useful means to that end. "The object of all science, whether natural science or psychology, is to coordinate our experiences and to bring them into a logical system," remarks Einstein.[1] The immediate object of

[1] Einstein, A. (1879-1955): *The Meaning of Relativity*, English translation by Adams, E. P. p. 1 (sixth edition, London, 1954).

science is the discovery and establishment of scientific laws—putative laws of nature—and the ultimate object is to coordinate these scientific laws by bringing them into a unifying, postulational system. "The whole aim of science is to find out facts, and to work out a satisfactory theory of them."[1] But the facts to be found out are general facts: laws of nature. In so far as the scientist is interested in particular facts it is less for their own sakes than for the sake of some general fact or for the sake of a complex of general facts which are embodied in a theory.

A basic function of a scientific law is that it explains each particular fact falling under it, and a basic function of a scientific theory is that it explains each particular scientific law falling under it. Since a scientific law is liable to falsification or modification in the light of further experience, it is customary for the reflective scientist to treat it as a working hypothesis; and since a scientific theory also depends for its acceptability on the outcomes of experience, it has to be treated as a complex working hypothesis. "If you brought all the writers on scientific method with the most varied views together, I imagine that every one of them would agree that the testing of a deduction from a broad working hypothesis (some would say a theory) was at least a part of science."[2]

Particular facts are thought of as falling under scientific laws in the sense that they are deductive consequences of them—they can be derived by strictly deductively logical procedures from a hypothesis or from hypotheses; and the validity of a hypothesis is tested by comparing its implications with relevant facts amenable to experience. It is clear from this that deduction, in the sense of derivation that could be made strictly deductive, plays an extremely

---

[1] Peirce: *Collected Papers VII*, p. 59 (Harvard, 1958).
[2] Conant, J. B. (1892-): *Science and Common Sense*, p. 51 (Oxford, 1951).

important part in the sciences: "A scientific system consists of a set of hypotheses which form a *deductive system*; that is, which is arranged in such a way that from some of the hypotheses as premises all the other hypotheses *logically follow*" [our italics];[1] "Concepts play an essential role in the genesis of science, and it is through concepts that scientific knowledge tends to be formed. . . . These mental representations of facts serve as a basis for our reasonings, and we utilise our concepts in the *deductions* which lead to predictions" [our italics].[2]

What are the functions of scientific explanation, what are its purposes? One view is that presented by Peirce:

"In order to define the circumstances under which a scientific explanation is really needed, the best way is to ask in what way explanation subserves the purpose of science. We shall then see what the evil situation is which it remedies, or what the need is which it may be expected to supply. Now what an explanation of a phenomenon does is to supply a proposition which, if it had been known to be true before the phenomenon presented itself, would have rendered that phenomenon predictable, if not with certainty, at least as something very likely to occur. It thus renders that phenomenon rational—that is, makes it a logical consequence, necessary or probable. Consequently, if without any particular explanation, a phenomenon is such as must have occurred, there is no room at all for explanation. If the phenomenon is such as need not have occurred on the special occasion, but must occur on occasions differing in no discoverable and exactly assignable pertinent respect from the special occasion on which the phenomenon in question actually occurs, still there is nothing for explanation to do, until it is ascertained in what respects, if any, the individual occasion differs from those other occasions. For example, I throw a die, and it turns up ace. Now I know already that this die will turn up ace once in six times; and I am persuaded that it would be hopeless to attempt, at present, to find any pertinent conditions fulfilled on this occasion which are not fulfilled every time the die is thrown. Hence, no proposed explanation of the die's turning up an ace can be in order, unless we can discover some peculiar and pertinent feature about the present occasion. Why should my lottery-ticket have

---

[1] Braithwaite (1900-): *Scientific Explanation*, p. 12 (Cambridge, 1953).
[2] Picard, E. (1856-1941): *La Science Moderne*, p. 17 (Paris, 1909).

drawn a blank, and somebody else's a prize? No explanation is called for. The question is silly.

"Let us now pass to the case of a phenomenon in which, apart from a particular explanation, there was antecedently no reason for expecting it, and as little for expecting it not to happen. Suppose, for example, that on the day of the Lisbon earthquake the brightest new star had appeared in the heavens. There might possibly have been some explanation for this; but there would have been no motive for searching for one. To have done so would, indeed, have been a foolish proceeding, for reasons we need not now consider.

"Thus, the only case in which this method of investigation, namely, by the study of how an explanation can further the purpose of science, leads to the conclusion that an explanation is positively called for, is the case in which a phenomenon presents itself which, without some special explanation, there would be reason to expect would *not* present itself; and the logical demand for an explanation is the greater, the stronger the reason for expecting it not to occur was. . . .

"Accepting the conclusion that an explanation is needed when facts contrary to what we should expect emerge, it follows that the explanation must be such a proposition as would lead to the prediction of the observed facts, either as necessary consequences or at least as very probable under the circumstances. A hypothesis then, has to be adopted, which is likely in itself, and renders the facts likely. This step of adopting a hypothesis as being suggested by the facts, is what I call *abduction*."[1]

In his account of scientific explanation Peirce is primarily concerned with scientific theories rather than with scientific laws. In what way does a scientific law that is a mere generalisation, say a universal statement and so of the form "All *s* is *t*", serve to explain a particular phenomenon to the effect that a member of *s* is also a member of *t*? Venn[2] maintained that it is a fact's being isolated from other facts that creates the need of an explanation of it. (He also gives other reasons.)

"But I suspect," says Peirce,[3] "that when Mr Venn speaks of *isolation*, he is thinking of there being other facts from which the given fact is separated; and that it is not *isolation* that he means, but *separation*. Now separation

[1] Peirce: *Collected Papers VII*, pp. 113-14, 121-2.
[2] Venn: *Empirical Logic* (London, 1889).
[3] Peirce: *Collected Papers VII*, p. 118.

is itself a kind of connection; so that if that be his meaning, the state of things which calls for explanation is a connection which is not satisfactory to the mind. In that case, it is incumbent on Mr Venn to explain himself more precisely, and to say in what respect it is unsatisfactory. If he were to say, 'unsatisfactory in being contrary to what ought to be expected', he would come to my position, precisely."

Now Venn gives as an illustration of an explanation by way of a scientific law a generalisation under which the particular fact to be explained falls. "We notice a plant that is flagging on a hot summer day: next morning it stands up again fresh and green. 'Why has it revived in the morning?'—'Oh they always do'."[1]

(In fairness to Venn, it should be added that he acknowledges the relative feebleness of this example, and gives stronger and more scientific ones.) Peirce comments:

"One may smile at the naïveté of this; and certainly, it is not an explanation in the proper sense of the word. Still, its general function is the same as that of explanation; namely, it renders the fact a conclusion, necessary or probable, from what is already well known. It might be called a *regularisation*, explanation and regularisation being the two types of *rationalisation*. The regularisation, stated in full, would be,

Plants of a certain class usually revive in the morning;
This plant belongs to that class;
∴ This plant might be expected to revive in the morning.

Now it is true that the effect of the regularisation is that the fact observed is less isolated than before; but the purpose of the regularisation is, I think, much more accurately said to be to show that it might have been expected, had the facts been fully known."[2]

Thus, Peirce holds that only theories can, strictly speaking, be said to explain facts, and they explain by showing why the facts could be expected to occur; he holds further that a scientific law can, in a distinct sense, be said to explain in so far as it gives an indication that the particular facts

[1] Venn: *Empirical Logic*, p. 495.
[2] Peirce: *Collected Papers VII*, p. 119; and cf. his *Collected Papers II*, p. 450 (Harvard, 1932).

falling under it are to be expected, and he calls this special type of explanation that is afforded by scientific laws *regularisation*.

10·03 The Nature of Abduction (Hypothesis) and Induction

"Abduction" (less often "retroduction" or a "presumption") is Peirce's name for the construction of a theoretical hypothesis in science.

"[Abduction] is the first step of scientific reasoning, as induction is the concluding step. Nothing has so much contributed to present chaotic or erroneous ideas of the logic of science as failure to distinguish the essentially different characters of different elements of scientific reasoning; and one of the worst of these confusions, as well as one of the commonest, consists in regarding abduction and induction taken together (often mixed also with deduction) as a simple argument. Abduction and induction have, to be sure, this common feature, that both lead to the acceptance of a hypothesis because observed facts are such as would necessarily or probably result as consequences of that hypothesis. But for all that, they are the opposite poles of reason, the one the most ineffective, the other the most effective of arguments. The method of either is the very reverse of the other's. Abduction makes its start from the facts, without, at the outset, having any particular theory in view, though it is motived by the feeling that a theory is needed to explain the surprising facts. Induction makes its start from a hypothesis which seems to recommend itself, without at the outset having any particular facts in view, though it feels the need of facts to support the theory. Abduction seeks a theory. Induction seeks for facts. In abduction the consideration of the facts suggests the hypothesis. In induction the study of the hypothesis suggest the experiments which bring to light the very facts to which the hypothesis had pointed."[1]

Peirce distinguishes three kinds of argument in science: deduction, induction, and abduction. In an acceptable deductive argument the conclusion must be true if the premises are, that is, the negation of the conclusion is logically incompatible with the premises. In an acceptable inductive argument the conclusion is probably true, that is, the conclusion, in relation to the premises, has a greater

[1] Peirce: *Collected Papers VII*, pp. 136-7; and cf. *Collected Papers II*, pp. 495-7.

probability than its negation, the probability of the inductive conclusion being measured by the ratio whose numerator is the number of long-term cases in which both premisses and conclusion are fulfilled and whose denominator is the number of long-term cases in which the premisses are fulfilled, cf. (7·071). In an acceptable abductive argument for a theory the conclusion has a certain "likelihood" in relation to the premisses, but this likelihood is not capable of numerical evaluation; it is logico-psychological plausibility rather than mathematical probability that makes the theory expressed in the conclusion an acceptable one.[1] Peirce regards deductive argument as being the application of a general rule to a particular case to yield some result; *e.g.* applying the general rule "All men are mortal" to the particular case "Enoch was a man" yields the result "Enoch is mortal";[2] and he holds that inductive and abductive arguments are different from this and from each other, an inductive argument consisting of the application of a particular case to some result to yield a general rule as conclusion, and an abductive argument consisting of the application of a general rule to some result to yield a case as conclusion. He illustrates these ideas as follows:[3]

"If, from a bag of beans of which we know that ⅔ are white, we take one at random, it is a deductive inference that this bean is probably white, the probability being ⅔. We have, in effect, the following syllogism: *Rule.*—The beans in this bag are ⅔ white. *Case.*—This bean has been drawn in such a way that in the long run the relative number of white beans so drawn would be equal to the relative number in the bag. *Result.*—This bean has been drawn in such a way that in the long run it would turn out white ⅔ of the time.

"If instead of drawing one bean we draw a handful at random and conclude that about ⅔ of the handful are probably white, the

---

[1] Cf., *e.g.* Peirce: *Collected Papers II*, p. 53.

[2] *Ibid.*, pp. 393-5 and 415; but elsewhere, cf. *Collected Papers VII*, pp. 67-71, Peirce considers inductive arguments whose conclusions have no numerical probabilities.

[3] *Ibid.*, pp. 58-9, 407-9, 497-8.

reasoning is of the same sort. If, however, not knowing what proportion of white beans there are in the bag, we draw a handful at random
and, finding ⅔ of the beans in the handful white, conclude that about ⅔
of those in the bag are white, we are rowing up the current of deductive
sequence, and are concluding a rule from the observation of a result
in a particular case. [This is induction.] . . .

"But this is not the only way of inverting a deductive syllogism so
as to produce a synthetic inference. Suppose I enter a room and
there find a number of bags, containing different kinds of beans.
On the table there is a handful of white beans; and, after some
searching, I find one of the bags contains white beans only. I at once
infer as a probability [likelihood], or as a fair guess, that this handful
was taken out of that bag. This sort of inference is called *making
an hypothesis*. It is the inference of a *case* from a *rule* and a *result*.
We have, then—

DEDUCTION

   Rule.—All the beans from this bag are white.
   Case.—These beans are from this bag.
∴ *Result.*—These beans are white.

INDUCTION

   Case.—These beans are from this bag.
   Result.—These beans are white.
∴ *Rule.*—All the beans from this bag are white.

HYPOTHESIS

   Rule.—All the beans from this bag are white.
   Result.—These beans are white.
∴ *Case.*—These beans are from this bag."

Peirce's conception of a scientific law as an inductive
conclusion that operates as a rule has, in recent times,
become widely propagated; though the notion of what
sort of rule it is has been variously interpreted.[1]

About abduction Peirce says further:

"An originary Argument, or *Abduction*, is an argument which
presents facts in its Premiss which present a similarity to the fact
stated in the Conclusion, but which could perfectly well be true

---

[1] See for example: Ramsey, F. P. (1903-30): *Foundations of
Mathematics*, p. 241 (London, 1931); Schlick, M. (1882-1936):
Gesammelte Aufsätze, p. 67 (Vienna, 1938); Ryle, G. (1900-): *The
Concept of Mind* ("inference-license"), (London, 1949). Toulmin, S. E.
(1922-): *The Philosophy of Science* (London, 1953).

without the latter being so, much more without its being recognised; so that we are not led to assert the conclusion positively but are only inclined toward admitting it. . . . For example, at a certain stage of Kepler's eternal exemplar of scientific reasoning, he found that the observed longitudes of Mars, which he had long tried in vain to get fitted with an orbit, were (within the possible limits of error of the observations) such as they would be if Mars moved in an ellipse. The facts were thus, in so far, a *likeness* of those of motion in an elliptic orbit. Kepler did not conclude from this that the orbit really was an ellipse; but it did incline him to that idea so much as to decide him to undertake to ascertain whether virtual predictions about the latitudes and parallaxes based on this hypothesis would be verified or not. This probational adoption of the hypothesis was an Abduction. An Abduction is Originary in respect to being the only kind of argument which starts a new idea."[1]

"*Presumption*, or, more precisely, *abduction*, ..., furnishes the reasoner with the problematic theory which induction verifies. Upon finding himself confronted with a phenomenon unlike what he would have expected under the circumstances, he looks over its features and notices some remarkable character or relation among them, which he at once recognises as being characteristic of some conception with which his mind is already stored, so that a theory is suggested which would *explain* (that is, render necessary) that which is surprising in the phenomena.

"He therefore accepts that theory so far as to give it a high place in the list of theories of those phenomena which call for further examination. . . .

"Presumption is the only kind of reasoning which supplies new ideas, the only kind which is, in this sense, synthetic. Induction is justified as a method which must in the long run lead up to the truth, and that, by gradual modification of the actual conclusion. There is no such warrant for presumption. The hypothesis which it problematically concludes is frequently utterly wrong itself, and even the method need not ever lead to the truth; for it may be that the features of the phenomena which it aims to explain have no rational explanation at all. Its only justification is that its method is the only way in which there can be any hope of attaining a rational explanation."[2]

Peirce's general idea of induction in relation to abduction —let us call this *explanatory induction*—is apparent from the following passage:

"*Induction* takes place when the reasoner already holds a theory more or less problematically (ranging from a pure interrogative

---

[1] Peirce: *Collected Papers II*, pp. 53-4; Kepler, J. (1571-1631): *Astronomia nova* (Prague, 1609).

[2] *Ibid.*, pp. 496-7.

apprehension to a strong leaning mixed with ever so little doubt); and having reflected that if that theory be true, then under certain conditions certain phenomena ought to appear (the stranger and less antecedently credible the better), proceeds to *experiment*, that is, to realise those conditions and watch for the predicted phenomena. Upon their appearance he accepts the theory with a modality which recognises it provisionally as approximately true."[1]

Thus, for Peirce, abduction is the process of thinking up explanations; induction is the process of testing by experience these generalisations and explanations and of drawing appropriate inferences from the data of such experience.

The logically important differences between the hypotheses of abduction and the generalisations of ordinary induction are explained by Peirce as follows:

"A certain anonymous writing is upon a torn piece of paper. It is suspected that the author is a certain person. His desk, to which only he has had access, is searched, and in it is found a piece of paper, the torn edge of which exactly fits, in all its irregularities, that of the paper in question. It is a fair hypothetic inference that the suspected man was actually the author. The ground of this inference evidently is that two torn pieces of paper are extremely unlikely to fit together by accident. Therefore, of a great number of inferences of this sort, but a very small proportion would be deceptive. The analogy of hypothesis with induction is so strong that some logicians have confounded them. Hypothesis has been called an induction of characters. A number of characters belonging to a certain class are found in a certain object; whence it is inferred that all the characters of that class belong to the object in question. This certainly involves the same principle as induction; yet in a modified form. In the first place, characters are not susceptible of simple enumeration like objects; in the next place, characters run in categories. When we make an hypothesis like that about the piece of paper, we only examine a single line of characters, or perhaps two or three, and we take no specimen at all of others. If the hypothesis were nothing but an induction, all that we should be justified in concluding, in the example above, would be that the two pieces of paper which matched in such irregularities as have been examined would be found to match in other, say slighter, irregularities. The inference from the shape of the paper to

---

[1] Peirce: *Collected Papers II*, pp. 495-6; and cf. *Collected Papers VII*, pp. 67-8 footnote.

its ownership is precisely what distinguishes hypothesis from induction, and makes it a bolder and more perilous step."[1]

"Induction is, plainly, a much stronger kind of inference than hypothesis; and this is the first reason for distinguishing them. Hypotheses are sometimes regarded as provisional resorts, which in the progress of science are to be replaced by inductions. But this is a false view of the subject. Hypothetic reasoning infers very frequently a fact not capable of direct observation. It is an hypothesis that Napoleon Bonaparte once existed. How is that hypothesis ever to be replaced by an induction? It may be said that from the premiss that such facts as we have observed are as they would be if Napoleon existed, we are to infer by induction that *all* facts that are hereafter to be observed will be of the same character. There is no doubt that every hypothetic inference may be distorted into an appearance of an induction in this way. But the essence of an induction is that it infers from one set of facts another set of similar facts, whereas hypothesis infers from facts of one kind to facts of another."[2]

"The following examples will illustrate the distinction between statistical deduction, induction, and hypothesis. If I wished to order a font of type expressly for the printing of this book, knowing, as I do, that in all English writing the letter *e* occurs oftener than any other letter, I should want more *e*'s in my font than other letters. For what is true of all other English writing is no doubt true of these papers. This is a statistical deduction. But then the words used in logical writings are rather peculiar, and a good deal of use is made of single letters. I might, then, count the number of occurrences of the different letters upon a dozen or so pages of the manuscript, and thence conclude the relative amounts of the different kinds of type required in the font. That would be inductive inference. If now I were to order the font, and if, after some days, I were to receive a box containing a large number of little paper parcels of very different sizes, I should naturally infer that this was the font of type I had ordered; and this would be hypothetic inference."[3]

10·04 Induction and Inductive Hypotheses

"In the contemplation of that uniformity in the course of nature," said John Stuart Mill,[4] "which is assumed in every inference from experience, one of the first observations that present themselves is, that the uniformity in

---

[1] Peirce: *Collected Papers II*, pp. 378-9.
[2] *Ibid.*, p. 386.
[3] *Ibid.*, p. 446.
[4] Mill, J. S. (1806-73): *A System of Logic*, Book III, Chapter IV, § 1 (London, 1843).

question is not properly uniformity, but uniformities. The general regularity results from the co-existence of partial regularities. The course of nature in general is constant, because the course of each of the various phenomena that compose it is so. A certain fact invariably occurs whenever certain circumstances are present, and does not occur when they are absent; the like is true of another fact; and so on. From these separate threads of connection between parts of the great whole which we term nature a general tissue of connection unavoidably weaves itself, by which the whole is held together. . . .

"The first point, therefore, to be noted in regard to what is called the uniformity of the course of nature is, that it is itself a complex fact, compounded of all the separate uniformities which exist in respect to single phenomena. These various uniformities, when ascertained by what is regarded as a sufficient induction, we call in common parlance, Laws of Nature."

The first task of science is to discover the structure of the separate uniformities pervading phenomena; and its second task is to devise economical putative uniformities from which each particular uniformity of as wide a sort as possible can be deduced. The first task is the formation of satisfactory inductive hypotheses, as scientific laws, and the second task is the creation of satisfactory theoretical hypotheses. Inductive hypotheses will be considered in this section; theoretical ones in **10·06**.

To call a statement in the empirical sciences a hypothesis is to indicate that its truth is not absolutely certain; the statement so described is regarded as being to some degree tentative or corrigible. In some, perhaps generic, sense of "probability", the statement that is a hypothesis has a mere probability. Now of course it is perfectly possible for the philosophically minded to hold that not only are *e.g.* inductively based universal statements such as "(Any

specimen of any of the) inert gases have very stable atoms"
necessarily hypotheses in being merely probable, but that
also observation statements, about specific occurrences, are
hypotheses too in having a mere probability, for anyone
might at any time be mistaken or inaccurate. This is the
doctrine that Peirce, an adherent of it, called *Fallibilism*.[1]
However, scientists as a group are not thus philosophically
minded, and they would not accept that each observation
statement must, in principle, be regarded as fallible; but
their acknowledgment of the existence of observational
and experimental errors of the kind dealt with in the
Calculus of Observations is perhaps incompatible with this
attitude.

An inductive generalisation, say of the form "All *s* is
t" (where *s* in particular might and commonly is the
intersection-set of several sets which between them provide
sufficient conditions for something to be a member of *t*),
is usually a generalisation from what is relatively a negligible number of observed instances of things that are
members of *s* being also members of *t*, no observed member
of *s* failing to be also a member of *t*, to all the possible
members of *s* being members of *t*, these possible members
of *s* being either vastly numerous or even innumerable.
Since there are so many possible cases which lie outside
our actual experience, it is quite unjustified rationally to
assert categorically that every single member of *s* is a
member of *t*, in the temporally universal sense of "is"
to cover past and future as well as present. And to
support this lack of there being a rational justification for
making a categorical generalisation from a sample is the
fact that past experience has shown many well established
generalisations to be controverted in the course of

[1] See Peirce: *Collected Papers I*, pp. 58-72, *e.g.*; a more recent,
and influential, exposition of the doctrine is in Reichenbach, H.
(1891-1953): *Experience and Prediction* (Chicago, 1938).

later observations. Inductive generalisations are, then, hypotheses.

It should be remarked in passing that Mill believed it possible to overcome the hypothetical nature of inductions, and to establish their truth conclusively; indeed, he went further and claimed to have worked out a handful of rules of experimental inquiry whose use would guarantee the successful and decisive establishment of causal laws, these laws being, in Mill's conception, the fundamental ones. Very few thinkers of his own time or subsequently have found themselves able to agree with Mill's views; on the contrary, almost all logicians and philosophers have regarded his basic doctrine of inductive proof as erroneous and discovered detailed faults in the particular methods of proof which Mill proposed. Nevertheless, Mill's clear and elaborate discussions have been of immense value in enunciating and clarifying relevant issues and serving as a stimulus to further investigation.[1]

"Suppose we define Inductive reasoning," says Peirce,[2] "as that reasoning whose conclusion is justified not by their being any necessity of its being true or approximately true but by its being the result of a method which if steadily persisted in must bring the reasoner to the truth of the matter or must cause his conclusion in its changes to converge to the truth as its limit." Using this definition, Peirce asserts that there are three principal kinds of inductive reasoning and that all three are indispensable. The first kind is what he usually calls *Pooh-pooh Induction*, and occasionally *Rudimentary* or *Crude Induction*. The

---

[1] Mill's teachings on the logic of science are in Books III and IV of his *System of Logic*. The most important earlier criticisms of Mill are by Whewell, W. (1794-1866): *The Philosophy of Discovery* (London, 1860); and Bradley, F. H. (1846-1924): *Principles of Logic* (Oxford, 1883). For later, constructive criticism the reader may consult Keynes: *Treatise on Probability*; Johnson, W. E. (1858-1931): *Logic II* (Cambridge, 1922).

[2] Peirce: *Collected Papers VII*, p. 65.

second kind consists, he says, in the argument from the fulfilment of predictions; and this kind has two varieties. The third kind is what he calls *Statistical Induction*; this has three varieties.

Pooh-pooh Induction.—"Induction is such a way of inference that if one persists in it one must necessarily be led to the truth, at last. It is true that this condition is most imperfectly fulfilled in the *Pooh-pooh* argument. For here the unexpected, when it comes, comes with a bang. But then, on the other hand, until the fatal day arrives, this argument causes us to anticipate just what does happen and prevents us from anticipating a thousand things that do not happen. I engage a stateroom; I purchase a letter of credit for fifty thousand dollars, and I start off determined to have a good time. On the way down the bay, my wife says to me, 'Aren't you afraid the house may be struck by lightning while we are gone?' *Pooh-pooh!* 'But aren't you afraid there will be a war and Boston will be bombarded?' *Pooh-pooh!* 'But aren't you afraid that when we are in the heart of Hungary or somewhere you will get the Asiatic plague, and I shall be left unable to speak the language?' *Pooh-pooh!* On the morning of the fourth day out there is a terrific explosion and I find myself floating about on the middle of the Atlantic with my letter of credit safe in my breast pocket. I say to myself, my *Pooh-pooh* argument broke down that time sure enough, but after all, it made my mind easy about a number of possibilities that did not occur, and even about this one for three days. So I had better be content with my lot."[1]

The Pooh-pooh argument "proceeds from the premiss that the reasoner has no evidence of the existence of any fact of a given description and concludes that there never

[1] Peirce: *Collected Papers II*, p. 480.

was, is not, and never will be any such thing. . . . It goes upon the roughest kind of information, upon merely negative information; but that is the only kind of information we can have concerning the great majority of subjects[1]

Induction from Fulfilment of Predictions.—First variety. This variety of this kind of induction is the weaker of the two; it is "where the predictions that are fulfilled are merely of the continuance in future experience of the same phenomena which originally suggested and recommended the hypothesis, expectations directly involved in holding the hypothesis".[2] Second variety. "The other variety of the argument from the fulfilment of predictions is where truths ascertained subsequently to the provisional adoption of the hypothesis or, at least, not at all seen to have any bearing upon it, lead to new predictions being based upon the hypothesis of an entirely different kind from those originally contemplated and these new predictions are equally found to be verified.

"Thus Maxwell, noticing that the velocity of light had the same value as a certain fundamental constant relating to electricity, was led to the hypothesis that light was an electromagnetic oscillation. This explained the magnetic rotation of the plane of polarisation, and predicted the Hertzian waves. Not only that, but it further led to the prediction of the mechanical pressure of light, which had not at first been contemplated."[3]

It seems clear that this second kind of induction is not one that consists of a straightforward generalisation from experience. It is the kind of induction called *explanatory induction* in **9·08**.

Statistical Induction.—First variety. This is the weakest variety of argument of this kind. In it

[1] Peirce: *Collected Papers VII*, p. 66. [2] *Ibid.*, p. 68.
[3] *Ibid.*, pp. 68-9; [Maxwell, J. C. (1831-79): "On a dynamic theory of the electromagnetic field", *Phil. Trans. Roy. Soc.*, 1865, **155**; cf. also *Philosophical Magazine*, 1862, (4) **23**, p. 22.]

"we have cases in which a class of individuals recur in endless succession and we do not know in advance whether the occurrences are entirely independent of one another or not. But we have some reason to suppose that they would be independent and perhaps that they have some given ratio of frequency. Then what has to be done is to apply all sorts of consequences of independence and see whether the statistics support the assumption. . . . The question to be decided is how far a given succession of occurrences are independent of one another and if they are not independent what the nature of the law of their succession is."[1]

An example of this variety of induction is the inferential determination of the statistical laws governing the appearance of certain characters in the members of a line of offspring within a biological species. Second variety.

"In the second variety of statistical induction we are supposed to know whether the occurrences are independent or not, and if not, exactly how they are connected, and the inquiry is limited to ascertaining what the ratio of frequency is, after the effects of the law of succession have been eliminated. . . . This second variety is the usual and typical case of statistical induction."[2]

Third variety. This is called an *Induction from a Random Sample*.

"An Argument from a Random Sample, is a method of ascertaining what proportion of the members of a finite class possess a predesignate, or virtually predesignate, quality, by selecting instances from that class according to a method which will, in the long run, present any instance as often as any other, and concluding that the ratio found for such a sample will hold in the long run."[3]

If from a sample of the set *s* one is to proceed justifiably, *i.e.* in a way that will in the long run lead to the truth, to a general characterisation of the whole set, as for example, to the effect that every member of *s* is a member of *t*, two precautions are necessary. The first is that the sample be a random, or virtually a random, one. Unless there are reasonable grounds for accepting that the membership of the sample is representative of the membership of the population as a whole, it will obviously not be reasonable

[1] Peirce: *Collected Papers VII*, pp. 69-71.   [2] *Ibid.*, p. 71.
[3] Peirce: *Collected Papers II*, p. 153.

to characterise the population as a whole simply on the basis of the character of the observed members, in the sample.

"The other rule is that the character, toward the ascertainment of the proportionate frequency of which in the lot sampled the sampling is done, must not be determined by the character of the particular sample taken. For example, we must not take a sample of eminent men, and studying over them, find that they have certain characters and conclude that all eminent men will have those characters. We must first decide for what character we propose to examine the sample, and only after that decision examine the sample. The reason is that any sample will be peculiar and unlike the average of the lot [population] sampled in innumerable respects. At the same time it will be approximately like the average of the whole lot in the great majority of respects."[1]

In short, the character or characters with which an inductive hypothesis to be tested is concerned must be predesignated. This second rule is not, of course, intended to prevent the devising of a generalisation in the light of what is given in experience; it does not prohibit the working backwards from facts to laws. But such a working backwards, Peirce insists, is abduction, not induction, and the abduction will need appropriate empirical testing.[2]

10·05 Induction and the Rule of Succession

We have pointed out that a generalisation from experience, embodied in a scientific law, has, it is generally agreed, some degree of probability (not necessarily of a numerical kind) that is something less than certainty. Since the eighteenth century there have been many attempts to bring all induction within the scope of the theory of mathematical probability or of some modified version of that theory. There are two main motives for making such attempts. One motive is to achieve the same rigour in evaluating an inductive argument as is possible for a

[1] Peirce: *Collected Papers I*, p. 39.
[2] Peirce: *Collected Papers VII*, p. 67, § 114.

deductive argument; since an inductive argument is always invalid from the standpoint of deductive logic since it passes from "Some s is t" to, *e.g.* "All s is t", the most plausible way of being able to give an objective criterion of its validity is in terms of probability as treated within a calculus of probabilities. Over mathematics there can be no dispute, it is thought. The first motive, then, is to be able to determine the degree of probability of an inductive conclusion in a precise, numerical way that is fully objective and thus achieve for inductive logic the same sort of power that is in the hands of deductive logic. The second motive is connected with the first. It is apparent that some inductive generalisations are more probable than others. What one would like is to be in a position to compare the probabilities of different generalisations in an objective manner, by having a precise, numerical standard. Let us add that many of those interested in the application of mathematical probability methods to scientific ideas have wanted to treat scientific theories as well as inductive generalisations by means of those methods.[1]

Two theorems due to Laplace are continually cited or used in accounts of the applicability of probability theory to induction. The first theorem is this: suppose there is a hugely large number $n + 1$ of urns u_k, each of which contains n white or black balls, the urn u_k containing k white and $n - k$ black balls ($k = 0, 1, 2, \ldots, n$); *if* an urn is chosen at random, m balls are randomly drawn in succession, each with replacement, from the urn, and all m balls are white, *then* the probability that all the balls in the chosen urn are white is $(m + 1)/(n + 1)$. There

[1] See for example, Laplace: *Essai philosophique des probabilités* (Paris, 1814), in *Oeuvres Complètes de Laplace VII*; De Morgan: *Formal Logic*; Boole: *The Laws of Thought*; and, more recently, Carnap: *Logical Foundations of Probability*, which gives references to other modern works in the same direction.

is no accepted name for this theorem; we shall call it the *Rule of Generalisation*. The second theorem is this: with precisely the same suppositions and hypotheses as for the previous theorem, the probability that the next ball drawn from the chosen urn will also be white is $(m + 1)/(m + 2)$. This theorem is generally called the *Rule of Succession*. We shall demonstrate these theorems at the end of this section.

Consider an inductive generalisation such as "All native European swans are white". Suppose that the set s of all the possible native European swans, past, present, and future, has n members. Let us treat the $n + 1$ urns u_k containing k white and $n - k$ black balls as models for all the possible colour constitutions of s, a white ball representing a white swan and a black ball a non-white swan. Accordingly, if m native European swans have been observed, all m have been white, and if these m observed members form a genuinely random sample of the whole population s, then, applying the Rule of Generalisation, we find that the probability of the generalisation "All native European swans are white" is $(m + 1)/(n + 1)$. Thus, it seems that any inductively based universal proposition can be evaluated in terms of mathematical probability. However, in so far as a probability value is an indication of the degree of acceptability of a proposition, the Rule of Generalisation hardly seems to be a suitable instrument to apply to inductive generalisations, for they will all be assigned a negligible probability value. Suppose it be granted that the native European swans we have observed are a completely random sample of all possible such swans (which they certainly are not), and suppose further that say a million native European swans have been observed and that none of them has had a colour other than white. But the number n of all possible European swans must be regarded as being incomparably larger than a million; it must be practically infinite. Let us conservatively put it as being a hundred thousand million. Then the probability that all native European swans are white is 1,000,001/100,000,000,001. Therefore, the odds against all native European swans being white is overwhelmingly great, being about 100,000 : 1. So, similarly, all our inductive generalisations are going to turn out to be almost surely false according to the Rule of Generalisation, if this is applicable. Hence, all inductive generalisations are ultimately just as improbable, practically speaking, as the least improbable—but this scarcely seems to be supported by experience. And experience is the final test. If we have a result that is incompatible with experience, we are led to affirm that the conditions of the Rule of Generalisation are not really applicable to the inductive situation. For example, we can say that there is no ground for believing (i) that the actual constitution of s is one of a hugely large number of possible constitutions all of which are equally probable, and (ii) that the probability of a native European swan's being white has the same value, viz. 1/2, as its being non-white.

In view of the impasse to which the application of the Rule of Generalisation leads, resort is often made to the much more famous Rule of Succession. The decisive advantage that this Rule has over the other is that it gives probability values that are independent of the number n of all the possible instances, and are dependent only on the number m of observed instances. Assuming that the conditions for the applicability of the Rule of Succession are fulfilled (which many, for the sort of reasons mentioned at the end of the previous paragraph, would deny), the probability that the next native European swan to be observed will be white if all the million ones already observed have been white is 1,000,001/1,000,002; thus the odds against the next one to be observed being white are less than a million to one. That this Rule, in spite of such comforting results, is not rationally applicable in general to inductions is shown by the fact that if merely a single instance belonging to a set has been observed and this instance has a certain character, then, by the Rule of Succession, the probability that the next instance will also have that character will be 2/3. What we have learned from experience in the course of many generations is completely at variance with this high probability value; very little reliance indeed can be placed upon a single observation, even if it is of a randomly chosen instance.[1]

We shall now demonstrate the two theorems referred to.

(10·051)   **The Rule of Generalisation Theorem:** Suppose there is a finite number $n + 1$ of urns u_k each containing n white and black balls, the urn u_k containing k white and $n - k$ black balls ($k \in N^{\geq}$); if an urn is chosen at random and a sample of size m, with replacement, is drawn from it and all the members of the sample are white, then the probability that all the balls in the chosen urn are white is $(m + 1)/(n + 1)$.

Demonstration: Call the event that all the m members of the sample are white "s", and call the event that all the members of the chosen urn are white "t". We seek to show that $P(t/s) = (m + 1)/(n + 1)$. Now $s \_ t = t$, since both s and t occur if and only if t occurs.

$$(10·052) \quad P(t/s) = \frac{P(s\_t)}{P(s)} \qquad \text{by (7·071)}$$

---

[1] For a clear and critical discussion of the two Laplacean Rules, see Broad, C. D. (1889-): "Induction and Probability I", *Mind*, 1918, **27**, 389-404; he requires the sampling to be without replacement, but, when n is great, the difference between sampling with and without replacement is, as was seen in Chapter VII, negligible. Also consult, for further developments, Broad: "Induction and Probability II", *Mind*, 1920, **29**, 11-45.

$$(10.053) \qquad = \frac{P(t)}{P(s)} \qquad \text{since } s_\smile t = t.$$

By (7.0710), if s_k is the event that $\mathbf{u}_k$ is chosen,

$$(10.054) \quad P(s) = \sum_{k \in \mathbf{N}_n^\geq} P(s_k)\, P(s/s_k)$$

$$(10.055) \qquad = \frac{1}{n+1} \sum_{k \in \mathbf{N}_n^\geq} P(s/s_k)$$

$$(10.056) \qquad = \frac{1}{n+1} \sum_{k \in \mathbf{N}_n^\geq} \frac{P(s_\smile s_k)}{P(s_k)}$$

$$(10.057) \qquad = \frac{1}{n+1} \sum_{k \in \mathbf{N}_n^\geq} \left[\binom{k}{n}^m \left(\frac{1}{n+1}\right) \Big/ \frac{1}{n+1} \right]$$

$$(10.058) \qquad = \frac{1}{n+1} \sum_{k \in \mathbf{N}_n^\geq} \binom{k}{n}^m$$

$$(10.059) \qquad = \frac{0^m + 1^m + 2^m + \ldots + n^m}{(n+1)\, n^{m+1}}.$$

Now set x equal to k/n, so that $x = 1/n$ and $0 \leq x \leq 1$. If n is great

$$(10.0510) \quad P(s) \doteq \frac{1}{n} \sum_{k \in \mathbf{N}_n} \binom{k}{n}^m$$

$$(10.0511) \qquad \doteq \int_0^1 x^m dx$$

$$(10.0512) \qquad - \frac{1}{m+1}.$$

$P(t) = 1/(n+1)$, since there are $n+1$ urns to choose from. Hence

$$(10.0513) \quad P(t/s) = \frac{1/(n+1)}{1/(m+1)} = \frac{m+1}{n+1}.$$

(10·0514)   **The Rule of Succession Theorem:** Suppose there is a finite number $n + 1$ of urns u_k each containing n white and black balls, the urn u_k containing k white and $n - k$ black balls ($k \in N_n^\geq$); if an urn is chosen at random and a sample of size m, with replacement, is drawn from it and all the members of the sample are white, then the probability that the next ball to be drawn from the chosen urn is also white is $(m + 1)/(m + 2)$.

Demonstration: Call the event that all the m members of the sample are white "s", and call the event that all the balls drawn in the enlarged sample of size $m + 1$ will be white "t". As before, $s\_t = t$. Also as before, $P(s) = 1/(m + 1)$ if n is great.

$$(10·0515)\ \ P(t/s) = \frac{P(s\_t)}{P(s)} = \frac{P(t)}{P(s)}.$$

Using (7·0710) as in the previous demonstration, we find that

$$(10·0516)\ \ P(t) = \frac{0^{m+1} + 1^{m+1} + 2^{m+1} + \ldots + n^{m+1}}{(n + 1)\, n^{m+2}}.$$

Similarly to the previous demonstration, if n is great,

$$(10·0517)\ \ P(t) \doteq \frac{1}{n} \underset{k \in N_n}{\Sigma} \left(\frac{k}{n}\right)^m$$

$$(10·0518)\ \ \ \ \ \ \ \doteq \int_0^1 x^{m+1} dx$$

$$(10·0519)\ \ \ \ \ \ \ = 1/(m + 2).$$

Therefore,

$$(10·0520)\ \ P(t/s) = \frac{1/(m + 2)}{1/(m + 1)} \doteq \frac{m + 1}{m + 2}.[1]$$

[1] The Rules of Generalisation and Succession are due to Laplace: "Sur la probabilité des causes par les événements", *Mémoires de l'Académie Royale des Sciences de Paris* (*Savants étrangers*), **6**, 621 *et seq.*; reprinted in *Oeuvres de Laplace VIII*, pp. 27-65. (It is a common mistake of the probability texts to assign the origin of these theorems to Laplace's *Théorie Analytique des Probabilités* (1812).)

EXERCISE

E10·5·1.   With the same suppositions and hypotheses as in (10·0514), show that the probability that the next p balls to be drawn from the chosen urn are also white is

$$(m + 1)/(m + p + 1).$$

10·06 Science and the Hypothetico-Deductive Method

Because of the serious difficulties, such as those indicated in the previous section, facing the attempts to bring induction within the scope of mathematical probability, many logicians of science have thought that scientific generalisations and theories are not to be considered as conclusions from empirical premisses, except perhaps in the sort of cases dealt with in ordinary statistics (cf. Chapter Eight).   If they are regarded as conclusions, they are either deductive ones, in which case they are always invalid, or they are inductive ones, in which case the degree of their validity is indeterminable or worse.   What these logicians maintain is that, in general, scientific generalisations and theories are not arrived at by processes of *reasoning* but are hypotheses prompted by experience; from these hypotheses deductions are made—this is where reasoning comes in—and predictions from the hypotheses are obtained; then these results of deduction are compared with empirical data to find out whether what the hypothesis says and implies is compatible with the facts of nature. If the hypotheses stand up to strenuous empirical scrutiny, they are retained, with justifiably greater confidence than before.   If they do not stand up, they are discarded or suitably modified.   Since every retained hypothesis is continually in direct or indirect use in science, it is continually subjected to falsification; the testing of hypotheses is not a once-for-all matter, unless and until falsification occurs.   However, it is important to realise that especially theoretical hypotheses are not used in isolation.   Predictions result not from a single hypothesis but from a conjunction of hypotheses. Abstractly, the common situation for theories is representable by

$$(10\cdot061) \quad (b_1.b_2\ldots b_n) \supset d \qquad CK^{n-1}b_1b_2\ldots b_nd;$$

if in fact the prediction d yielded by the conjunction of the b_i is false, then at least one of the hypotheses b_i must be rejected:

$$(10\cdot062) \quad [(b_1.b_2\ldots b_n) \supset d).\sim d] \supset$$
$$[\sim b_1 \vee \sim b_2 \vee \ldots \vee \sim b_n]$$
$$CK^nb_1b_2\ldots b_ndNdA^{n-1}Nb_1Nb_2\ldots Nb_n.$$

According to this view of the subject, then, science operates through the use of the hypothetico-deductive method, and each scientific explanation is a hypothetico-deductive system.[1]

When science is considered as operating through the construction, and the testing of the predictive consequences, of hypotheses, a hypothesis being retained until it is falsified, emphasis is placed on attempting to falsify hypotheses rather than to verify them. For this point of view, a hypothesis must have predictive consequences if it is to be of scientific value, and it is desirable that at least some of these should be precise and readily checked in experience. As Peirce puts it:

"It is a great mistake to suppose that the mind of the active scientist is filled with propositions which, if not proved beyond all reasonable cavil, are at least extremely probable. On the contrary, he entertains hypotheses which are almost wildly incredible, and treats them with respect for the time being. Why does he do this? Simply because any scientific proposition whatever is always liable to be refuted and dropped at short notice. A hypothesis is something which looks as if it might be true and were true, and which is capable of verification or refutation by comparison with facts. The best hypothesis, in the sense of the one most recommending itself to the inquirer, is the one

---

[1] This view was first elaborated by Jevons: *The Principles of Science* (London, 1873); see, *e.g.* p. 267 of the third edition (1879). Later exponents of the view include Peirce and, contemporarily, Popper, K. (1902-): *Die Logik der Forschung* (Vienna, 1935), published in English as *The Logic of Scientific Discovery* (London, 1958).

which can be the most readily refuted if it is false. This far outweighs the trifling merit of being likely. For after all, what is a *likely* hypothesis? It is one which falls in with our preconceived ideas. But these may be wrong. Their errors are just what the scientific man is out gunning for more particularly."[1]

"Having, then, by means of deduction, drawn from a hypothesis predictions as to what the results of experiment will be, we proceed to test the hypothesis by making the experiments and comparing those predictions with the actual results of the experiment. Experiment is very expensive business, in money, in time, and in thought; so that it will be a saving of expense, to begin with that positive prediction from the hypothesis which seems least likely to be verified. For a single experiment may absolutely refute the most valuable of hypotheses, while a hypothesis must be a trifling one indeed if a single experiment could establish it."[2]

A scientific theory is, in many respects, like a mathematical one. It will contain some fundamental postulates, definitions, and consequences derived from these by means of auxiliary tools, especially in physics, mathematical ones. A physical theory could be transformed, with great difficulty, into a rigorously deductive system, and, with relatively little difficulty, into a demonstrative postulational system. Its postulates express abstract relationships and so far are not different essentially from postulates of a system of pure mathematics. But in physical theories the formulae receive a definite and unique interpretation which enables the truth or falsity of the theory to be tested empirically by comparing consequences of the postulates with facts: the postulates must, directly or indirectly, be about observables, and what exactly the postulates say about observables must be capable of general agreement among all scientists concerned, that is there must be room for only a single interpretation.

A rather different account of the nature of physical theory is that given by Campbell:

"A theory is a connected set of propositions which are divided into two groups. One group consists of statements about some

---

[1] Peirce: *Collected Papers I*, p. 48.
[2] Peirce: *Collected Papers VII*, pp. 124-5.

collection of ideas which are characteristic of the theory; the other group consists of statements of the relation between these ideas and some other ideas of a different nature. The first group will be termed collectively the "hypothesis" of the theory; the second group the "dictionary" The hypothesis is so called, in accordance with the sense that has just been stated, because the propositions composing it are incapable of proof or of disproof by themselves; they must be significant, but, taken apart from the dictionary, they appear arbitrary assumptions. They may be considered accordingly as providing a "definition by postulate" [implicit definition] of the ideas which are characteristic of the hypothesis. The ideas which are related by means of the dictionary to the ideas of the hypothesis are, on the other hand, such that something is known about them apart from the theory. It must be possible to determine, apart from all knowledge of the theory, whether certain propositions involving these ideas are true or false. . . . The theory is said to be true if propositions concerning the hypothetical ideas, deduced from the hypothesis, are found, according to the dictionary . . . to imply laws. . . . And the theory is said to explain certain laws if it is these laws which are implied by the propositions concerning the hypothetical ideas."[1]

10·07 Operationalism

We have seen, in Chapter Five and in earlier sections of the present chapter, that in the last analysis scientific ideas must be tied to experience: hypotheses of generalisation or theory must be refutable by observations or experiments. This strongly marked feature of science has led various scientists and logicians of science to make rather more stringent the nature of the concepts or statements that may be entertained in science, in order to exclude any "metaphysical", *i.e.* non-empirical, elements from science. There is the desire to describe and explain phenomena without invoking what could be regarded as unreal abstractions—fictions. An example of this attitude is expressed in the following passage from d'Alembert:

"All that we see distinctly in the motion of a body is that the body traverses a certain distance and that it takes a certain time to traverse

---

[1] Campbell: *Physics, The Elements*, pp. 122-3 (Cambridge, 1920). See also, for similar approaches under Campbell's influence, Ramsey, F. P.: *The Foundations of Mathematics*, paper on Theories; Braithwaite: *Scientific Explanation*.

that distance. It is from this one idea that all the principles of mechanics should be drawn, if we wish to demonstrate them in a clear and accurate way; so no one need be surprised that for this reason I have turned my thoughts away from causes of motion to consider solely the motions that they produce; and that I have entirely excluded forces inherent in bodies in motion, obscure and metaphysical entities which can only cast shadows on a science that is in itself clear. . . .

"When we speak of the force of bodies in motion, either we have no clear idea of what the word means or we can only mean in general the property of moving bodies by which they overcome the obstacles that they encounter, or resist them. It is therefore not by the distance that a body traverses with uniform motion, or by the time that it takes to traverse that distance, or finally, by the simple, unique, and abstract consideration of its mass and velocity that we can at once estimate the force; it is solely by the obstacles that a body encounters and by the resistance that these obstacles offer to it. The greater the obstacle that a body can overcome, the greater may we say is its force, provided that, without meaning to express by this word a hypothetical entity which resides in the body, we use the word only as an abbreviated way of expressing a fact, just as we say that one body has twice as much velocity as another instead of saying that in equal times it traverses twice the distance, without intending to mean by this that the word velocity represents an entity inherent in the body."[1]

The doctrine that the sciences should exclude all "metaphysical entities" and limit themselves to what is given directly in experience was first systematically maintained by Comte who called this doctrine *Positivism*.[2] This doctrine has had very considerable influence on the development of modern science, especially after Einstein's theory of Special Relativity showed the powerful advantages of a positivistic approach to the concept of time and related concepts. A much discussed modern attitude affiliated to positivism is known as *Operationalism*. According to this doctrine, named and developed by Bridgman, "we mean by any concept nothing more than a

[1] d'Alembert, J. le R. (1717-83): *Traite de Dynamique*, revised edition (Paris, 1758; first edition 1743), xvi-xix.
[2] Comte, A. (1798-1857): *Cours de Philosophie Positive* (Paris, 1830-42).

set of operations; the concept is synonymous with the corresponding set of operations."[1] Thus, the concept of length is to be defined simply by reference to those procedures that are involved in measuring distances; such procedures as employing certain rods in certain ways. The meaning of a concept is the set of operations that are performed when it is used. The advantages of operational definitions are chiefly that they are constructive and objective and often lead to interesting discoveries or theoretical advances. Undoubtedly much in science tends in the operationalist direction; more and more as science advances are concepts introduced and defined in terms of the operations which will bring about the actual construction of exemplifications of the concept or which will enable exemplifications to be recognised. Operationalism is a particular expression of the scientific trend towards replacing vague and subjectively varied ideas by precise and public criteria. On the other hand, it leads to the following difficulty among others, that different ways of measuring what would normally be regarded as the same quantity would become measurements of different quantities; for instance, the concept of distance with respect to earth-bound measurements of distance with rods would be a different concept from the concept of astronomical distance where distances have to be calculated at least in part so that the operations involved here are not identical with those in the former case.[2]

[1] Bridgman, P. W. (1882-): *The Logic of Modern Physics*, p. 5 (New York, 1927).

[2] A detailed criticism of operationalism is given by Lindsay, R. B. (1900-): "A critique of operationalism in physics", *Philosophy of Science*, 1937, **4**, 456-70. See, in reply, Bridgman: "Operational analysis", *Philosophy of Science*, 1938, **5**, 114-31. Apart from the books and papers already referred to in Chapter V and this chapter, the reader may usefully consult the following: On induction and theory: Duhem, P. M. M. (1861-1916): *La théorie physique, son objet, sa structure*, second edition (Paris, 1914), (English translation,

1954); Mach, E. (1838-1916): *Popular Scientific Lectures*, English translation, third edition (Chicago, 1898), the chapters on the economical nature of physical inquiry, on transformation and adaptation in scientific thought, and on the principle of comparison in physics; Whewell: *Novum Organum Renovatum*, third edition (London, 1858). For the logic of science in general: Kattsoff, L. O. (1908-): *Physical Science and Physical Reality* (Groningen, 1957) (with plentiful bibliography, especially for recent works); Margenau, H. (1901-): *The Nature of Physical Reality* (New York, 1950) (with bibliography); Feigl, H. (1902-) and Brodbeck, M., editors: *Readings in the Philosophy of Science* (New York, 1953). For the historical background of modern science: Burtt, E. A. (1892-): *Metaphysical Foundations of Modern Science*, second edition (London, New York, 1932); Butterfield, H. (1900-): *The Origins of Modern Science*, second edition (London, 1957). Whitehead: *Science and the Modern World* (Cambridge, 1925).

Many works by philosophers on the philosophy of science deal at length with what is called *The Problem of Induction* or *Hume's Problem*. This Problem may be expressed thus: how to justify the general belief that the discovery that all observed objects having the (possibly complex) character *A* have also had the (possibly complex) character *B*, is rationally relevant to, and is supporting evidence for, accepting that, until contrary evidence appears, it is more rational and sensible to believe that at any rate the next object having *A* will (probably) also have *B*, and to act accordingly, rather than to believe that the next object having *A* will probably not also have *B*, and to act accordingly. On this issue, see: Hume, D. (1711-76): *A Treatise of Human Nature* (London, 1739-40), Book I, Part III; (in view of Hume's individual-subjective epistemology, his book should have been called *A Treatise of Humean Nature*; but, inconsistently, he assumes, especially in his arguments against the validity of induction, that all other human beings have essentially the same powers and incapacities as his own and that such powers and incapacities will persist unchanged throughout subsequent generations—thereby assuming what his own conclusions cannot allow); Mill: *A System of Logic*, Book II; Russell: *The Problems of Philosophy* (London, 1912), Chapter 6; Keynes: *A Treatise on Probability*, Parts III, V; Williams, D. C. (1899-): *The Ground of Induction* (Oxford, 1947); Will, F. L.: "Will the Future be like the Past?" *Mind*, 1947, **56**, 332-47; Edwards, P. (1923-): "Russell's doubts about induction", *Mind*, 1949, **58**, 141-63; Strawson, P. F. (1919-): *An Introduction to Logical Theory* (London, 1952), Chapter 9.

ANSWERS AND HINTS FOR SOLUTIONS TO EXERCISES

E2·6

1. valid. **2.** invalid. **3.** invalid. **4.** invalid. **5.** valid.

6. Prefix $\sim$ or infix $\supset$. **7.** yes. **8.** yes. **10.** yes.

E2·7

12-16. Inclusive: all t.p.s.s **17.** valid. **18.** valid.

19. $(1-s)\,t + (1-t)\,s - (1-s)\,t\,(1-t)\,s,$
$$= s^2\,(t - t^2) + s\,(t^2 - 3t + 1) + t.$$

20. (a) $(1-p)\,p$, is a t.p.s.;

(b) $(1 - (1 - (p + q - pq)))\,((1-p)\,(1-q)),$
$$= (p + q - pq)\,(1-p)\,(1-q), \text{ is a t.p.s.;}$$

(c) and (d) are t.p.s.s but (e) is not a t.p.s.

E2·9

21.

$(p$	$\supset$	$q)$	$\supset$	$(\sim$	p	$\mathbf{V}$	$q)$
0	0	0	0	1	0	0	0
0	1	1	0	1	0	1	1
1	0	0	0	0	1	0	0
1	0	1	0	0	1	0	1

27. $(p \;\; \mathbf{V} \;\; q) \;\; \supset \;\; (p \;\; \mathbf{V}\,(\sim \;\; p \quad . \quad q))$
$1_4 \;\; 0_2 \;\; 0_5 \;\; 1_1 \;\; 1_3 \;\; 1_2 \;\; 0_6 \;\; 1_4 \;\; 1_3 \;\; 1_7$
The converse is $(p\,\mathbf{V}\,(\sim p\,.q)) \supset (p\,\mathbf{V}\,q).$

39. (a) s/s; (b) (s/s)/(t/t); (c) (s/t)/(s/t); (d) s/(t/t).

40. (e) $[(s \setminus s) \setminus (t \setminus t)] \setminus [(s \setminus s) \setminus (t \setminus t)].$

E2·13

42. Use (2·102), sub(stitution) w.r.t. (with respect to) q and rep(lacement).

43. Use (2·104), sub and rep. **44.** Use (2·104), sub and rep.

45. Obtain (2·1311) as in text, then use sub and rep.

46. Apply rep to (2·104), then sub w.r.t. p, q, and r, yielding (a) $(\sim p \supset \sim \sim \sim p) \supset ((p\,\mathbf{V} \sim p) \supset (p\,\mathbf{V} \sim \sim \sim p))$; obtain (2·1318) and use sub so as to obtain (b) $\sim p \supset \sim \sim \sim p$; apply MP to (b) and (a).

341

47. Apply MP to E2·13·46 and (2·1316), obtaining (a) $p \lor \sim \sim \sim p$; use rep and sub on (2·103); apply MP and then rep.

48. See **2·15**.

49. $CpCqp$; $CCpqCCqpCqq$; $CCpqCCrpCrq$; $AKpqCpNq$; $CApNpApNNNp$; $CNNpp$.

50. See **2·15**.

51. In axiom (a), $q/CNpq$; use axiom (c), MP; in consequent q/p, r/p; use axiom (b) and MP.

52. Apply sub and rep to E2·13·51. **53.** Apply rep to axiom (c).

54. In axiom (a), q/Apq; use rep, axiom (c), and MP.

55. $+ + abc = + a + bc$. **56.** $a + bc = + ab\, ac$.

57. If $ab = ac$ and $a \neq 0$, then $b = c$.

E2·17

59. (i) $s°$; (ii) $s \supset (s \supset s)$ — axs (2·161); (iii) $s \supset s$ — MP; (iv) s — MP.

64. As E2·17·59. **65.** Use (2·163).

66. Use (2·161) in form $t \supset (s \supset t)$, and (2·162).

67. Use (2·1713), (2·161), and then (2·168). **68.** Use (2·168) and MP.

69. Use (2·169) and MP. **70.** Use (2·1723) and (2·165).

71. Compare (2·1719) to (2·1723).

E2·18

72. (i) $Ast°$; (ii) Csu—from (i), by D(eduction) T(heorem); (iii) Ctu— from (i), by DT; now use (2·165) and MP.

73. Establish $s \supset t$, $t \supset u$, $s \vdash u$. **74.** Establish $(s.t) \supset u$, s, $t \vdash u$.

75. Establish, using (2·169), s, $\sim s \vdash t$. **76.** Use E2·18·75.

77. Establish $s \supset t$, $u \supset s$, $u \vdash t$. **78.** Establish s, u, $Cst \vdash u$.

79. Use E2·18·72.

80. Establish, using (2·161) and (2·168), s, $t \vdash Kst$.

81. Establish $CsCCtu$, t, $s \vdash u$. **83.** Establish Cqr, Cpq, $p \vdash r$.

84. (a) Establish Cpq, Cqr, $p \vdash r$; (b) use (2·1610); (c) use (2·169).

88. Compare demonstration of (2·195).

90. Apply DT and use (2·168).

91. If $s \vdash t. \sim t$, then, since $t. \sim t \vdash \sim s$, $s \vdash \sim s$; also $\sim \sim s \vdash s$, as shown in text; hence $\sim \sim s \vdash \sim s$; apply DT and use (2·1610).

92. Use E2·18·72.

93. (a) Use (2·163); (b) compare E2·17·59; (c) use E2·18·90-91 w.r.t.; (a) and (b); (d) use (2·164); (e) compare E2·17·59; (f) use E2·18·90-91 w.r.t. (d) and (e); (g) same, w.r.t. (c) and (f); (h) use (2·171) and E2·18·89.

E2·19

94. Use (2·164) and E2·17·62.

95. Use (2·161) in form $u_2 \supset (u_1 \supset u_2)$, and (2·168).

96. Use (2·167), (2·171), (2·169) in form $\sim\sim t \supset (\sim t \supset \sim s)$, (2·1718) and (2·165), to obtain $\sim s \vee \sim t$, $s.t \vdash \sim s$; but $\sim s \vee \sim t$, $s.t \vdash s$; apply E2·18·90-91.

97. If $s \vdash t$ and $s_1 \vdash \sim u$, then $s.s_1 \vdash t.\sim u$; now $t.\sim u$, $t \supset u \vdash u$, and $t.\sim u$, $t \supset u \vdash \sim u$; apply E2·18·90-91.

98. (E2·17·60) (i) s°; (ii) $s \supset t$—from (i), by DT; (iii) t—(i), (ii), MP. Others similarly.

99. Apply E2·18·90-91.

100. As in solution to E2·19·96, $\sim s \vee t$, $s.t \vdash \sim s$; hence $\sim\sim s \vee \sim\sim t$, $\sim s.\sim t \vdash \sim\sim s$; but by E2·19·99 and E2·18·72, $s \vee t \vdash \sim\sim s \vee \sim\sim t$; so $\sim s.\sim t$, $s \vee t \vdash \sim\sim s$; yet also $\sim s.\sim t$, $s \vee t \vdash \sim s$; apply E2·18·90-91.

101. Apply MP.

E2·20

103-110. These epitheorems can be established by using methods similar to those employed in the text for establishing the analogous epitheorems.

111. With "W_1" as in demonstration of (2·2021), we have both $\vdash W_1$, from hypothesis, and $\vdash \sim W_1$, from (2·2018).

E3·6

1. (2·171) (i) $\sim\sim b^\circ$; (ii) $\sim\sim b \supset (\sim b \supset b)$ — axs (3·069); (iii) $\sim b \supset b$—(i), (ii), MP; (iv) $(\sim b \supset b) \supset b$ — axs (3·0610); (v) b — (iii), (iv), MP.

2. Construct a proof along the lines of the following proof schema:

(i) $[(b.\sim b) \supset (b \supset d)] \supset [((b.\sim b) \supset b) \supset ((b.\sim b) \supset d)]$ — axs (3·062);

(ii) $[(b.\sim b) \supset (\sim b \supset (b \supset d))] \supset [((b.\sim b) \supset \sim b) \supset ((b.\sim b) \supset (b \supset d))]$ — axs (3·062);

(iii) $[\sim b \supset (b \supset d)] \supset [(b.\sim b) \supset (\sim b \supset (b \supset d))]$ — axs (3·061);

(iv) $\sim b \supset (b \supset d)$ — axs (3·069);

(v) $(b.\sim b) \supset (\sim b \supset (b \supset d))$ — (iv), (iii), MP;

(vi) $((b.\sim b) \supset \sim b) \supset ((b.\sim b) \supset (b \supset d)) - $ (v), (ii), MP;

(vii) $(b.\sim b) \supset \sim b - $ axs (3·067);

(viii) $(b.\sim b) \supset (b \supset d) - $ (vii), (vi), MP;

(ix) $((b.\sim b) \supset b) \supset ((b.\sim b) \supset d)) - $ (viii), (i), MP;

(x) $(b.\sim b) \supset b - $ axs (3·066);

(xi) $(b.\sim b) \supset d - $ (x), (ix), MP.

E3·8

7. 3; 1, tf; 4 : 2, 3, imp in; 5 : 1, 4, imp in.

8. 2 : 1, alt in; 3 : 1, alt in; 4 : 1, 2, imp in; 5 : 1, 3, imp in.

14. 3 : 1, tf; 4 : 2, 3, imp ex; 5 : 4, 2, neg in; 6 : 5, negneg ex; 7 : 1, 6, imp in.

E3·10

15. In section of order 2: (i) $b°$; (ii) $b - $ (i), re; in section of order 1: (iii) $b \supset b - $ (i), (ii), imp in.

16. In section of order 2: (i) $\sim b \supset b°$; in section of order 3: (ii) $\sim b°$; (iii) $\sim b \supset b - $ (i), tf; (iv) $b - $ (ii), (iii), imp ex; in section of order 2: (v) $\sim \sim b - $ (iv), (ii), neg in; (vi) $b'' - $ (v), negneg ex; in section of order 1: (vii). $(\sim b \supset b) \supset b'' - $ (i), (vi), imp in.

38. Suppose s has signs of negation only; then it is of form $N^{2i}v$ or of the form $N^{2i+1}v$, where v is a p.v.; but neither of these forms is tautologous. If s has signs of conjunction only, then, in the standard construction of its truth-table, it takes the t.v. falsity in each row except the first, and so is not tautologous. In the case of alternation, s takes the t.v. falsity in the last row of the truth-table.

E3·13

41. In section of order 2: (i) $(x) [b(x).d(x)]°$; in section of order 3 general w.r.t. x: (ii) $(x) [b(x).d(x)] - $ (i), tf; (iii) $b(x).d(x) - $ (ii), uq ex; (iv) $b(x) - $ (iii), con ex; (v) $d(x) - $ (iii), con ex; in section of order 2: (vi) $(x) b(x) - $ (iv), uq in; (vii) $(x) d(x) - $ (v), uq in; (viii) $(x) b(x).(x) d(x) - $ (vi), (vii), con in; in section of order 1: (ix) $(x) [b(x).d(x)] \supset [(x) b(x).(x) d(x)] - $ (i), (viii), imp in.

55. $(\exists x) b(x) \supset (x) b(x).$

E4·2

1. (4·0211): $x = x\_\grave{u} = x\_(x\_çx) = (x\_x)\_(x\_çx) = (x\_x)\_u = x\_x.$ (4·0212): same, interchanging u and $\grave{u}$, $\_$ and $\_$. (4·0213): suppose, for all x of W, $x\_\grave{u}_1 = x$ and $x\_\grave{u}_2 = x$; then

$\dot{u}_2 = \dot{u}_2 \_ \dot{u}_1 = \dot{u}_1 \_ \dot{u}_2 = \dot{u}_1$. (4·0214): same as previous, interchanging u and $\dot{u}$, $\_$ and $\_$. (4·0215): $x \_ u = (x \_ u) \_ u = u \_ (x \_ u) = (x \_ \varsigma x) \_ (x \_ u) = x \_ (\varsigma x \_ u) = x \_ \varsigma x = u$. (4·0216): same as previous, interchanging u and $\dot{u}$, $\_$ and $\_$. (4·0217): $x \_ (x \_ y) = (x \_ u) \_ (x \_ y) = x \_ (u \_ y) = x \_ (y \_ u) = x \_ u$ (by (4·0215)) $= x$. (4·0218): same as previous, interchanging u and $\dot{u}$, $\_$ and $\_$. (4·0219): suppose x has two complements $\varsigma_1 x$ and $\varsigma_2 x$; then $\varsigma_2 x = u \_ \varsigma_2 x = (x \_ \varsigma_1 x) \_ \varsigma_2 x = (x \_ \varsigma_2 x) \_ (\varsigma_1 x \_ \varsigma_2 x)$ $= \dot{u} \_ (\varsigma_1 x \_ \varsigma_2 x) = (\varsigma_1 x \_ x) \_ (\varsigma_1 x \_ \varsigma_2 x) = \varsigma_1 x \_ (x \_ \varsigma_2 x) = \varsigma_1 x \_ u =$ $\varsigma_1 x$. (4·0222): suppose $x \_ y = x \_ z$ and $x \_ y = x \_ z$; then $y = y \_ (y \_ x) = y \_ (z \_ x) = (y \_ z) \_ (y \_ x) = (y \_ z) \_ (x \_ z) =$ $z \_ (y \_ x) = z \_ (x \_ z) = z$. (4·0223): $x \_ x = x = x \_ \dot{u} = x \_$ $(\varsigma x \_ \varsigma \varsigma x) = (x \_ \varsigma x) \_ (x \_ \varsigma \varsigma x) = u \_ (x \_ \varsigma \varsigma x) = x \_ \varsigma \varsigma x$; and, by interchanging u and $\dot{u}$, $\_$ and $\_$, one can show $x \_ x = x \_ \varsigma \varsigma x$; now apply (4·0222).

5. Is a factor of; is a subregion of.

6. If $x < y$, then $x \_ y = y$, and so $x = x \_ (x \_ y) = x \_ y$; conversely, if $x \_ y = x$, then $y = y \_ (y \_ x) = y \_ (x \_ y) = y \_ x = x \_ y$ and so $x < y$.

7. Use (4·0211). 8. Use (4·025).

9. Using the hypotheses, $x \_ z = x \_ (y \_ z) = (x \_ y) \_ z = y \_ z = z$.

10. Use (4·0211).

11. $(x \_ y) \_ x = (x \_ x) \_ y = x \_ y$; apply E4·2·6.

12. Using elementary Theory of Numbers, if u has no square factor, it is either a prime or a product of distinct primes;[1] call such a number a *Boolean number*; set 1 as the $\dot{u}$, interpret $\_$ as l.c.m., $\_$ as h.c.f., and ς as $u/$; e.g. $\{1, 2\}$, $\{1, 2, 3, 6\}$ are BAs associated with Boolean numbers 2 and 6. To obtain a Boolean number (apart from a prime) multiply the first n primes together; the associated BA has 2^n members, for the total number of factors of u is $\binom{n}{0} + \binom{n}{1} + \ldots + \binom{n}{n} = (1 + 1)^n = 2^n$, cf. E7·6·11. Since there are infinitely many prime numbers, cf. **4·10**, it follows that there are infinitely many BAs and ones having different numbers of members. (One must, of course, show that (4·021) to (4·0210) are verified by the arithmetical set-up.)

I have called E4·2·12 "Sheffer's Theorem" because it is, I have found, closely associated with an example given by Sheffer, *loc. cit.*; but the formulation and the above demonstration of it are due to the present author; at any rate, they were arrived at independently of other's results.

---

[1] By the Fundamental Theorem of Arithmetic, if $n \in \mathbb{N}$, then n is decomposible uniquely into a product $p_1^{e_1} p_2^{e_2} \ldots p_m^{e_m}$ of integral powers of distinct primes. If n has no square factor (other than 1), each $e_i = 1$, and so n is a product of distinct primes.

E4·3

13-17. See Huntington's paper cited in text.

19. No; cf. solution to E4·2·12.

20. (4·027): $\_x\_yz = \_\_xy\_xz$; (4·035): $\_ç\_çxçyç\_çxy = x$.

21. Each of (4·031) to (4·038) is directly in BAH$_1$ as an axiom or rule, except for (4·035). (4·035): $ç (çx\_çy)\_ç (çx\_y) = (x\_y)\_$ $(ççx\_çy) = (x\_y)\_(x\_çy) = x\_(y\_çy) = x$, by E4·2·2, E4·2·3, (4·0222), (4·028), (4·029) and (4·024).

23. This follows from the fact that the axioms (4·021) to (4·029) are in "dual" pairs.

E4·4

25. If a B.p. f has 2 variables and its canonical transform has 2^2 c.m.B.p.s., then, x and y being metalinguistic variables denoting distinct variables, $f = (x\_y)\_(x\_çy)\_(çx\_y)\_(çx\_çy) =$ $(x\_(y\_çy))\_(çx\_(y\_çy)) = (x\_u)\_(çx\_u) = x\_çx = u$. The general case, when f has n variables, follows by Math. Induction. Conversely, the x_i being metalinguistic variables denoting distinct variables, if $f(x_1, x_2, \ldots, x_n) = u$, then $f = (x_1\_çx_1) =$
$$((x_1\_u)\_(çx_1\_u)) = (x_1\_(x_2\_çx_2))\_(çx_1\_(x_2\_çx_2));$$
now expand each of these by using the distributive law and then using the fact that $x = x^\frown u$ to bring in successively the other variables.

26. $(x\_y)\_(x\_çy)$; not tautologous.

27. $(x\_y)\_(x\_çy)\_(çx\_y)$; not tautologous.

28. $(x\_y)\_(x\_çy)\_(çx\_çy)$; not tautologous.

29. $(x\_y)\_(x\_çy)\_(çx\_y)\_(çx\_çy)$; tautologous.

30. $(x\_y\_z)\_(x\_y\_çz)\_(x\_çy\_z)\_(x\_çy\_çz)$; not tautologous.

31. $(x\_y\_çz)\_(x\_çy\_z)\_(çx\_y\_çz)\_(çx\_çy\_z)\_(çx\_çy\_çz)$; not tautologous.

32. $(y\_z)\_(y\_çz)\_(çy\_z)$; not tautologous.

35. There are 2^n c.m.B.p.s in a particular set of n variables $x_1, x_2, \ldots, x_n$; the number of different Boolean polynomials in these variables is the number m of ways of choosing 0, 1, 2, $\ldots$, 2^n c.m.B.p.s out of these 2^n c.m.B.p.s; therefore, cf. E7·6·11,
$$m = \binom{2^n}{0} + \binom{2^n}{1} + \binom{2^n}{2} + \ldots + \binom{2^n}{2^n} = (1 + 1)^{2^n} = 2^{2^n}.$$
Hence (*a*) when $n = 1$, $m = 4$, (*b*) when $n = 2$, $m = 16$, and (*c*) when $n = 3$, $m = 256$.

E4·5

38. In section of order 3: (i) $Ks \subseteq tt \subseteq w^\circ$; (ii) $s \subseteq t - $ (i), con ex; (iii) $t \subseteq w - $ (i), con ex; (iv) $PstEs \subseteq tPxCx \in sx \in t - $ df (4·057) in; (v) $Es \subseteq tPxCx \in sx \in t - $ (iv), uq ex; (vi) $PxCx \in$

$sx \in t$ — (ii), (v), mutimp ex; (vii) $Et \subseteq wPxCx \in tx \in w$ — (iv), uq ex; (viii) $PxCx \in tx \in w$ — (iii), (vii), mutimp ex; in section of order 5: (ix) $x \in s^\circ$; (x) $PxCx \in sx \in t$ — (vi), tf; (xi) $Cx \in sx \in t$ — (x), uq ex; (xii) $x \in t$ — (ix), (xi), imp ex; (xiii) $PxCx \in tx \in w$ — (viii), tf; (xiv) $Cx \in tx \in w$ — (xiii), uq ex; (xv) $x \in w$ — (xii), (xiv), imp ex; in containing section of order 4 general w.r.t. x: (xvi) $Cx \in sx \in w$ — (ix), (xv), imp in; in original section of order 3: (xvii) $PxCx \in sx \in w$ — (xvi), uq in; (xviii) $Es \subseteq wPxCx \in sx \in w$ — (iv), uq ex; (xix) $s \subseteq w$ — (xvii), (xviii), mutimp ex; in containing section of order 2 general w.r.t. s, t and w: (xx) $CKs \subseteq tt \subseteq ws \subseteq w$ — (i), (xix), imp in; in section of order 1: (xxi) $PstwCKs \subseteq tt \subseteq ws \subseteq w$ — (xx), uq in.

44. 2. **45.** 4. **46.** 8.

47. The number of subsets of $\{x_1, x_2, \ldots, x_n\}$ is the number m of ways of choosing 0, 1, 2, .., n members from that set; cf.,

$$\text{E7·6·11,} \quad m = \binom{n}{0} + \binom{n}{1} + \ldots + \binom{n}{n} = (1 + 1)^n = 2^n.$$

E4·6

48. Union-set's members are 1, 2, 3, 4, 5; intersection-set's members are 2, 5.

49. Union-set is equal to $\{2, 3, 4, 5\}$; intersection-set is equal to $\emptyset$.

50. 6, 7, 8, 9, 10. **58.** See solution to E4·2·1 for (4·0222).

59-60. Proceed by showing that if x is a member of the left-hand side set, it is also a member of the right-hand side set; then show converse.

61-64. Use the definitions of the "if and only if" sort given in the text; proceed as in **59-60.**

65-66. Proceed as in **59-60.**

E4·7

67. $\emptyset\_\emptyset = \emptyset$; $\emptyset - \emptyset = \emptyset$.

68. If t and w are any members of Us, then $(t\_w) \subseteq s$ and so $(t\_w) \in Us$, and $(t - w) \subseteq s$ and so $(t - w) \in Us$.

70. (b) By elementary arithmetic, every number is a factor of itself; if a number x is a factor of y and y is a factor of x, then x is the same as y; and if x is a factor of y and y is a factor of z, then x is a factor of z.

71. Since all the members of the subset are members of the partly ordered set, the conditions (i) to (iii) of E4·7·70 apply to them;

e.g. for each x of the subset, $x \leq x$ since, by (i) of E4·7·70, for each x of the partly ordered set, $x \leq x$.

72. (*a*) By (ii), $(x \leq y) \mathbf{V} (y \leq x)$. Suppose $(x \leq y).(y \leq x)$; then, by (ii) of E4·7·70, $x = y$, contrary to present hypothesis that $x \neq y$. (*b*) Interpret " $\leq$ " in ordinary sense of being less than or equal to. (*c*) Cf. solution to E4·7·71. (*d*) Let the members of s be $x_1, x_2, \ldots, x_n$. By (i) and (*a*), of any two members x_i and x_j of s, either $x_i \leq x_j$ or (exclusively) $x_j \leq x_i$. Suppose that, of any k members x_{i_1} to x_{i_k}, $x_{i_1} \leq x_{i_2} \leq \ldots \leq x_{i_k}$. Consider any other member $x_{i_{k+1}}$; either $x_{i_k} \leq x_{i_{k+1}}$ or (exclusively) $x_{i_{k+1}} \leq x_{i_k}$; if the former, then $x_{i_{k+1}}$ is the final member of the subset of the $k + 1$ members, and if the latter then x_{i_k} is. It follows by Math. Induction that any finite chain has a final member. Analogously it can be shown that such a chain has an initial member.

76. Let s denote $\{1, 2\}$; this set is a consistent model of the axiomatic system for partial ordering if $\leq$ denotes being a factor of. Treat "if . . . then" as material implication and interpret $1 \leq 1$ as meaning $1 + 1 = 3$, $2 \leq 2$ as $2 + 2 = 4$, $3 \leq 3$ as $3 + 3 = 6$, $1 \leq 2$ as $1 + 2 = 6$, $1 \leq 3$ as $1 + 3 = 6$, $2 \leq 1$ as $2 + 1 = 6$, $2 \leq 3$ as $2 + 3 = 6$, $3 \leq 1$ as $3 + 1 = 6$, and $3 \leq 2$ as $3 + 2 = 6$; then axiom (i) is falsified but axioms (ii) and (iii) are verified. Interpret $1 \leq 1$ as meaning $1 + 1 = 2$, $2 \leq 2$ as $2 + 2 = 4$, $3 \leq 3$ as $3 + 3 = 6$, $1 \leq 2$ as $1 + 2 = 3$, $1 \leq 3$ as $1 + 3 = 6$, $2 \leq 1$ as $2 + 1 = 3$, $2 \leq 3$ as $2 + 3 = 6$, $3 \leq 1$ as $3 + 1 = 6$, and $3 \leq 2$ as $3 + 2 = 6$; then axiom (ii) is falsified but axioms (i) and (iii) are verified. Interpret $1 \leq 1$ as meaning $1 + 1 = 2$, $2 \leq 2$ as $2 + 2 = 4$, $3 \leq 3$ as $3 + 3 = 6$, $1 \leq 2$ as $1 + 2 = 3$, $1 \leq 3$ as $1 + 3 = 6$, $2 \leq 1$ as $2 + 1 = 6$, $2 \leq 3$ as $2 + 3 = 5$, $3 \leq 1$ as $3 + 1 = 6$, and $3 \leq 2$ as $3 + 2 = 6$; then axiom (iii) is falsified but axioms (i) and (ii) are verified.[1] $\{1, 2\}$ and $\{1, 2, 3, 6\}$ are consistent models of the axiomatic system for partial ordering if $\leq$ denotes being a factor of; and these sets are not capable of being put in $1 - 1$ correspondence, so that the system with the axioms (i) to (iii) of partial ordering is not categorical.

---

[1] Another solution: to show the independence of axiom I (of axiom II; of axiom III), let $\leq$ signify "is a proper divisor of" over $\mathbf{N}$ (let $\leq$ signify "is a factor of" over $\mathbf{Z}$; let $x \leq y$ signify "$| x - y | < 2$" over $\mathbf{N}_3$ and let $x = y$, which in all the other cases has its normal meaning, signify "$| x - y | \leq 1$" over $\mathbf{N}_3$). (For the meaning of the Clarendon symbols, see **4·07** and **6·05**.)

77. {1, 2, 6} and {1, 2, 6, 12} are consistent models of the axiomatic system for linear ordering; hence that system is simply-consistent and not categorical (since those two sets cannot be put in $1 - 1$ correspondence).

E4·8

78. (a) (1, 1), (1, 2), (2, 1), (2, 2); (b) (1, 1), (1, 2), (1, 3); (c) (1, 1), (1, 2), (2, 1), (2, 2), (3, 1), (3, 2); (d) no members.

82. Let $s = \{1\}$, $t = \{2\}$ and $w = \{3\}$; then $(s \times t) \smile w = \{(1, 2), 3\}$ whereas $(s \smile w) \times (t \smile w) = \{(1, 2), (1, 3), (3, 2), (3, 3)\}$.

83. (a) If $(x, y) = (y, x)$, then $\{\{x\}, \{x, y\}\} = \{\{y\}, \{y, x\}\}$; hence, since $\{x, y\} = \{y, x\}$, $\{x\} = \{y\}$, and so $x = y$. (b) If $(x_1, y_1) = (x_2, y_2)$, then $\{\{x_1\}, \{x_1, y_1\}\} = \{\{x_2\}, \{x_2, y_2\}\}$, which is possible only if $x_1 = x_2$ and $y_1 = y_2$; conversely, if $x_1 = x_2$ and $y_1 = y_2$, then $(x_1, y_1) = \{\{x_1\}, \{x_1, y_1\}\} = \{\{x_2\}, \{x_2, y_2\}\} = (x_2, y_2)$.

89. By definition, cf. 6·05, $|m| = m$ if m is non-negative and $|m| = -m$ if m is negative.   Now if $i \equiv j \pmod{m}$, then, for some integer n, $i - j = nm$.   Let $i = n_1 m + r_1$ ($0 \le r_1 < |m|$) and let $j = n_2 m + r_2$ ($0 \le r_2 < |m|$).   Then $r_1 - r_2 = i - n_1 m - j + n_2 m = (n + n_2 - n_1)m$, so that $m \mid (r_1 - r_2)$. But since $(r_1 - r_2) < |m|$, $r_1 - r_2$ must equal 0 since 0 is the only integer less than $|m|$ that can have m as a factor.

90. All congruences being mod m, if $ab \equiv 0$, then $m \mid ab$ and so, if m is a prime, $m \mid a$ or $m \mid b$, i.e. $a \equiv 0$ or $b \equiv 0$; conversely, if m is not a prime, then $ab \equiv 0$ does not imply $a \equiv 0$ or $b \equiv 0$, as shown by example: $3 \times 4 \equiv 0 \pmod 6$ but neither $3 \equiv 0 \pmod 6$ nor $4 \equiv 0 \pmod 6$.

E4·9

92. 1 and 2, 2 and 4, 3 and 6, 4 and 8, 5 and 10, . . . can be made to mutually correspond; the rule of association is: n of $\mathbf{N}$ corresponds with $2n$ of $\mathbf{N}_e$.

94. Cf. demonstration of (4·112).

E4·11

95. If $s \smile t = \emptyset$, establish $1 - 1$ correspondence between s and $\mathbf{N}_e$ and $1 - 1$ correspondence between t and $\mathbf{N}_o$; since $\mathbf{N}_e \smile \mathbf{N}_o$ is countable, $s \smile t$ will be countable (using the Lemma: if $s \infty s_1$ and $t \infty t_1$, then $\overline{\overline{s \smile t}} = \overline{\overline{s_1 \smile t_1}}$). If $s \smile t \ne \emptyset$, then establish and use the Lemma: every infinite subset w of $\mathbf{N}$ is countable; (let the members n_k of w be in natural order, so $w = \{n_1, n_2, \ldots,$

n_k, n_{k+1}, ...} where $n_k < n_{k+1}$; then $w \backsim N$, n_k of w corresponding with k of N).

96. Use E4·11·95 and Math. Induction.

97. One procedure is to set s_i ($i \in N$) in $1 - 1$ correspondence with $\{p_i^n : p_i$ is the ith prime in the natural order, $n \in N\}$; *e.g.* $s_2 = \{3, 9, 27, 81, ...\}$. The union-set of these (countably many) sets of powers of primes is infinite and is a subset of N; use the second Lemma mentioned in solution to E4·11·95.

99. The family of all the finite subsets of N is countable, as can be shown by using Math. Induction w.r.t. the sets β_n, $n \in N$, of ordered n-tuples of members of N. Now let a be a countable subset of UN and let the members of a be s_1, s_2, ..., s_n, ..., where, for each positive integral n, s_n is an infinite sequence of positive integers. Construct an infinite sequence s of positive integers as follows: if the nth member of s_n ends in the digit m, let the nth member of s end in the digit $m + 1$ unless $m = 9$, when let it end in the digit 0. Then s differs from each s_n in at least one term, *viz.* the nth. Hence a is a proper subset of UN. Therefore UN is not itself countable for if it were countable it would be a proper subset of itself, which is impossible. (This method of demonstration is due to Cantor and is known as *Cantor's Diagonal Method*.)

E5·10

1. No s is $t - s_{-}t = \dot{u}$; some s is $t - s_{-}t \neq \dot{u}$.

2. No s is $t - PxCbxNdx$; some s is not $t - SxKbxNdx$.

3. If $s_{-}\varsigma t = \dot{u}$ and $w_{-}\varsigma s = \dot{u}$, then $w_{-}\varsigma t = \dot{u}$. Demonstration in outline: $w_{-}\varsigma t = (w_{-}\varsigma t)_{-}u = (w_{-}\varsigma t)_{-}(s_{-}\varsigma s) = (w_{-}\varsigma t_{-}s)_{-}$ $(w_{-}\varsigma t_{-}\varsigma s) = \dot{u}_{-}\dot{u}$ (by hypotheses) $= \dot{u}$.

4. If $s_{-}t = \dot{u}$ and $w_{-}\varsigma s = \dot{u}$, then $w_{-}t = \dot{u}$: $w_{-}t = (w_{-}t_{-}s)_{-}$ $(w_{-}t_{-}\varsigma s) = \dot{u}_{-}\dot{u}$ (by hypotheses) $= \dot{u}$.

5. If $s_{-}t = \dot{u}$ and $w_{-}t \neq \dot{u}$, then $w_{-}\varsigma s \neq \dot{u}$: suppose $w_{-}\varsigma s = \dot{u}$; then $w_{-}t = (w_{-}t_{-}s)_{-}(w_{-}t_{-}\varsigma s) = \dot{u}_{-}\dot{u}$ (by first hyp. and supposition resp.) $= \dot{u}$, contrary to second hypothesis; therefore supposition must be rejected.

6. If $s_{-}t \neq \dot{u}$ and $s_{-}\varsigma w = \dot{u}$, then $w_{-}t \neq \dot{u}$: suppose $w_{-}t = \dot{u}$; then $s_{-}t = (s_{-}t_{-}w)_{-}(s_{-}t_{-}\varsigma w) = \dot{u}_{-}\dot{u}$ (by supposition and second hyp. resp.) $= \dot{u}$, contrary to first hypothesis.

7. If $s_{-}\varsigma t \neq \dot{u}$ and $s_{-}\varsigma w = \dot{u}$, then $w_{-}\varsigma t \neq \dot{u}$: suppose $w_{-}\varsigma t = \dot{u}$; then $s_{-}\varsigma t = (s_{-}\varsigma t_{-}w)_{-}(s_{-}\varsigma t_{-}\varsigma w) = \dot{u}_{-}\dot{u}$ (by supposition and second hyp. resp.) $= \dot{u}$, contrary to first hypothesis.

8. If $s_{-}\varsigma t = \dot{u}$ and $t_{-}w = \dot{u}$, then $w_{-}s = \dot{u}$: $w_{-}s = (w_{-}s_{-}t)_{-}$ $(w_{-}s_{-}\varsigma t) = \dot{u}_{-}\dot{u}$ (by second and first hyps. resp.) $= \dot{u}$.

9. If $s\_t \neq \dot{u}$, $(s\_e)\_w = \dot{u}$ and $(s\_t)\_çe = \dot{u}$, then $s\_çw \neq \dot{u}$: suppose $s\_çw = \dot{u}$; then $s\_t = (s\_t\_w\_e)\_(s\_t\_w\_çe)\_$ $(s\_t\_çw\_e)\_(s\_t\_çw\_çe) = \dot{u}\_\dot{u}\_\dot{u}\_\dot{u}$ (by second, third hyps., supposition and supposition (or third hyp.) resp.) $= \dot{u}$, contrary to first hypothesis.

10. If $s\_çt = \dot{u}$, $w\_e = \dot{u}$ and $t\_çw = \dot{u}$, then $s\_e = \dot{u}$: s_e $= (s\_e\_t\_w)\_(s\_e\_t\_çw)\_(s\_e\_çt\_w)\_(s\_e\_çt\_çw) = \dot{u}\_\dot{u}\_\dot{u}\_\dot{u}$ (by second, third, first and first hyps. resp.) $= \dot{u}$.

11. If $s\_çt = \dot{u}$, $w\_e = \dot{u}$ and $çe\_ççt = \dot{u}$, then $w\_s = \dot{u}$: (a) $çe\_ççt$ $= çe\_t$, and $w\_s = (w\_s\_e\_t)\_(w\_s\_e\_çt)\_(w\_s\_çe\_t)$ $(w\_s\_çe\_çt) = \dot{u}\_\dot{u}\_\dot{u}\_\dot{u}$ (by second, second or first hyps., (a) and third hyp., and first hyp. resp.) $= \dot{u}$.

12. (3) $CKPxCbxdxPxChxbxPxChxdx$;
    (4) $CKPxCbxNdxPxChxbxPxChxNdx$;
    (5) $CKPxCbxNdxSxKhxdxSxKhxNbx$.

E6·5

1. (a) $(x + y)z = z(x + y) = zx + zy = xz + yz$; (b) supposing $x + y = x + z$, then $y = 0 + y = (-x + x) + y = -x + (x + y) = -x + (x + z) = (-x + x) + z = 0 + z = z$.

2. $x + x0 = x1 + x0 = x(1 + 0) = x1 = x = x + 0$; hence, by E6·5·1 (b), $x0 = 0$. Let $xy = 0$; supposing $x \neq 0$, $xy = 0 = x0$, and so, by (6·0513), $y = 0$.

3. $y + (x + -y) = y + (-y + x) = (y + -y) + x = 0 + x = x$. Hence there is at least one z, viz. $x + -y$, such that $y + z = x$. Suppose there is another (member of Z denoted by) z such that $y + z = x$; then $y + z = x = y + (x + -y)$, and so, by E6·5·1 (b), $z = x + -y$.

4. (a) (i) $xy + (x(-y) + (-x)(-y)) = (xy + x(-y)) + (-x)$ $(-y) = x(y + -y) + (-x)(-y) = x0 + (-x)(-y) = 0 + (-x)(-y) = (-x)(-y)$; but (ii) also the original left-hand expression in (i) $= xy + (x + -x)(-y) = xy + 0(-y)$ $= xy + 0 = xy$; hence, $(-x)(-y) = xy$. (b) $-(-x) = 0 + -(-x) = (x + -x) + -(-x) = x + (-x + -(-x)) = x + 0 = x$. (c) $x + (-1)x = 1x + (-1)x = (1 + -1)x = 0x = x0 = 0 = x + -x$; therefore, by E6·5·1 (b), $(-1)x = -x$.

5. (a) By definition, if $x + z < y + z$, then $y + z - x - z, = y - x$, $\in N$; therefore $x < y$. Conversely, if $x < y$, then $y - x \in N$ and so $y - x + 0, = y - x + z - z, = (y + z) - (x + z)$, $\in N$; therefore $x + z < y + z$. (b) Suppose $0 < z$. If $x < y$, then $y - x \in N$. N is closed under multiplication, and so $z(y - x), = zy - zx, \in N$; therefore $zx < zy$. Conversely, if $zx < zy$, then $z(y - x) \in N$. Since $z \in N$, $y - x \in N$, and so $x < y$.

6. With N as I, suppose $çs \neq \emptyset$. Since N is well-ordered, $çs$ is well-ordered and so has an initial member m. $1 \in s$, so $1 \notin çs$ and therefore $1 < m$. Hence $m - 1 \in s$ and so, by hypothesis, $(m - 1) + 1$, $= m$, $\in s$, which contradicts that $m \in çs$. So the supposition that $çs \neq \emptyset$ must be rejected since it leads to a contradiction.

8. Use E6·5·7, with u for the s and t for the N. (The "u" here is not to be confused with the "u" of Boolean Algebra.) The demonstration of E6·5·8 rests on (6·0515). But, conversely, E6·5·8 implies (6·0515): let s be a non-empty subset of N. If $1 \in s$, s has a smallest member, viz. 1. If $1 \notin s$, it contains, since by hypothesis $s \neq \emptyset$, some m_0 of N. For each n of N let $b(n)$ signify "$n < m$ for each m of s". $b(m_0)$ is false; and $b(m) \supset b(m + 1)$ will be false for some (and only one) m of s, from which it follows that $b(m)$ is true and $b(m + 1)$ is false. $m + 1$ is the smallest member of s.

9. Let s be the set of integers $n > x$ for which $b(n) \in çu$, where t is I. Suppose $s \neq \emptyset$; then s has an initial member m. Therefore $b(k) \in u$ for all $x < k < m$. But, by hypothesis, if $b(k) \in u$, then $b(m) \in u$, contrary to the consequence of the supposition that $b(m) \in çu$. Hence the supposition must be rejected.

12. Let $\theta = /s$, $t/$ and $\psi = /w$, $e/$. If $\theta < \psi$, then, by definition, $s \subset w$. Let x be any rational number such that $x \in w$, and $x \notin s$. Then $/\{y : y < x\}, \{z : z \leq x\}/$ is a rational real number ϕ such that $\theta < \phi < \psi$.

13. Let e be the set of all the rationals in s and w be the set of all the rationals in t. Then $/e$, $w/$ is a cut in Q. Hence, $/e$, $w/$ defines a real number ϕ. Either $\phi \in s$ or $\phi \in t$. Suppose $\phi \in s$ and suppose that ϕ is not the greatest member of s. Then, for some real number ϕ_1, $\phi_1 \in s$ and $\phi < \phi_1$. By E6·5·12, there is some rational r such that $\phi < r < \phi_1$. Now since $\phi_1 \in s$, $r \in e$. But this gives us a contradiction, since a member of the first component e of $/e$, $w/$ cannot be greater than the real number ϕ which $/e$, $w/$ defines. Similarly if $\phi \in t$.

14. Let $\alpha = \{\theta:$ for some ψ of s, $\theta > \psi\}$, and let $\beta = R - \alpha$. No member of α is a 1b of s, and every member of β *is* a 1b of s. Show that α and β satisfy the hypotheses of Dedekind's Theorem E6·5·13; then either α has a smallest or β has a greatest member. α has not a smallest member, for let θ be the supposedly smallest member of α. Then there is at least one ψ of s such that $\theta > \psi$. Choose θ_1 such that $\psi < \theta_1 < \theta$; this is possible by E6·5·12. Since $\theta_1 > \psi$, $\theta_1 \in \alpha$ and $\theta_1 < \theta$, so that θ is not the smallest member of α. Hence β has a greatest member, and this is the glb of s.

15. Analogously to E6·5·14, reversing order signs and substituting "ub" for "lb".

16. Suppose, contrary to Principle, that for some θ and ϕ, $n\theta \leq \phi$ for every n of N. The set s of all the multiples $n\theta$ then has ϕ as an ub, so that it has a lub ψ, by E6·5·15. Hence $n\theta \leq \psi$ for every n of N, and so $(n+1)\,\theta \leq \psi$ for every n of N. Therefore $n\theta \leq \psi - \theta$ for every n of N, and so, after all, ψ is not the lub of s: thus there is a contradiction.

E6·7

17. $[LMT^{-2}]$.   **18.** $[L^{-1}MT^{-2}]$.   **19.** $[LT^{-2}]$.   **20.** $[T^{-2}]$.
21. $[L^2T^{-2}]$.   **22.** xy^2 m; xy m sec^{-1}.

E6·8

23. $q\,(u^2/r)$.   **24.** $q\,(r^2d\omega^2)$.   **25.** $q\,(F/r)$.   **26.** $q\,(sg)$.

27. Let L_1 (L_2), M_1 (M_2), and T_1 (T_2) be the units of S_1 (S_2). Then for some real numbers l, m, and t, $L_1 = lL_2$, $M_1 = mM_2$, and $T_1 = tT_2$. If a quantity Q is measured in terms of S_1, its magnitude is, for some real number q, $qL_1^x M_1^y T_1^z$ where x, y, and z are given by the dimensional equation $[Q] = [L^x M^y T^z]$. So the magnitude of Q in terms of S_2 is $q\,(l^x m^y t^z)\,(L_2^x M_2^y T_2^z)$.

E6·11

28. (a) Arithmetic mean: 36·29 sec; variance: 0·42 (0·4189) sec; standard deviation: 0·65 (0·6472) sec.   (b) Arithmetic mean: 74·01 sec; variance: 0·199 (0·19890) sec; standard deviation: 0·446 (0·44598) sec.

29. (a) Arithmetic mean: 299790·7 km sec^{-1}; (b) coefficient of variation: 0·002 (0·001916) per cent.; probable error: 3·874 km sec^{-1}; standard error: 2·031 km sec^{-1}.

E7·5

7. Consider the random experiment of tossing a two-headed coin once; $1 - \{\overline{H}\}$, $a = \{\emptyset;\ 1\}$.

E7·6

11. Use Math. Induction.

14. With a B.p. in n variables there are associated 2^n c.m.B.ps. The total number of distinct B.ps., including $\grave{u}$, in the n variables is

$$\underset{k \in \mathbf{N}_{2^n}^{\geq}}{\Sigma} \binom{2^n}{k}, = 2^{2^n}$$

15. 4.   **16.** n^m.

17. 2^n; in constructing a truth-table for a p.s. of n variables, one draws all possible ordered samples of size n from $\{0, 1\}$, *i.e.* {truth, falsity}.

18. $(1/6)^n$.　　**19.** Probability $= \binom{4}{2} \binom{48}{3} / \binom{52}{5}$.

20. $\binom{13}{7} \binom{13}{5} \binom{13}{1} \binom{13}{0} / \binom{52}{13}$　　　　**21.** $\binom{4}{2} \binom{4}{2} \binom{4}{2} \binom{36}{7} / \binom{52}{13}$.

22. $1/n^m$; $1/(n(n-1)(n-2)\ldots(n-m+1))$.

E7·7

23. $\mathrm{P}\,(s/t) = 75/257$; $\mathrm{P}\,(s_2/t) = 80/257$.　　**26.** $\binom{4}{2} \binom{48}{3} / \binom{52}{5}$.

27. $\binom{4}{1} \binom{4}{2} \binom{44}{2} / \binom{52}{5}$.　　**28.** $4 \binom{13}{5} / \binom{52}{5}$.　　**29.** $5 \binom{4}{1} / \binom{52}{5}$.

30. $4 \times 5! / \binom{52}{5}$.

32. 25; solve the inequality $(35/36)^n < 1/2$, *i.e.* $n (\log 36 - \log 35) > \log 2$, obtaining that $n > 24{\cdot}604$.

34. (ii) (*a*) $\underset{i\epsilon\mathbf{N}_6}{\Sigma}\, i\mathrm{P}\,(s_i) = \frac{1}{6}(1 + 2 + 3 + 4 + 5 + 6) = \frac{21}{6} = 3{\cdot}5$.

(ii) (*b*) If s_i is the event of scoring i, where $2 \leq i \leq 12$, then
$$\overset{12}{\underset{i=2}{\Sigma}}\, i\mathrm{P}\,(s_i) = \overset{7}{\underset{i=2}{\Sigma}}\, i\frac{(i-1)}{36} + \overset{12}{\underset{i=8}{\Sigma}}\, i\frac{(12-i+1)}{36} = \frac{252}{36} = 7.$$

45. $2{\cdot}4 \times 10^{-29}$. $\mathrm{P}\,(s_{160}) = 5{\cdot}854 \times 10^{-31}$; even if, contrary to fact, all the events s_{160+i} $(i \in \mathbf{N}_{40})$ had as great a probability value as this, the maximum probability in total would be no greater than $41 \times \mathrm{P}\,(s_{160})$, $= 2{\cdot}4 \times 10^{-29}$.

46. If $\epsilon -$ is the greatest index smaller than ϵ, then $\overset{\max i}{\underset{\min i}{\Sigma}}\, i^2\mathrm{P}\,(s_i)$
$$= \overset{\epsilon -}{\underset{\min i}{\Sigma}}\, i^2\mathrm{P}\,(s_i) + \underset{i \geq \epsilon}{\Sigma}\, i^2\mathrm{P}\,(s_i) \geq \underset{i \geq \epsilon}{\Sigma}\, i^2\mathrm{P}\,(s_i) \geq \underset{i \geq \epsilon}{\Sigma}\, \epsilon^2\mathrm{P}\,(s_i)$$
$$= \epsilon^2 \underset{i \geq \epsilon}{\Sigma}\, \mathrm{P}\,(s_i) = \epsilon^2\mathrm{P}\,(\underset{i \geq \epsilon}{\cup}\, s_i); \quad \therefore\; \mathrm{P}\,(\underset{i \geq \epsilon}{\cup})s_i \leq \frac{1}{\epsilon^2}\overset{\max i}{\underset{\min i}{\Sigma}}\, i^2\mathrm{P}\,(s_i).$$

47. Tchebyshev's Inequality is expressible as $\mathrm{P}\,(|\,X\,| \geq \epsilon) \leq \frac{1}{\epsilon^2}\Sigma\,X^2\mathrm{P}\,(X)$, where X denotes a "random variable" and $\mathrm{P}\,(|\,X\,| \geq \epsilon)$ denotes the probability of the union-set of all those events for which the values of $|\,X\,|$ are $\geq \epsilon$. Hence,
$$\mathrm{P}\,(|\,S_n - np\,| \geq n\epsilon) \leq \frac{1}{n^2\epsilon^2}\Sigma\,(S_n - np)^2\,\mathrm{P}\,(S_n - np)$$
$$= \frac{1}{n^2\epsilon^2} \times \text{variance of }\; S_n = \frac{1}{n^2\epsilon^2} \times np\,(1-p)\; [\text{by E7·7·42}]$$
$$= p\,\frac{(1-p)}{n\epsilon^2}, \text{ and this converges to 0 as } n \to \infty.$$

E8·4

1. The means of the samples are 4·6, 3·7, 5·0, 3·0, and 4·2 respectively. The variance of the first sample is 9·6 (86·30 ÷ 9).

E8·5

5. $N (s\_t\_w) = 58 + 42 + 47 - 22 - 19 - 16 + 12 = 159 - 57 = 102.$

E8·6

7. Mean, median, and mode all have the value 5.

E8·7

8. With a significance level of 5 per cent., no.

9. With a significance level of 5 per cent., 62.

10. No.   **11.** No.

E9·5

9. By (2·163) and (2·164) we have: $s \vee (t \vee t_1)$, $s \vdash s \vee t_1$, and and $s \vee t_1 \vdash t \vee (s \vee t_1)$, so that $s \vee (t \vee t_1)$, $s \vdash t \vee (s \vee t_1)$; and $s \vee (t \vee t_1)$, $t \vee t_1 \vdash t \vee (s \vee t_1)$, by E2·18·72 applied to the epitheorems $t \vee t_1$, $t \vdash t \vee (s \vee t_1)$ and $t \vee t_1$, $t_1 \vdash t \vee (s \vee t_1)$. Hence, again by E2·18·72, $s \vee (t \vee t_1) \vdash t \vee (s \vee t_1)$. Finally use Deduction Theorem.

10. Simply establish the analogue of E2·18·72 for PCWR, then proceed as in E9·5·9, and finally use E2·20·104.

E9·6

17. If b (1) occurs as a step in a section of order k of a proof structure ($k \geq 1$), and a section of order $k + 1$, within that section, is general w.r.t. the positive integral variable n, and contains b (n) as supposition and $b (n + 1)$ as a subsequent step, then (n) b (n) [Pnbn] may legitimately occur as a subsequent step in the original section. ("n" is used as a metalinguistic variable.)

LIST OF ABBREVIATIONS

Each number indicates the place of the first occurrence of the abbreviation in the text.

I. JOURNALS

Acad. Roy. Belgique (**3·10**) = Académie Royale Belgique.

Akad. Wiss. Wien, *Math.-naturwiss. Klasse* (**3·10**) = Akademie der Wissenschaften in Wien, *Mathematisch-naturwissenschaftliche Klasse.*

Amer. J. Math. (**2·03**) = *American Journal of Mathematics.*

Amer. Math. Monthly (**4·03**) = *American Mathematical Monthly.*

Ann. of Math. (2), (**2·08**) = *Annals of Mathematics,* Second Series.

Ann. Math. Stat. (**7·03**) = *Annals of Mathematical Statistics.*

Biol. Bull. (**5·09**) = *Biological Bulletin.*

Bull. Amer. Math. Soc. (**2·08**) = *Bulletin of the American Mathematical Society.*

C. R. Soc. Sc. Lett. Varsovie, cl. *III* (**2·08**) = *Comptes Rendus des Séances de la Société des Sciences et des Lettres de Varsovie,* classe III.

Fund. Math. (**2·08**) = *Fundamenta Mathematicae.*

Jber. D.M.V. (**7·07**) = *Jahresbericht der Deutschen Mathematiker-Vereinigung.*

J. Roy. Stat. Soc. (**8·05**) = *Journal of the Royal Statistical Society.*

J. Symbolic Logic (**3·13**) = *Journal of Symbolic Logic.*

Journal f.d. reine u. angew. Math. (**6·05**) = *Journal für die reine und angewandte Mathematik.*

Math. Ann. (**4·05**) = *Mathematische Annalen.*

Math. Z. (**2·08**) = *Mathematische Zeitschrift.*

Monatsh. Math. Phys. (**2·08**) = *Monatschfte der Mathematik und der Physik.*

Phil. Trans. Roy. Soc. (**7·07**) = *Philosophical Transactions of the Royal Society.*

Proc. Camb. Phil. Soc. (**4·08**) = *Proceedings of the Cambridge Philosophical Society.*

Proc. Nat. Acad. Sc. (**4·07**) = *Proceedings of the National Academy of Sciences.*

Rev. de Mét. et de Morale (**4·11**) = *Revue de Métaphysique et de Morale.*

Riv. di Mat. (**2·05**) = *Rivista di Matematica.*

Ruch filoz. (**2·03**) = *Ruch filozoficzny.*

Sitzungsber. preuss. Akad. Wiss. Berlin (**3·03**) = *Sitzungsberichte der preussischen Akademie der Wissenschaften in Berlin.*

Trans. Amer. Math. Soc. (**2·09**) = *Transactions of the American Mathematical Society.*

Trans. Camb. Phil. Soc. (**4·02**) = *Transactions of the Cambridge Philosophical Society.*

II. OTHER ABBREVIATIONS[1]

alt   (**3·08**) = alternation.

BA   (**4·02**) = Boolean Algebra.

BAH_1 (**4·02**) = Huntington's first axiomatic system for Boolean Algebra.

BAH_2 (**4·03**) = Huntington's later axiomatic system for Boolean Algebra.

cm   (**6·03**) = centimetre.

c.m.B.p. (**4·04**) = canonical minimal Boolean polynomial.

con   (**3·03**) = conjunction.

df   (**2·11**) = definition.

---

[1] The meaning of each of these abbreviations has been explained in the text. The present collected list is for reference, in case the student, in reading, has forgotten the meaning.

d.s. $(2\cdot08)$ = deductive system.

ex $(3\cdot08)$ = expulsion.

FC $(3\cdot01)$ = Functional Calculus of the First Order.

FCIT $(3\cdot09)$ = Intuitionist Functional Calculus of the First Order, in terms of Tarski's axiom schemata system of 1938 (see $2\cdot15$).

FCT $(3\cdot01)$ = Functional Calculus of the First Order, in terms of Tarski's 1938 system.

$FL_1\dot{L}T$ $(3\cdot05)$ = object language, using Łukasiewicz-Tarski notation, for the Functional Calculus of the First Order.

$FL_2\dot{L}T$ $(3\cdot05)$ = metalanguage, using Łukasiewicz-Tarski notation, for the Functional Calculus of the First Order.

FL_1PR $(3\cdot05)$ = object language, using Peano-Russell notation, for the Functional Calculus of the First Order.

FL_2PR $(3\cdot05)$ = metalanguage, using Peano-Russell notation, for the Functional Calculus of the First Order.

f.s. $(3\cdot05)$ = functional schema.

ft $(6\cdot03)$ = foot (or feet).

f.v. $(3\cdot05)$ = functional variable.

glb $(6\cdot05)$ = greatest lower bound.

imp $(3\cdot08)$ = implication.

in $(3\cdot08)$ = introduction.

ind $(7\cdot07)$ = independent.

L_1 $(2\cdot15)$ = object language for the Propositional Calculus.

L_2 $(2\cdot15)$ = metalanguage for the Propositional Calculus.

L_1ŁT   **(2·15)** = object language, using Łukasiewicz-Tarski notation, for the Propositional Calculus (Tarski's 1938 system).

L_2ŁT   **(2·15)** = metalanguage, using Łukasiewicz-Tarski notation, for the Propositional Calculus (Tarski's 1938 system).

L_1PR   **(2·15)** = object language, using Peano-Russell notation, for the Propositional Calculus (Tarski's 1938 system).

L_2PR   **(2·15)** = metalanguage, using Peano-Russell notation, for the Propositional Calculus (Tarski's 1938 system).

lub   **(6·05)** = least upper bound.

m   **(6·04)** = metre.

MP   **(6·11)** = *Modus Ponens*.

m.p.s.   **(2·15)** = metalinguistic propositional schema.

m.p.v.   **(2·15)** = metalinguistic propositional variable.

mutimp **(4·05)** = mutual implication.

neg   **(3·08)** = negation.

negneg **(3·08)** = double negation.

PC   **(2·01)** = Propositional Calculus.

PCF   **(E2·20)** = Frege's axiomatic system for the Propositional Calculus.

PCIT   **(3·09)** = Intuitionist Propositional Calculus, in terms of Tarski's 1938 system.

PCŁ   **(E2·13)** = Łukasiewicz's axiomatic system for the Propositional Calculus.

PCT   **(2·15)** = Tarski's axiom schemata system for the Propositional Calculus.

PCWR **(2·10)** = Whitehead and Russell's axiomatic system for the Propositional Calculus.

p.e.   (**6·11**) = probable error of the arithmetic mean.

p.f.   (**3·02**) = propositional function.

p.s.   (**2·03**) = propositional schema.

p.v.   (**2·03**) = propositional variable.

q.e.   (**3·03**) = quantificational expression.

re   (**3·08**) = repetition.

RR   (**2·11**) = Rule of Replacement.

RS   (**2·11**) = Rule of Substitution.

s.e.   (**6·11**) = standard error of the arithmetic mean.

sec   (**6·03**) = second.

sec^{-1} (**6·03**) = per second.

SFCIT   (**3·09**) = suppositional method version of FCIT (see above).

SFCT   (**3·08**) = suppositional method version of FCT (see above).

tf   (**3·08**) = transference.

t.p.s.   (**2·06**) = tautologous propositional schema.

t.v.   (**2·02**) = truth value.

LIST OF SYMBOLS

The meaning of each symbol has been explained in the text on its introduction; in this list the number accompanying a symbol indicates the place of the first occurrence of the symbol in the text.

A	2·12	$s(x)$	4·09	1	2·04
b, d, h	3·05	$\wedge sx$	4·09	$\leftrightarrow$	2·09
b, d, h	3·05	$/s, t/$	6·05	$\sim$	2·05
bxy	3·05	s, t, u	2·15	v	2·05
$b(x, y)$	3·05	$s(1, m)$	2·18	·	2·05
bxy	3·05	U	6·03	$\supset$	E2·03
b(x, y)	3·05	U_L	6·04	$\equiv$	E4·08
C	2·12	U_M	6·04	W	4·07
$C(x_iU)_n$	6·11	U_T	6·04	/	E2·09
ç	4·02	Us	E4·07	\	E2·09
E	2·12	u	4·02	$\vdash$	2·16
$E(x_iU)_n$	6·10	$\grave{u}$	4·02	$\vdash_n$	2·18
e_iU	6·10	$V(x_iU)_n$	6·11	°	2·16
f_i	6·10	$V^2(x_iU)_n$	6·11	( )	3·03
J	4·07	v	2·20	$\emptyset$	4·05
K	2·12	v′	2·20	I	4·06
N	4·07	W	4·02	$=$	4·02
N_e	4·10	x, y, z	3·05	$\doteqdot$	2·20
N_i	4·07	(x, y)	4·08	$\overline{\equiv}$	4·05
N_o	4·10	&xy	4·08	$\underline{\cup}$	4·05
$N^{\geq}$	4·07	x_qU	6·10	$\not\equiv$	4·05
$N^{\geq}_i$	4·07	x, y, z	3·05	$\underline{\cap}$	4·05
N'	2·12	xéc	4·09	{ }	4·05
N	E8·05	xéf	4·09	{ : }	4·05
$(n)_m$	7·06	xéms	4·07	$\cup$	4·10
$\binom{n}{m}$	7·06	xérel	4·08	$\cup$	7·05
$n!$	7·06	xérs	4·07	$\cap$	4·10
P	3·03	Z	6·05	$\wedge$	7·06
P	7·05	$\forall$	3·03	$\smile$	4·02
$P(s/t)$	7·07	$\exists$	3·03	$-$	4·02
p, q, r	2·03	Π	7·05	$\dotminus$	4·06
Q	E4·11	Σ	6·10	$+$	4·07
Q	6·03	α, β, γ	4·07	$\times$	4·08
Q	2·20	$\in$	4·05	$\beth$	4·11
R	6·05	$\notin$	4·05	$\gtrless$	E4·02
r_iU	6·10	θ, ϕ, ψ	6·05	$\lesseqgtr$	E4·07
S	3·03	μ_m	E7·07	$\simeq_1$	6·05
s, t, w, e	4·05	μ'_m	E7·07	$\|$	6·05
$\overline{\overline{s}}$	4·11	ω	E4·07	[ ]	6·06
s_i	4·10	$\mathfrak{C}$	7·04	$	$	4·08
		$\aleph_o$	4·11	$\doteq^1$	7·02
		0	2·04		

[1] Sign of approximate equality.

363

BEHMANN, H.

INDEX OF AUTHORS

ACKERMANN, W., 28, 54, 69
d'Alembert, J. le R., 336-7
Archimedes, 191
Aristotle, 150, 152, 304
Ayer, A. J., 284

BABINGTON SMITH, B., 270
Bar Hillel, Y., 147
Bayes, T., 241
Baylis, C. A., 117
Bennett, A. A., 117
Bernard, C., 150, 157, 165, 298
Bernays, P., 28, 37, 48, 91, 147, 295
Bernoulli, Jacques, 213, 221, 238, 246
Beth, E. W., 295
Birkhoff, G., 117, 189
Bocheński, I. M., 304
Bôcher, M., 288-9, 298
Boole, G., 104, 106, 117, 119, 126, 327
Borel, E., 289
Bourbaki, N., 139-40
Boyle, R., 258
Bradley, F. H., 322
Braithwaite, R. B., 311, 336
Bridgman, P. W., 337-8
Briggs, H., 238
Brinkley, D., 268
Broad, C. D., 330
Brodbeck, M., 339
Brookes, B. C., 267
Brouwer, L. E. J., 84-5, 147
Brown, G. S., 270
Brownlee, K. A., 264
Burali-Forti, C., 28
Burtt, E. A., 339
Butterfield, H., 339

CAJORI, F., 236, 291
Campbell, N. R., 177, 335-6
Cantor, G., 118, 131-2, 145-6, 350
Carnap, R., 28, 30, 214, 327

Church, A., 28, 100, 296
Cochran, W. G., 268
Comte, A., 337
Conant, J. B., 310
Cramér, H., 213, 222-5, 244, 267
Curry, H. B., 28, 44
Czuber, E., 244

DANIELL, P. J., 128
Darwin, C. R., 162-4
Dedekind, R., 188, 190
De Morgan, A., 106-7, 327
Dick, W. F. L., 267
Doob, J. L., 220
Duhem, P. M. M., 338
Duns, J. W., 255

EDWARDS, P., 339
Einstein, A., 309, 337
Ellis, R. L., 217
Euclid, 27, 140, 301

FEATHER, N., 212
Feigl, H., 339
Feller, W., 244
Fisher, R. A., 263-4, 278
Fitch, F. B., 75, 97, 147
Focken, C. M., 196
Foucault, L., 255
Fourier, J. B. L., 196
Fraenkel, A., 147
Frege, G., 12, 28-9, 42, 63, 146

GALILEI, G., 152, 154
Gauss, C. F., 275
Gentzen, G., 75, 97
Gergonne, J. D., 290
Glivenko, V. I., 89
Gödel, K., 90, 94, 308
Goodstein, R. L., 26, 219-20

HANSON, N. R., 173
Hardy, G. H., 302
Hausdorff, F., 130

Haybittle, J. L., 268
Helmholtz, H., 177
Herbrand, J., 48, 74
Hérigone, P., 291
Herschel, J. F. W., 154-6, 158-61, 168, 174
Heyting, A., 67, 85
Hilbert, D., 28, 48, 54, 69, 91, 104, 295
Hogben, L., 214, 275, 278
Hume, D., 339
Huntington, E. V., 103, 108, 113-14, 131, 295-6, 346

JAŚKOWSKI, S., 97
Jevons, W. S., 106, 334
Johnson, W. E., 322

KALMÁR, L., 53
Kant, I., 256-7, 288
Kattsoff, L. O., 339
Kelley, J. L., 147
Kendall, M. G., 262-3, 267, 270, 273
Kepler, J., 317
Keynes, J. M. (Lord), 214, 322, 339
Kleene, S. C., 42, 295, 308
Kolmogorov, A. N., 227
Koopman, B. O., 239
Kuratowski, C., 132

LADRIÈRE, J., 308
Lanchester, F. W., 196
Langford, C. H., 100
Laplace, P. S., 214, 239, 245, 275, 327, 330, 332
Larmor, J., 196
Lazear, J. W., 253-4
Leibniz, G. W., 124, 136
Lemmon, E. J., 100
Leśniewski, S., 28, 31, 39
Lewis, C. I., 100
Lindley, D. V., 267
Lindsay, R. B., 338
Loève, M., 244
Łukasiewicz, J., 15, 28, 35, 37, 174, 304

LÖWENHEIM, L.

MACH, E., 339
MacLane, S., 189
Mann, H. B., 264
Margenau, H., 339
Maxwell, J. C., 324
de Méré, A. G., 245
Michelson, A. A., 182
Mill, J. S., 319-20, 322
Miller, J. C. P., 267
von Mises R., 213, 218-20
de Moivre, A., 275
de Montaigne, M., 150
Mood, A. M., 267
Moore, E. H., 136, 140, 295
Moore, R. L., 295

von NEUMANN, J., 28, 39, 147
Newton, I., 166, 238, 288
Neyman, J., 244, 278
Nidditch, P. H., 75, 97, 126, 282, 284, 301, 303-4

O'CONNOR, D. J., 284

PADOA, A., 295
Parry, W. T., 100
Pascal, B., 151-2, 231, 245, 249-50
Pasch, M., 295, 297
Peano, G., 18, 67, 69, 104, 118, 124, 289, 294-6
Pearson, E. S., 278
Pearson, K., 263
Peirce, C. S., 17, 67, 287-8, 310-19, 321-6, 334-5
Périer, F., 250-3
Picard, C. E., 311
Pieri, M., 289, 295-7
Pittendrigh, C. S., 273
Poincaré, H., 148
Polyá, G., 203
Popper, K. R., 334
Post, E. L., 15, 21, 51, 53
Prior, A. N., 100

QUETELET, L. A. J., 275
Quine, W. V. O., 147

RAMSEY, F. P., 336
Rayleigh, 3rd Lord, 195
Reichenbach, H., 321
Ritt, J. F., 189
Rosser, J. B., 42, 135
Russell, B. A. W. (Earl), 17-18, 32, 64, 67, 73, 124, 131, 135, 137, 146-7, 295
Ryle, G., 316

SCHLICK, M., 316
Schröder, E., 114, 117
Schweitzer, A. R., 295
Sheffer, H. M., 31, 108, 345
Sierpiński, W., 145
Simpson, E. B., 255
Simpson, G. G., 273
Simpson, J. Y., 254-5
Smart, W. M., 204-5
Steinitz, E., 187
Stewart, D., 287
Stolz, O., 191
Stone, M. H., 130
Strawson, P. F., 339
Stuart, A., 267
Sutton, W. S., 167-8

TARSKI, A., 28, 35, 39-40, 50, 53, 86

Tchebyshev, P. L., 247, 354
Thurston, H. A., 189
Tiffany, L. H., 273
Tippett, L. H. C., 270
Todhunter, I., 244
Topping, J., 203
Torricelli, E., 249
Toulmin, S. E., 316

VEBLEN, O., 114, 295
Venn, J., 217, 312-13

WALD, A., 278
Whewell, W., 322, 339
Whitehead, A. N., 18, 32, 67, 73, 117, 124, 135, 212, 339
Wiener, N., 133
Will, F. L., 339
Williams, D. C., 339
Wittgenstein, L., 15, 22

YOUNG, J. W., 295
Yule, G. U., 262, 273

ZERMELO, E., 147
Żyliński, E., 31

SKOLEM, T. (1887-1963?)

INDEX OF TERMS AND SUBJECTS

ABDUCTION, 314-19
Alternation, 16-19, 128
Archimedean continuity, 191
Axiom, 27-9, 155-6, 289-94
— schema, 28, 38-40
Axiomatic method, 27-30, 282, 289-301

BAH₁, 101-8, 114
BAH₂, 108-14
Boolean algebra, 101-18, 130, 174, 213, 226, 261-2
— polynomial, 114-18, 238
Bounds, 188-91

CANONICAL form, 115-18
Cartesian product, 132, 232
Chain, 131
Class, 105-6, 118
— equivalence, 135
— null, 106, 119
Classification, 160, 174
Coefficient of variation, 209
Combination, 236
Combinatory analysis, 231-8, 244-5
Complementation, 106, 126-7
Completeness, 53, 113, 293-4, 308
Conditions, logical, 8-9, 11
Congruences, 135-6, 308
Conjunction, 16-17, 19
Consistency, 49-50, 293-4
Correspondence, 137-9, 143-5
Countable, 143
Counting, 175-7
Cut, Dedekind, 188-9

DEDUCTION, 1, 282-3
— theorem, 45, 74
Definition, 124, 290-1
— impredicative, 148, 189
Demonstration, 282-4, 291-3
Deviation, 207
— standard, 209, 245

Diagonal method, 350
Difference of sets, 125-6
— symmetric, 128, 228
Dimension, 191-2
Dimensional analysis, 191-200
— expression, 192-5
— homogeneity, 196
Disjoint sets, 143
Distribution, binomial, 246-7, 275, 278
— frequency, 268, 273-7
— hypergeometric, 237
— normal, 273-7
— probability, function, 245
Duality, 114

EPITHEORY, 44-5
Error, probable, of mean, 209-10
— standard, of mean, 210
— — — proportion, 280
— of observation, 2, 7, 200-12, 253, 257-8
Events, random, 225-6
— independent, 240
Expectation, 206, 245
Experience, 149-52, 157, 162, 164-5, 309-10
Experiment, 149, 152, 154-6, 166, 168-9, 248-61, 318
Experiments, design of, 264-5
— statistical, 223-5, 266, 268-73
Explanation, 161-4, 309-14, 317-18, 324, 336

FCT, Chapter III
Field, 187
— of sets, 130
Finiteness, 143-4
Formula, 64, 284
— closed, 284
— open, 284
Frequency definition of probability, 217-20
Function, 136-8, 238, 246

Functional calculus, Chapter III, 103, 174, 261, 296
— schema, 70
— variable, 69
Fundamental theorem of arithmetic, 345

GROUP, 187, 296

HISTOGRAM, 273
Hypothesis, null, 266, 278-80
— scientific, 164, 248-50, 253-4, 258-9, 310, 314, 316-22, 324, 333-4, 336
— in proof, 41-2
Hypothetico-deductive, method, 333-6
— system, 289

IMPLICATION, 9, 11, 14, 17-19, 22-3, 30, 221
Indexed family of sets, 139-41
Induction, mathematical, 45, 190, 296, 308, 352
— scientific, 314-30, 333, 339
Infinite set, 143
— sequence, 139, 218-20
Integral domain, 187, 190, 305-8
Interpretation, 101, 104-7, 288-9
Intersection, 106, 109, 123-4, 140-1, 226
Intuitionism, 84-6, 94

K-IDENTITY, 91

LANGUAGES, 30, 38-40, 44-5, 69-71
Law of large numbers, 247
— scientific, 149, 155-64, 195-6, 255-62, 310, 312-19
Least squares, 212
Limit, 218
Logic, classical, 12, 85-6
— modal, 5, 6, 100

MATHEMATICS, pure, 1-8, 12-13, 27, 64, 84-5, 215, Chapter IX
Mean, 206, 208-11, 245

Measurement, 2, 7-8, 173, 175-85, 200-12, 257-8
Median, 276
Membership of sets, 118-19
de Méré's problem, 245
Mode, 209
Model, 105-7, 110
Module of sets, 129
Modulus, 189
Modus ponens, 33, 41, 72
Moments, probability, 245-6

NEGATION, 15, 19, 35, 137
Normal distribution, 209, 273-5, 277
Notation in FC, PC, 18-19, 22, 31, 35, 38-9, 67-71
Numbers, 144, 147, 186-91, 296-7
— cardinal, 144, 147
— irrational, 187-8
— prime, 139-40
— rational, 147, 187-8
— real, 187-91
Numeric, 178

OBSERVATION, 149-52, 155-7, 166-73
Operationalism, 337-8
Ordered, field, 187-189
— n-tuple, 232
— pair, 131-2
— sampling, 233-4
Ordering, 130-1

PARADOXES, 146, 148
Parameter, 263
PCF, 63, 296
PCŁ, 37, 63, 296
PCT, 40-64, 221, 301
PCWR, 32-8, 62-3, 104, 113, 301
Permutation, 236
Population, 233
Postulate, 28
Prediction, 157-9, 223, 323-4, 333-5
Primitives, axiomatic, 289-90
Probability, 2-3, 7-8, Chapter VII, 262-81, 311-21, 324-34
— conditional, 239
— of causes, 241-3

Projection, 133-4
Proof, 6, 34-6, 41-2, 64, 75-84, 282-4, 299, 302-8
— structure, 75-7
Proposition, 12-13, 64-6, 104-7, 284
Propositional, calculus, Chapter II, 64, 104-7, 221, 296, 304
— function, 64-6
— schema, 13-14
— variable, 13

QUANTIFIERS, 66-8, 296
Quantity-types, 181, 191, 193-4

RANDOMNESS, 204-5, 219, 223-6, 262, 266, 269-73
Relations, 107, 133-5
Residual, 207
Ring of sets, 129-30
Rules, formation, 30, 33-4, 38-40, 70-1
— of deduction, 29, 32-3, 41, 72-3, 75, 77-82, 86, 95-7, 103, 109, 120-4, 135, 306-8

SAMPLING, 233-7, 263-73, 279, 315-19, 321, 325-6, 328
Satisfiability, 111
Set theory, 118-48
SFCT, 78-82, 86, 120
Significance, 266, 278-81
Statistic, 262-3
Statistics, 7-8, 213, 217, 221-5, 262-81
Stochastics, 213, 221
Subset, 119-20

Supposition, 76
Suppositional method, 64, 75-84, 86-9, 94-100, 120-3, 135, 304-8
Syllogism, 174, 304

TAUTOLOGY, 22
Tchebyshev's inequality, 247
Tertium non datur, 49, 84-5, 148
Testability, 152, 157, 162-3, 334-7
Theorem, 6, 34, 40-2, 76, 282-91, 297-301
Theory, auxiliary, 293
— scientific, 149, 161-9, 309-10, 317-18, 320, 333-6
Truth, 6, 12-13, 84-5, 150-2, 282, 284-9
— table method, 15-17, 19-26, 90-1, 101, 238
— value, 12, 15-16

UNCOUNTABLE set, 147
Union, 106, 123-4, 140-1, 226
Unit, 179-81, 200
Universal statement, 175
Universe of discourse, 106, 126

VALUE, absolute, 189
— of function, 136
Variable, attached term, 69
— bound, 68
— free, 68
— functional, 69
— propositional, 13
Variables, term, 64-6, 68-71
Variance, 208, 245

PRINTED IN GREAT BRITAIN BY UNIVERSITY TUTORIAL PRESS LTD
FOXTON, NEAR CAMBRIDGE